STEPHAN PAETROW

HISTORY
IN MOTION

ZF Friedrichshafen AG from 1915 to 2015

Hoffmann und Campe

This book commemorates the 100th anniversary
of ZF Friedrichshafen AG.

Publisher: ZF Friedrichshafen AG, Friedrichshafen
Corporate Communication, Matthias Lenz
Editorial Management: Gisela Mattes
1st edition 2015
© 2015 ZF Friedrichshafen AG, Friedrichshafen, Germany;
HOFFMANN UND CAMPE VERLAG GmbH, Hamburg, Germany
Published by HOFFMANN UND CAMPE VERLAG GmbH, Hamburg, Germany
www.hoca.de
Author: Stephan Paetrow
Translation: Samantha Riffle
Post-production: PX2@Medien, Hamburg, Germany
Printed by: Eberl Print, Immenstadt, Germany
Printed in Germany
ISBN 978-3-455-50392-0
This is a HOFFMANN UND CAMPE Corporate Publishing book
distributed by HOFFMANN UND CAMPE VERLAG.

Ein Unternehmen der
GANSKE VERLAGSGRUPPE

TABLE OF CONTENTS

FOREWORD

The ZF Group celebrates its 100th anniversary in 2015, and many people around the world will be marking this momentous event alongside the company and its employees: international customers, suppliers, and business partners, but also industry associations, politicians, the media, and the public as a whole. For outsiders, it might at first seem odd that the mayor of Friedrichshafen would be granted the honor of writing the foreword to the book chronicling these 100 years of history. But this is a perfect example of the special relationship between this global company and the city where it was founded.

ZF is the largest employer in the Friedrichshafen region, but it is also so much more than that. Through the Zeppelin Foundation, the city has held a majority share in ZF Friedrichshafen AG since 1947. The mayor serves as chairman of the Zeppelin Foundation and as a member of the supervisory board at ZF Friedrichshafen AG, and the scope of that responsibility is extensive, both locally and globally. The proceeds from the foundation's assets – of which ZF's profits comprise a large part – benefit the citizens of Friedrichshafen in many different ways, primarily through charitable, social, and cultural projects. The construction of the ZF Forum, the global company's new headquarters in Friedrichshafen, will further strengthen ZF's ties to the city. This new location will allow ZF to present itself to visitors and citizens as an open, transparent company, and to convey what the company represents: its past, present, and future.

There is more to ZF than the city where it was founded, however. With its 2015 acquisition of TRW, ZF will employ approximately 134,000 people at nearly 300 locations around the globe, generating annual sales of more than 30 billion euros. Against the backdrop of this impressive growth, one has to wonder whether it still makes sense for this global player to remain tied to the Zeppelin Foundation and, consequently, to the city of Friedrichshafen. As a representative of the company's main shareholder, the Zeppelin Foundation, I can provide a clear answer to this question: yes, it does still make sense. If we look back at history, we can see that the foundation has proven itself to be a responsible shareholder, consistently aware of its duties to the company and its employees, and always making sustainability its top priority.

ZF is one of the largest technology companies in the world today because it plans for the long term. And while ZF has to hold its own against the international competition like any other organization, the support of the Zeppelin Foundation as majority shareholder provides the company with a certain degree of staying power. ZF has the ability to develop new products and technology in a sustainable way – a way that will help them succeed in the global marketplace. And in times of economic instability, ZF can rest assured that the shareholders' primary goal is ensuring the continued existence of the company.

100 years of ZF history are also 100 years of German history. This book does not turn a blind eye to any of the crises, large or small, that the country and the company faced during the past century. Even the years between in 1933 and 1945 – a dark chapter for ZF, Germany, and the whole world – are addressed openly and transparently. For ZF, this is a matter of historical responsibility – a responsibility the company fully accepts.

On the whole, this book is a success story – and an impressive one at that. But we would expect nothing less from a company which, today, numbers among the global market's most important technological leaders. Even more fascinating than the "what" of ZF's history, however, is the "how:" little by little, the reader is able to piece together the big picture from a multitude of individual events told from the perspective of the people at ZF who experienced them first-hand. And in this way, a series of moving moments becomes "History in Motion."

To the readers of this book: I hope you find it enlightening and inspiring. And to ZF Friedrichshafen AG: I wish you the very best for the future!

ANDREAS BRAND
Mayor of the City of Friedrichshafen,
Chairman of the Zeppelin Foundation, and
Member of the Supervisory Board at ZF Friedrichshafen AG

THE LONG PROLOGUE TO ZF'S FOUNDING:

BORN IN THE CRADLE OF AIRSHIP MANUFACTURING

The civilian transport airship LZ 127 above the Hafenbahnhof (port railway station) in Friedrichshafen, 1928.

Friedrichshafen may be the city of Zeppelins, but these giants of the skies weren't the only thing that helped to turn the former summer residence of the Württemberg kings into a burgeoning industrial city. As in so many parts of the world, change began with the railroads. A train from the city of Ravensburg, north of Friedrichshafen, arrived in the latter city for the first time on November 8, 1947.[1] The Südbahn, or southern line, was completed in June 1850; it connected Heilbronn to the shores of Lake Constance, and still does today. In Friedrichshafen, the Stadtbahnhof (city railway station, completed in 1847) and Hafenbahnhof (port railway station, completed in 1850) were constructed to accommodate this line.[2] The latter station joined the railroads to the steamboat traffic on Lake Constance; steamboat transportation had first got its start in Friedrichshafen in 1824. The city was now an important transit hub; however, its population remained relatively modest. In 1871, Friedrichshafen was home to just 3,052 people – compared to approximately 10,000 in nearby Constance. Until the late 19th century, it was as though time stood still in Friedrichshafen – the city only awoke from its slumber when important guests paid a visit, such as Russian Czar Alexander II in 1880.

Count Ferdinand von Zeppelin (1838–1917)[3], who would ultimately be responsible for making Friedrichshafen a household name, had little interest in settling there at first. The son of Sigmaringen-based Hofmarschall Friedrich von Zeppelin and native of Constance Amélie Macaire d'Hogguèr, the daughter of a wealthy cotton magnate, Ferdinand von Zeppelin was born on July 8, 1838 in Constance, on Dominican Island in Lake Constance. He grew up in Girsberg Palace, which was part of the Swiss town of Emmishofen at the time. After completing his schooling, the young Count joined the military, earning the rank of lieutenant in the Württemberg Army. In 1858, he took up a program of study in political science, mechanical engineering, and chemistry in Tübingen. He spent 1863 and 1864 in the northern United States as an observer during the Civil War. This was the first time Zeppelin had ever seen a tethered balloon used for military reconnaissance purposes; he also had the opportunity to ride in a balloon himself, away from the battlefield, and it was a defining moment for him. Back in Württemberg, the Count continued his military career. He served as a General Staff Captain in the Württemberg Cavalry during the Franco-Prussian War of 1870/71, where he led a reconnaissance mission behind enemy lines near Haguenau in the Alsace region. This brought him a certain degree of fame – not least because renowned German writer Theodor Fontane immortalized this event in his war reports.[4]

Balloons to break blockades

However, it was another event during the war that eventually led Zeppelin to become a pioneer of airship manufacturing: while German troops laid siege to Paris between September 1870 and January 1871, the French sent up a total of 67 balloons, one at a time, to carry news and passengers across

Count Ferdinand von Zeppelin (1838–1917) is considered the father of rigid airship manufacturing.

Proof has been furnished that transoceanic travel is technologically possible, although the calculations regarding its profitability remain problematic.

ALFRED COLSMAN

the German blockade. The city was completely surrounded, but more than three quarters of the balloons – transporting approximately 2.5 million letters and at least 91 passengers – reached their destination.[5] French Minister of the Interior Léon Gambetta, who was tasked with organizing resistance in the countryside against the German invasion, managed to escape the capital this way. It is unclear whether Ferdinand von Zeppelin was already considering building an airship at this point, but it would stand to reason. After all, if these balloons – which could not even be steered – could be used so effectively against a superior military force, what incredible possibilities could they offer if they didn't depend on the direction the wind was blowing?

As a patriot, Zeppelin must have felt that technological progress in this area was all the more urgent, because France – Germany's enemy during this war – was clearly far ahead of the Germans in conquering the airspace. In November 1783, physicist Jean-François Pilâtre de Rozier and army officer François d'Arlandes had already mounted the first successful manned flight in history in a hot air balloon designed by the Montgolfier brothers. In December of the same year, physicist Jacques Alexandre César Charles also helped a competing technology, the hydrogen balloon, get off to a strong start – this technology, incidentally, was the basis for the airships that would later be developed. The gas balloon, or Charlière, set new records with its cruising altitude of more than 2.1 miles and flight duration of around two hours. And balloon travel in France only grew more advanced after that point. The French military used a balloon for reconnaissance purposes for the first time in 1794 – nine years before the first German

balloonist, Friedrich Wilhelm Jungius of Prussia, came onto the scene. The first flight of a motorized airship also took place in France: in September 1852, engineer Henri Giffard traveled a distance of nearly 17 miles in a 145-foot-long, football-shaped balloon powered by a steam engine.

At first, Ferdinand von Zeppelin was only interested in the theoretical aspects of aviation. On April 25, 1874, he read a lecture that German Postmaster General Heinrich von Stephan had given on the subject of global postal services and airship travel. In this lecture, Stephan addressed the development of transportation as a whole since the era of the ancient world and ultimately came to the conclusion that conquering the skies with aircraft suited to transporting people and mail was the next logical step. If the advanced technologies of steam engines and balloon travel were combined, Stephan continued, it might really be possible to create an aircraft that could be steered. However, all of the engines available at the time were too heavy for this purpose. Stephan consequently suggested using a combustion engine based on the patent held by Luxembourgian inventor Étienne Lenoir, as inventor Paul Haenlein had done in 1872. Ferdinand von Zeppelin was so fascinated by Stephan's remarks that he made an entry in his diary; this was the first time he ever documented his plans to build an airship in writing.

Leaving the military to design airships

At first, however, the Count continued to climb the ranks in Württemberg's military and government. After being promoted to the rank of Colonel in 1884, he headed to Berlin the following year; beginning in 1887, he served as an envoy of the

King of Württemberg. Two years later, however, Zeppelin incurred the wrath of German Emperor Wilhelm II by writing a critical memorandum; this put an end to his time in Berlin, and Zeppelin also retired from active military service. At that point, he finally began to dedicate all of his energy to the project of constructing an airship.

In order to overcome the aerodynamic and static issues associated with a project of this nature, Zeppelin needed help from an experienced engineer. In 1892, he found just the man for the job: Theodor Kober. Together, the two of them drafted a concept for a "dirigible aircraft with multiple supporting bodies arranged consecutively." The frame of this aircraft would be constructed of an innovative material called aluminum. In 1894, the draft design was reviewed by a commission headed by physicist Hermann von Helmholtz – and politely rejected. But Zeppelin was persistent and ultimately managed to obtain a patent for the design.[6] Kober and Zeppelin were aware that

in order to construct the skeleton of an airship, they would need a relatively lightweight, break-proof, stable material; nothing else would do. At the time, the only material that met all of their requirements was "Victoria" aluminum. In Germany, there was only one manufacturer who could supply this special metal: Lüdenscheid-based industrialist Carl Berg, who also happened to be the father-in-law of future ZF co-founder Alfred Colsman. Berg's technicians had already constructed an airship with an aluminum frame once before: in 1897, for Hungarian airship pioneer David Schwarz. However, Schwarz passed away before the test flight, which was scheduled to take place at the Tempelhof airfield in Berlin. His widow sold her husband's remaining plans and drawings to Zeppelin in 1898. And while Schwarz's death was a tragedy, it also had a silver lining – it cleared the way for Zeppelin to partner with Carl Berg, solving the issue of procuring materials to construct frames for the airships of the future.

The LZ 1 lifts off above Lake Constance on July 2, 1900. The airship had five passengers on board and remained airborne for 18 minutes.

Friedrichshafen becomes the city of Zeppelins

In the meantime, Zeppelin had managed to find a number of supporters for his idea at the Association of German Engineers (VDI), which he had joined in 1896. In June 1898, Zeppelin organized the founding of the Gesellschaft zur Förderung der Luftschiffahrt (Company for the Promotion of Airship Travel) in Stuttgart; its shareholders included Gottlieb Daimler and Carl von Linde. Ferdinand von Zeppelin had gone to great pains to scrape together approximately 55 percent of the 800,000 marks in share capital for the company himself. Collecting these funds was a monumental effort, but it paid off – Zeppelin was essentially able to determine the company's strategy himself. The fact that the new company chose Friedrichshafen as the location for its headquarters was due to the support it received from King Wilhelm II of Württemberg. Unlike the German Emperor who shared his name, Wilhelm II of Württemberg had supported Zeppelin's airship plans from the very beginning. By royal decree, Zeppelin's company was granted a plot of land in the king's domain of Manzell – today part of the Friedrichshafen metropolitan area – with direct access to Lake Constance. There, the Count built a floating hangar to construct the first Zeppelin airship, the LZ 1. On July 2, 1900, the prototype lifted off over Lake Constance for the first time. The flight lasted 18 minutes, and potential investors were nowhere in sight.

FROM A MODERN-DAY PERSPECTIVE, the dimensions of the Zeppelin airships are staggering: the Airbus A380, the largest passenger airplane in the world, is "only" 240 feet long, while the LZ 127, the most successful Zeppelin, measured in at a length of

776.3 feet

Despite the fact that the Gesellschaft zur Förderung der Luftschiffahrt dissolved in the same year as this first flight, Ferdinand von Zeppelin managed to build two more airships, financed by donations, lottery proceeds, and a significant amount of private funds. During this period, mechanical engineer Ludwig Dürr also became heavily involved in the design process; he later earned the position of head designer at the Zeppelin Group. With the construction of the LZ 3, the company was finally able to recoup the enormous investments it had originally made; this new airship successfully completed several test flights, causing the government in Berlin to reevaluate its position on airship travel. The military ultimately purchased the LZ 3 and used it as a training ship. This was further proof that the technology was viable, and it also caused another observer to have a change of heart: economist and journalist Hugo Eckener, who had written a series of critical articles about Count von Zeppelin and his projects in the years between 1900 and 1906, was now convinced that the rigid airship would catch on.[7] In the years that followed, Eckener would make a name for himself as an airship pilot, and later as head of the Zeppelin Group.

The "Zeppelinspende" public donation campaign

Before it came to that, however, a catastrophic event shook the very foundations of everything Zeppelin had built thus far – but ultimately became the starting point for his greatest triumph. The chain of events that eventually led to the founding of ZF was set in motion when the War Ministry in Berlin informed Zeppelin's company that it would consider placing an order for four airships – if Zeppelin could prove that his airships could remain airborne for 24 hours. Consequently, a test flight with the LZ 4 airship was scheduled for summer 1908. After the LZ 4 landed in a field near Echterdingen, however, it was caught up in a gust of wind, collided with a fruit tree, and almost immediately burned to a crisp. The situation seemed hopeless: in practical terms, the commercial success of the

The site of the accident in Echterdingen, with the burned-out frame of the LZ 4 on August 5, 1908.
This catastrophe triggered one of the largest public donation campaigns in German history.

airship should still have been a long way off, particularly since shortly before the accident, a plan to found a company with a Krupp-led industrial consortium as a shareholder had failed. But the accident resulted in an outpouring of support from the entire German population; many people in Switzerland also donated to support the struggling airship business. Within a very short period of time, the donation campaign collected more than six million marks – which meant that Ferdinand von Zeppelin now had enough resources to start a new airship company. On September 8, 1908, before the donation campaign had even officially ended, he founded Luftschiffbau Zeppelin GmbH. Alfred Colsman was chosen to manage the fledgling business. On December 30 of the same year, the Zeppelin Foundation was established – upon receiving approval from the authorities, it went into operation on April 1, 1909. The foundation held 60 percent of the shares in Luftschiffbau Zeppelin GmbH; Count von Zeppelin himself held the rest.

With this stable source of financing, the groundwork had been laid for the Count and his collaborators to continue manufacturing airships. And while the airships that followed may not have delivered what their creator promised – either financially or militarily – it would be incorrect to dismiss the entire project as a failure. After all, like manned space flight, airship manufacturing facilitated numerous technological and societal advancements in related fields, including lightweight aluminum designs, industrial hydrogen production, new findings in navigation and meteorology, greater sophistication in industrial architecture thanks to the construction of enormous hangars, and – last but not least – important innovations in driveline technology for both engines and transmissions. In that sense, if we look at the economic history of Friedrichshafen, airship manufacturing set the pace of growth, as numerous subsidiaries also sprang up under the umbrella of the Zeppelin Group. And these subsidiaries quickly outgrew their intended role, becoming flourishing companies in their own right. This book tells the story of one of those successful subsidiaries: ZF Friedrichshafen AG.

1915 – 1933

From the company's founding to the end of the Weimar Republic

Zeppelins take to the skies, but their transmission systems are loud and prone to malfunctions. Then Alfred von Soden, head of the Zeppelin testing department, remembers a Swiss patent that can help.

ZAHNRADFABRIK EMERGES:

VISIONARY TECHNOLOGY AND REAL WAR

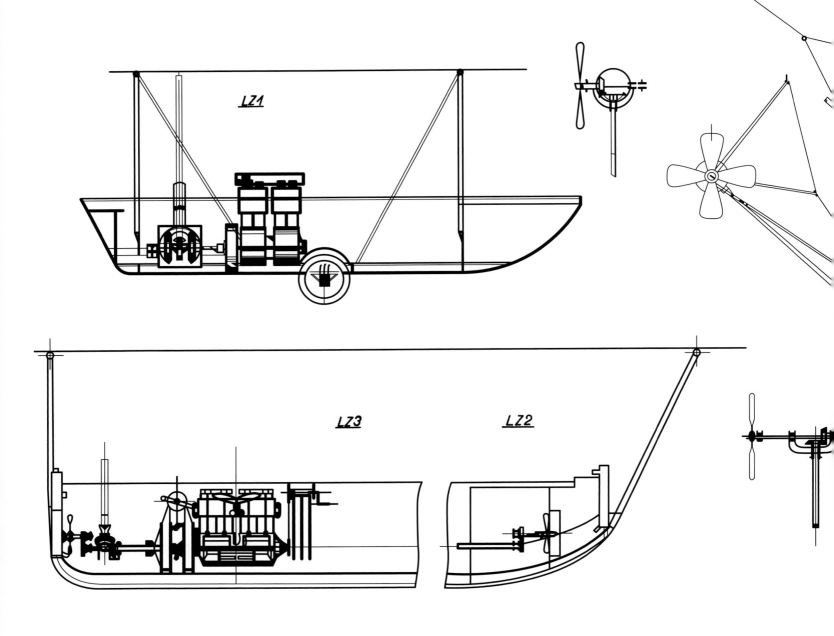

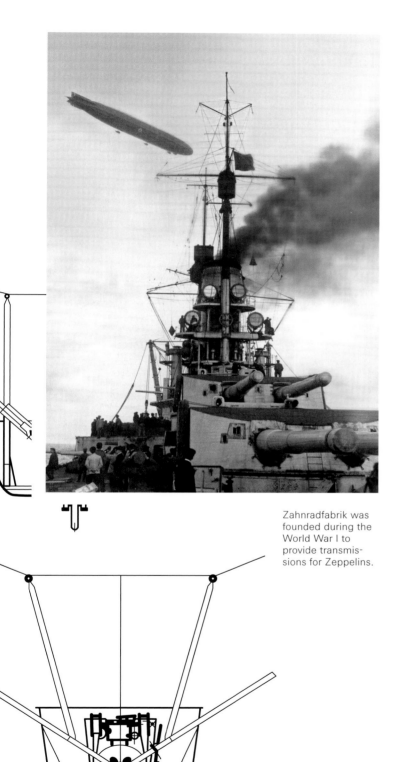

Zahnradfabrik was founded during the World War I to provide transmissions for Zeppelins.

After leaving the armed forces in 1890, Count Ferdinand von Zeppelin (1838-1917) worked tirelessly to make his dream a reality. The airships he constructed were partly intended to facilitate civilian flights, but their primary purpose was to serve German military interests. In the summer of 1915, one year after the World War I broke out, it seemed as though the Count had nearly achieved his goal. The army and navy of Imperial Germany used these massive flying machines for reconnaissance missions and even conducted the first aerial bombardments; their opponents had no defense against this new threat. However, the Zeppelins were plagued by serious technical problems, particularly in their drivelines. The emergence of ZF is directly tied to the attempt to remedy these issues. Alfred Colsman, who had managed Luftschiffbau Zeppelin GmbH since 1908, retrospectively summarized the events surrounding ZF's founding:

"As long as the power from the Zeppelin's engine was conveyed to the propeller transmission via long steel shafts, the noise from the propeller transmission on the side of the machine – as well as from the driveline in the pilot's car – was almost unbearable; consequently, we had numerous discussions about reducing the noise level. Count Alfred von Soden, who headed the testing department in airship construction at the time, and who was very involved with the issue of transmissions, told us one day that Swiss engineer Max Maag had managed to manufacture mathematically precise gears in Zurich. Gears made on these Maag machines allowed us to hope that we could reduce transmission noise and increase safety, which is why I initiated licensing negotiations with Maag-Zahnräder A.-G. in Zurich [...]."[1]

Von Soden's enthusiasm for the gear manufacturing process patented by Maag began before the outbreak of the World War I. In summer 1914, the Count reportedly saw the innovative spur gear grinding machine for the first time in Zurich; at that point, it had just gone into production. An earlier gear planing machine also constructed by

Maag had been delivered to Luftschiffbau Zeppelin GmbH in Friedrichshafen back in August 1912.[2]

Max Maag and the search for the perfect gear

Engineer Max Maag had traveled a long and rocky road to reach that point. Born in 1883 in the village of Dorf am Irchel near Zurich in Switzerland, the son of a rural school teacher first studied mechanical engineering and then took a job at Maschinenfabrik C. Wuest & Co. in Seebach. As a provider of elevators and cranes, the company also produced gears. The head design engineer was already working on a milling machine for this purpose; when he went on vacation, Maag supposedly started optimizing the prototype himself.[3] In the process, he also conducted the first studies on changing the geometry of gears – which mostly resulted in mockery from his senior supervisor. Even at his next job, at Werkzeugmaschinen-Fabrik Oerlikon, Maag was still unable to implement his novel ideas. Eventually, he decided to strike out on his own, opening an office in Zurich in 1910. In the years that followed, Maag first developed a complete theoretical gearing system, the core of which was the involute gear profile – now considered the industry standard.

Manufacturing gears according to this system was an extremely complex process, however, because individual gear geometries had to be developed for different pairs of gears. Maag found an ingenious solution to this production problem. Rather than allowing for only a small selection of defined tooth profiles, he developed a standardized milling tool with an adjustable cutting edge. On January 23, 1912, Maag registered this "process for producing involute gear profiles on cylindrical, bevel, and helical gears" for a patent in the German Empire.[4] This was followed by 13 further patent registrations in other countries. However, a patent registered by Englishman Sam Sunderland in October 1908 stood in the way of Maag's goal of constructing a machine tool based on this patented process.[5] In April 1912, Maag and Sunderland came to an agreement on licensing for Sunderland's gear planing machine. Based on this agreement, Maag and his partner Albert Weiss from Schweizerische Werkzeugmaschinenfabrik Oerlikon began constructing an improved model using the gearing process Maag had patented. From the very beginning, Maag was aware of the potential that this invention harbored. In September 1912, he wrote:

"The grinding machine that operates based on my Process II (adjustment of the flank angle) is currently under construction and will be operational in approximately 2 months. During the construction process for this machine, all experience garnered in the manufacturing of gears was assessed to the fullest extent [...]. As a result, for example, we avoided using any type of jig. The producing edge of the grinding wheel is perfectly straight and is automatically kept that way as the machine operates. Thanks to all of these precautions, the machine will be able to produce profiles of previously impossible precision, which is why it should be of overwhelming interest to the automobile industry in particular."[6]

MAX MAAG
(1883–1960)
The Swiss engineer developed a system for manufacturing low-vibration gears that ZF was the first company in Germany to utilize.

Maag gears on the rocky road to volume production

However, as is so often the case with innovative processes, the devil was in the details. The assumption that the precisely planed gears could be installed in vehicle transmissions without any further finishing processes turned out to be incorrect – a fact that Maag discovered the hard way when he tested his process on vehicles from Belgian luxury car manufacturer Minerva Motors:

"I was present for the tests with these gears, which were initially installed without being hardened. The finely planed gears gave rise to the greatest of hopes. However, when they were hardened, they performed little better than the company's old gears. I had to leave with my head hanging in shame."[7]

After a few failed attempts, by 1913, Maag finally managed to design a machine to regrind the hardened gears; the machine's grinding wheels automatically adjusted themselves to compensate for wear and tear, thanks to a diamond that regularly scanned the surface of the wheels. On January 12, 1913, Max Maag was granted a patent for the machine in the German Empire.[8] In the months that followed, the inventor moved into a space in a former automobile factory, and set up a production facility with the support of his associate and financier Jakob Muggli. Maag was now ready to conquer the market, with the help of his patents. However, by this point, his company had already been operating on the precipice of a financial

One of the first Maag spur gear shaping machines at Zahnradfabrik Friedrichshafen, 1916.

abyss for quite some time. It was in desperate need of solvent customers in the transmission industry who appreciated innovation when they saw it.

The founding of Zahnradfabrik

For this reason, Luftschiffbau Zeppelin GmbH's interest in licensing production was wholly in line with Max Maag's financial objectives. The inventor from Zurich could approach the situation with confidence, as his patented process for the precision manufacturing of high-quality gears was the best on the market. What's more, because Germany was embroiled in the World War I at the time, Germans were unable to negotiate with all of their usual international partners. In that sense, the fact that Maag's company was headquartered in neutral Switzerland was extremely beneficial. Negotiations began in spring 1915. Colsman and von Soden participated on the German side; the opposing side was represented by Maag himself, alongside Jakob Muggli.

On August 20, 1915, in the offices of Luftschiffbau Zeppelin GmbH, Colsman and Maag signed a notarized agreement that formalized the establishment of Zahnradfabrik Gesellschaft mit beschränkter Haftung: a limited liability company headquartered in Friedrichshafen. LZ contributed 52 percent of the total share capital of 50,000 marks; 48 percent came from Max Maag. Alfred von Soden and Theodor Winz, an authorized officer at LZ, were appointed general managers. The articles of association stipulated that shares of the company could only be sold to third parties with the approval of all shareholders, who had right of first refusal. Another interesting aspect is the purpose of the company as described in section 2 of the articles of association: "the manufacturing of gears and transmissions for aircraft, motor vehicles, and motor boats." The original motivation for founding ZF may have been airship manufacturing, which was considered vital to the war effort at the time, but the company's founders von Soden, Colsman, and Maag apparently had more exten-

sive peacetime production – such as for the automobile industry – in mind from the very beginning. It was clear that airship transmissions alone would not generate enough profits to sustainably finance volume production of gear transmissions.

Zahnradfabrik received the capital it needed to set up its own factory – initially 1.5 million marks – in the form of a low-interest loan from LZ. If the transmission and gear business proved profitable, the financing agreement dated August 20, 1915 stipulated that the company would receive an additional 1.5 million marks. If Zahnradfabrik were ever to plan branches at other German locations, LZ would have certain privileges regarding capital and revenue there as well – only if LZ chose not to take advantage of these options could Maag's Zahnradfabrik in Zurich open additional factories in Germany on its own or in cooperation with third parties. In that sense, ZF – or its parent company LZ – was guaranteed a sort of monopoly for Maag gears on the German market, at least in its early stages.

A licensing agreement limited ZF's exclusive use of the technology to "aircraft, motor vehicle, and motor boat manufacturing." It also stipulated that the inventor would receive a total of one million marks in licensing fees, which is equivalent to more than 3.2 million euros today. The amount was to be paid in annual installments; the first installment of 200,000 marks was due immediately after the founding of Zahnradfabrik in Friedrichshafen. Additionally, ZF was obligated to stamp all gears produced with the Maag logo and advertise them as "Maag gears" in all promotional materials.

Zahnradfabrik between war and peace

Ultimately, however, the first series of gears and transmissions produced would not be shipped out until early 1917. The ongoing war made it difficult for the company to set up its production facility, as this report on the founding years of ZF written in August 1920 states:

"The company began working on numerous preliminary experimental and test orders for gears

ZAHNRÄDER
mit neuartig geschliffenen Zahnflanken
sowie ganze Getriebe für den gesamten Fahrzeugbau
kinematisch richtig · mathematisch genau
ZAHNRADFABRIK ⚙ZF⚙ **FRIEDRICHSHAFEN** a.B
G.M.B.H.

Above: Employees of the Zahnradfabrik engineering department, with
aviation products, 1919.
Right: The commercial register entry
for "Zahnradfabrik," September 1915.
Left: Ad for Zahnradfabrik GmbH,
1917. Clearly visible is the reference
to the gear-cutting system developed
by Max Maag.

in a makeshift factory in 1916, but the military administration started to make things difficult in fall of that same year. Not only did the administration refuse to assign Zahnradfabrik the civil servants and workers that it desperately needed; it also required that the company's existing workers report for military service. Additionally, the company was denied access to the material it needed to finish constructing the factory, as Zahnradfabrik's products were not considered strategically necessary to the war effort. Zahnradfabrik consequently faced a decision: completely discontinue production and the construction of the new factory, or find an activity that would make it indispensable to the war effort. The company's management chose the latter option. Aircraft transmissions had become an extremely urgent issue at that time, and they were well within Zahnradfabrik's manufacturing capabilities."[9]

Aircraft transmissions were a new category of products at that point, meaning that ZF had no experience to draw on. After a long string of attempts and failures, the first model range was finally ready for production in mid-1918 – military organizations and private investors alike began eagerly placing orders. However, shortly after ZF began processing those orders, the end of the war in 1918 brought production to a screeching halt once again. The very focus on militarily strategic production that was intended to allow ZF to continue setting up its facilities in 1916 was now proving disastrous for the young company. In early 1919, all of the company's orders for aircraft transmissions were canceled. The peace treaty of Versailles, which Germany signed on June 28, 1919, formally prohibited the country from rebuilding its air force. What's more, ZF was initially unable to find more than a small handful of civilian customers, because most potential buyers for transmissions and gears were preoccupied with the complicated process of converting their own production facilities from wartime to peacetime production.

The company only utilized a maximum of 20 percent of its production capacity during the entire year of 1919. Added to that were difficulties in procuring raw materials and fuel, as well as a general sense of unease among the company's employees, even months after the war had ended. Unlike regions such as Munich or the Ruhr Valley, the area around Lake Constance was not temporarily managed as a communist republic; however, there was a very real fear that companies here would also be socialized.

ZF becomes an automotive supplier

Beginning in fall 1919, Zahnradfabrik's financial situation began to improve – in fact, by early 1920, the company's order books were so full that employees had to work night shifts. ZF hired many more workers; by August 1920, the company employed approximately 600 people. This rapid recovery was primarily a result of the brisk demand from the automobile industry. The quality of the gears produced according to the Maag process and the fact that ZF provided complete transmissions specially constructed for automobiles were unique selling points on the German market. The company also continued to develop innovative products with strong sales potential, chief among them the Soden transmission, which was still in the trial phase at that point. Consequently, in summer 1920, Zahnradfabrik was in a position to be optimistic:

"Ownership of the Maag licenses and machines, the exemplary production equipment, the company's many years of experience in the construction of gears and transmissions, the joint ownership of the patents for the Soden transmission, a transmission that had been constructed based on entirely new perspectives and that was suitable for both passenger cars and trucks – all of these factors will give Zahnradfabrik an undeniable advantage over other similar companies [...]. The fact that Zahnradfabrik is the first factory in Europe that manufactures special transmission for the automobile industry deserves particular mention."[10]

Faced with liquidation, ZF buys time

And yet, ZF continued to struggle with serious problems. For example, manufacturing a single transmission took at least five or six months, which meant that Zahnradfabrik was unable to react to short-term fluctuations in demand. The company's financial situation was an even more severe burden. By mid-1920, ZF had received a total of approximately 10.5 million marks in loans from LZ, plus a further two million from Maag Zahnräder A.G. – or, rather, from its governing boards. As so often the case with newly established industrial companies, Zahnradfabrik's profits did not yet reflect the investments that had been made. Including the losses carried forward from the previous years, the company recorded a loss of more than 6.8 million marks in the 1920 fiscal year.[11] According to Zahnrad-

Three-gear transmission developed by ZF in 1919. Compact design was a hallmark of many ZF products.

fabrik's management, at least another four million marks in investments would be required to raise the company's manufacturing to a productive level. Neither Luftschiffbau Zeppelin GmbH nor Maag-Zahnräder A.G. was capable of providing the sum required, so Zahnradfabrik had to start looking for additional investors. As the general manager of Zahnradfabrik, Count von Soden negotiated with a series of renowned companies that had the funds to serve as potential investors: Gutehoffnungshütte in Oberhausen, Bergische Stahl-Industrie G.m.b.H. in Düsseldorf, Thyssen in Mülheim, and Krupp in Essen. ZF's strongest hope was for an investment from Nuremburg- and Augsburg-based MAN; however, in the end, none of the negotiations ended in a positive result. Meanwhile, a fresh injection of capital had become absolutely necessary for the company to continue to operate. On October 16, 1920, Alfred Colsman, director of parent company LZ, apparently ran out of patience. An extraordinary shareholders' meeting was held, where he put the dissolution of ZF up for debate:

"The question now under discussion is whether we should proceed to liquidate Zahnradfabrik, or whether we can procure the additional 2 to 5 million marks, and how."[12]

In this situation, the decisive factor may have been the fact that Alfred von Soden, as general manager, did not share Colsman's pessimism regarding ZF. He indicated, as soberly and optimistically as possible, that the break-even point in manufacturing had already been reached:

"Count von Soden expressly [...] emphasizes that it would be a fallacy to assume Zahnradfabrik is still operating at a loss. He stated that this is not the case; in fact, manufacturing is generating a very adequate profit, and development is proceeding at a normal pace."[13]

In the end, von Soden and his authorized officer Habermaas received the additional two million marks in working capital from LZ. Zahnradfabrik had bought time, but its future remained uncertain.

ALFRED VON SODEN-FRAUNHOFEN

(1875 – 1944)

Alfred von Soden-Fraunhofen in a cuirassier's uniform, circa 1894/95. By serving as an officer in the military, von Soden did what society expected of him as a young nobleman and the son of a Bavarian government minister.

Count Alfred von Soden-Fraunhofen, co-founder and first general manager of ZF, was born on November 21, 1875 in Neufraunhofen, Germany.[1] After graduating from high school at Wilhelmsgymnasium in Munich in 1894, he joined the Bavarian military as a cuirassier in the 1st regiment of the heavy cavalry. After one year, von Soden became an "aspiring officer" and withdrew from active service. As a reservist, he was promoted to lieutenant in 1898, senior lieutenant in 1907, and cavalry captain in 1913. In 1895, von Soden began studying law in Munich. At the same time, he also attended lectures on experimental physics. After passing his first state examination in law, he decided that he would prefer to study mechanical engineering – initially against the wishes of his parents, who felt that the subject was inappropriate for a member of the aristocracy. Their feelings were in line with the prevailing attitude of the time, but in December 1903, von Soden completed his engineering diploma.

In November 1902, just under one year before completing his studies, von Soden had already started working for Daimler-Motoren-Gesellschaft in Stuttgart. He began as an assistant production manager in the rail department and later became a tester in the automobile department. In 1906, the young engineer and one of his college friends developed a diesel engine, which he presented to Maschinenfabrik Augsburg-Nürnberg (MAN). In 1908, he was hired by MAN in Nuremberg to continue working on this engine, which was known as the "Vogel" engine. In his free time, too, von Soden was a passionate designer, active in a wide range of different fields. His name is linked to inventions such as a shrapnel-filled bullet, a toy top, "invisible" suspenders, a shaver, a slide trumpet, and a spirit lamp.

Starting a family and working in airship construction

In the meantime, von Soden – a young baron – had attended a ball held by the Bavarian foreign office, where he met Countess Mechthild Adelmann von Adelmannsfelden; the two were married in May 1905 and had six sons and three daughters. In October 1906, von Soden traveled to Lake Constance, where he saw an airship for the first time – the LZ 3. Von Soden already knew the man who had initiated the construction of these airships, Count Ferdinand von Zeppelin, from his time at Daimler, where the engines for the first airships had been manufactured. Initially, the two noblemen remained nothing but friendly acquaintances; it wasn't until February 1910 that the airship pioneer from Lake Constance offered von Soden the opportunity to join Luftschiffbau Zeppelin GmbH as the head of a testing department that the company was about to establish. Despite extreme skepticism among his colleagues at MAN – who did not set much store by aviation – von Soden decided to take the job, moving his growing family to Friedrichshafen and taking the airships LZ 6 and LZ 7 on their first test flights that same year.

While von Soden dedicated himself to improving engines, transmissions, and aircraft propellers, Europe plunged into the maelstrom of the World War I. As an officer in the reserves, Soden reported for duty at his Munich regiment on August 1, 1914 and was made commander of a munitions convoy. He was later stationed on the western German front as a local commander in the Somme region. In April 1915, von Soden was recalled to Friedrichshafen. Count Zeppelin and many of Germany's military officers felt that the airships being constructed there would give them

Alfred von Soden's engineering diploma, 1903.

the upper hand in the war effort, and they asked Soden to assist in the manufacturing process to the best of his ability. The steadily improving performance of the propulsion engines being utilized in airships meant that the transmissions also had to be refined. The massive vibrations and noise generated during the transmission of energy made it clear that the bevel gears available at the time simply were not up to the task.

Idea for using the Maag process

Soden was familiar with the technologically superior process developed by Swiss engineer Max Maag, and he consequently put Maag forward as a potential business partner. His focus, initially, was on setting up a "department for transmission manufacturing Friedrichshafen" within Luftschiffbau Zeppelin GmbH.[2] However, the negotiations with Maag – in which von Soden took part alongside Alfred Colsman – actually resulted in the establishment of a new company: Zahnradfabrik GmbH, headquartered in Friedrichshafen. In 1916, as the Battle of Verdun was raging on the western German front and the Zeppelins were increasingly losing their military dominance in the skies to squadrons of Allied airplanes, the von Soden family ascended one rank higher in the hierarchy of the time. Maximilian von Soden-Fraunhofen, father of ZF general manager Alfred, had handed in his res-

Von Soden's exhibitor's pass for the Paris Automobile Show, 1933.

ignation as Bavarian minister of the interior that December. King Ludwig III, a man of the people with close ties to the Catholic Center Party of which Maximilian von Soden was a member, accepted his resignation from politics. In recognition of all of von Soden's achievements, the King raised the family to the earldom, awarding von Soden the title of Count.[3] He received the title in December 1916, and it was officially entered into the matricula of the aristocracy on January 31, 1917. In legal terms, however, this new title had little relevance for Alfred von Soden, as all aristocratic privileges were abolished when the Weimar Constitution went into effect on August 14, 1919.

Technical director of Zahnradfabrik

Of greater practical relevance was Alfred von Soden's appointment as technical director of Zahnradfabrik Aktiengesellschaft – formerly Zahnradfabrik GmbH – in Friedrichshafen in 1921. In this role, von Soden served as one of the most important driving forces behind ZF's technological development. His innovative spirit mainly produced results in the emerging automobile manufacturing segment. The Soden transmission, developed in 1921, featured a preselection switch for the individual gears; it was a feat of engineering that was far ahead of its time.[4] Soden's efforts to simplify and standardize automobile transmissions were a financial success, leading to the development of the "standardized transmission" in 1925. In partnership with a group of outstanding engineers, Soden worked on improving the shifting process in these transmissions while simultaneously minimizing noise emissions. The results of this fruitful cooperation included the Aphon transmission introduced in 1929 and the multi-synchronizer transmission, which went into production in 1934.

Distance, but not open opposition –
Von Soden in the Nazi era

Von Soden, whose contemporaries described him as humble, polite, and deeply religious, rejected

Alfred von Soden with his wife Mechthild during the last decade of his life. The Member of the Board of Management at ZF was already suffering from frequent health problems at this point.

the racist, aggressive ideology of the Nazis. However, in a combination of economic pragmatism, patriotism, and a sense of duty to the authorities, he supported Zahnradfabrik's conversion to wartime production in his position as technical director. In that sense, Soden indirectly contributed to enabling and prolonging Germany's actions during the war. Given his position within the company, his appointment as "defense economy manager" was a logical consequence. And yet, there are indicators that he maintained a distanced attitude toward the Hitler regime. Von Soden never became a member of the NSDAP, and he is said to have intentionally delayed his sons' entry into the Hitler Youth.[5] The foreword to the chronicle marking ZF's anniversary in 1940 bears von Soden's signature and the title "In Grave Times"; despite its patriotic tone, it still avoids using the Nazi vocabulary common at the time.[6] Rather than referring to Hitler at the end of the Text, von Soden mentions Count Zeppelin.

In 1940, the year that marked the company's 25th anniversary, von Soden was awarded an honorary doctorate in engineering from the Technical University of Stuttgart. At that point, he was visibly suffering from leukemia; his illness had been progressing since the early 1930s. Von Soden did not live long enough to witness the final months of the war and the decline of the company he had cofounded. Count Alfred von Soden-Fraunhofen died on June 14, 1944, and was buried at Neufraunhofen Manor in a private ceremony attended by his family. The local Nazi leadership prohibited any public ceremony honoring the ZF co-founder.

CONVERSION TO A STOCK CORPORATION AND YEARS OF INFLATION:

TECHNOLOGICAL VISIONS, ECONOMIC CONSTRAINTS

The ZF management team in 1923 (with Alfred von Soden, 2nd from right). Above: Lever-type transmission for cars, produced by ZF, 1922.

With the injection of a further two million marks in capital from Luftschiffbau Zeppelin GmbH (LZ) in October 1920, Zahnradfabrik was free of its liquidity problems for the time being. However, the fundamental dilemma that the company had faced since the end of the war remained. On the one hand, Zahnradfabrik had the technological potential to become the German and European market leader for automobile transmissions. But on the other, the company was burdened with a mountain of debt that was frightening away banks and potential investors. Shareholders LZ and Maag were not prepared to be the sole providers of the capital required to further expand the business, and Zahnradfabrik's capital base grew thinner and thinner. On March 11, 1921, an extraordinary shareholders' meeting was held in Romanshorn, Switzerland, on the southern shore of Lake Constance. Alfred Colsman, representing LZ, reported on the attempts that he and Alfred von Soden had made to acquire external investors for Zahnradfabrik:

"Thus far, our attempts have failed. ZF's situation has not improved since the last shareholders' meeting, and it must be viewed in a pessimistic light today. At the moment, additional funds totaling 3 million marks [are] required to augment the company's working capital and to procure a number of necessary machines. Given the dire situation in which Zahnradfabrik finds itself and the fact that LZ and Maag hold an unfavorable ratio of shares in ZF, LZ [cannot] provide these funds. Since we can assume that given the current conditions, the Maag Group also will not supply these 3 million marks, a complete restructuring of ZF is proposed, involving a merger of shares and the simultaneous conversion of Zahnradfabrik into a stock corporation."[1]

The stock corporation's overall capital, Colsman continued, would total five million marks, and shares would be distributed between LZ and Maag at a ratio of 4.25 to 0.75. The proposal also implied that neither of the two shareholders would insist on being repaid for previous investments, which totaled approximately 17 million marks. A debt forgiveness program of this magnitude would be enough to save Zahnradfabrik, particularly since converting the company to a stock corporation would make it easier to procure funds on the capital market. However, Colsman's proposal was a bitter pill for fellow shareholder Maag to swallow. By holding the threat of ZF's inevitable bankruptcy over Maag's head if the plan did not go through, the LZ director hoped to cut Maag's share in the profits from 50 percent (in Zahnradfabrik GmbH) to 15 percent (in the stock corporation still to be founded). However, representatives of the Swiss licensor demanded at least 30 percent. Protracted negotiations followed; it wasn't until another extraordinary shareholders' meeting on March 30, 1921, that the parties finally made a breakthrough. The ownership structure of Zahnradfabrik Friedrichshafen AG was set at four million marks for LZ and one million marks for Maag – dividends were divided at a ratio of 80 to 20.

Zahnradfabrik becomes a stock corporation

On May 27, 1921, the stock corporation was founded in the offices of Stuttgart-based notary Mr. Heimberger.[2] In addition to Alfred von Soden – general manager and future technical director of ZF – Alfred Colsman (for LZ), Max Maag, and Georg Fischer (for Maag) were in attendance, as were future supervisory board directors Baron Conrad von Bassus and Count Alexander von Brandenstein-Zeppelin. The entire year of 1921 was retroactively declared the stock corporation's first fiscal year. Directly after the company was founded, Zahnradfabrik Friedrichshafen AG and Maag AG signed a new licensing agreement. There were a few important differences between this new agreement and the one from 1915: first, opted to forgo licensing fees. Maag only earned money from the company's profit-sharing agreement with Zahnradfabrik Friedrichshafen AG – but in return, Maag was now able

*By the time people had the chance to spend the money
they'd earned, it had already lost its value.*

JOSEF KUTTNER

to operate on the German marketplace, independently of ZF. Second, ZF was now expressly permitted to sell transmissions that included Maag gears outside of the German territory covered by the license, although the company could not sell the individual gears themselves. Third, the agreement allowed ZF to use other production processes as an alternative to Maag's gear-cutting method. And finally, Maag agreed to sell Soden transmissions – both parties were convinced that the product had strong commercial potential.

Zahnradfabrik on an economic roller coaster

ZF now had the organizational structures in place that would allow it to exploit its technological potential in order to turn a profit. Alfred von Soden and his colleague from the board of management, businessman and former authorized officer Gustav Habermas, now had to deliver what they had promised the shareholders when the company was on the verge of liquidation. However, the unstable economic situation in the German Empire threw further uncertainties into the mix. Between spring and fall 1921, the German automobile industry – which was extremely important for ZF – experienced a sales crisis, followed by a temporary boom. At the same time, the devaluation of the mark was gradually reaching dangerous dimensions, particularly considering the fact that ZF had to buy the majority of its machines from Maag in Switzerland, where the currency was stable. The following excerpt from the company's 1921 annual report gives an impression of the kind of difficulties the first members of the board of management faced:

"After the economic crisis began, we were [...] forced to lay off large numbers of workers and civil servants: around 140 in total. Staff numbers reached their lowest point in summer, with 445 civil servants and workers employed at the company. We were unable to prevent a great number of diligent, well-trained employees from leaving us during this period – it was not what we wanted. Even back then, we were already aware that if we ramped up production again, we would have difficulty finding new staff to fill the required positions, as there are few employees in the region who are skilled in precision work, and the severe housing shortage in Friedrichshafen means that ZF cannot recruit employees from outside the area."[3]

In cooperation with the Zeppelin Welfare Association, Zahnradfabrik worked to counteract the housing shortage by laying aside large sums of money for the construction of new homes. In the stock corporation's first fiscal year alone, the funds set aside for this purpose totaled 500,000 marks – approximately one quarter of the company's gross profits. There was another problem that ZF was largely powerless to combat, however: the insufficient infrastructure in the region meant that the power frequently went out at the plant. In November 1921 alone, production during working hours (7:30 to 11:45 a.m. and 1:15 to 5:20 p.m.) came to a standstill 82 times as a result of power outages. All companies in Friedrichshafen were affected by these blackouts. For this reason, LZ, Maybach Motorenbau, and ZF cooperated with the local government to invest in two diesel-powered emergency generators, which largely stabilized the electricity supply beginning in 1922.

A license to print money – the inflation crisis of 1923

In the meantime, currency inflation in Germany

had spiraled completely out of control. The government of the German Empire was in large part to blame for this hyperinflation; by devaluing the currency, government officials hoped to artificially reduce the country's sovereign debt and the reparation payments owed to foreign countries. Additionally, this policy allowed the government to provide generous financial assistance to striking workers in the French- and Belgian-occupied Ruhr region – in a currency that ultimately wasn't worth the paper it was printed on. Many employers took drastic measures to provide their employees with some measure of financial security. Because shipments of new banknotes could no longer keep pace with the hourly devaluation of the mark, Zahnradfabrik also began printing its own emergency currency at the Druckerei Gessler printing house. Decades later, Josef Kuttner, head of accounts at the time, recalled the months of summer and fall 1923:

"During that period, wages and salaries were paid daily. When the ZF money was printed, the accountants had to supervise the printing process at the printing house. The process would often last until two or three o'clock in the morning. And by the time people had the chance to spend the money they'd earned, it had already lost its value. Usually, it was just enough to buy a cup of coffee at Café Bücher."[4]

Zahnradfabrik's balance surplus for the 1923 fiscal year was 81.2 quadrillion paper marks. But because a stick of butter often cost several billion marks during this period, this bizarre balance was really only useful for accounting purposes. According to the board of management composed of Alfred von Soden and new commercial director Hans Cappus: "The existing paper mark balance is not a standard that can be used to evaluate the state of our company."[5] It wasn't until the introduction of the "Rentenmark" – a currency whose value was backed up by deeds of trust on real estate and property – on November 15, 1923, that the situation began to return to normal. In 1924, Zahnradfabrik was once again able to present an orderly balance sheet: one that was in print for the first time.

In 1923, inflation was occurring so rapidly that many companies, including ZF, printed their own bank notes.

Consistent quality in uncertain times

Despite the numerous practical problems it faced, Zahnradfabrik was able to build up a strong reputation for its manufacturing. The products from Friedrichshafen were synonymous with high precision and consistency, as the following letter of reference written by MAN in August 1924 demonstrates:

"We would be glad to respond to your request that we comment on the quality of the services you provided to us, and we will elaborate on our business relationship, which has existed since 1915. We are aware that we demanded a great deal in terms of the performance of your workshops and machines, particularly as regards precision and accuracy, and we are happy to say that we are wholly and completely satisfied with your excellent, precise work. We would like to particularly emphasize the fact that our partnership involves much more than just single product versions or prototypes; we placed regular orders for volume production of designs that had been tested for many years, such as complete variable-speed transmissions with a clutch and rear-axle driving mechanisms."[6]

ZF could produce similar statements from nearly all of the renowned automobile manufacturers in the German Empire. There was one product in particular that truly represented the high technological standard that ZF had achieved in the 1920s: the Soden transmission. When the Zahnradfabrik stock corporation was founded, Count Alfred von Soden had transferred all of the patents

The Soden transmission (left) was available in different sizes for various vehicles –
a forerunner of the standard transmission that would be developed in the future.

34

related to this technology to the company – or at least the ones that were under his name and not already held by Zahnradfabrik.

The Soden transmission as a milestone

Volume production of the Soden transmission began in 1921. The new product was presented at the Berlin Automobile Exhibition in October of that same year, and it received a very positive response from automobile manufacturers. Werner Beisel, a leading expert on the Soden transmission, describes the benefits of the unit as follows:

"The Soden transmission clearly differed from non-synchronous manual transmissions – the only transmissions available at the time – in a number of ways. The transmission was evidence of ZF's efforts to make it easier for drivers to operate their vehicles. It was still a manual transmission, but the fact that the gear could be manually selected at any point in time and that gear preselection would subsequently kick in – and that this process only required the driver to activate the clutch pedal – was already a first step toward an automatic transmission. Incidentally, the company's first automatic transmission for passenger cars, the 3HP12, went into volume production in 1965 – exactly 50 years after the company was founded."[7]

ZF made every effort to popularize the new transmission among manufacturers and customers. The company even produced an ad in the style of the silent films of the time; it portrayed a group of people sharing a ride in a car, and it juxtaposed the struggles they faced using a standard manual transmission against the carefree driving experience that a vehicle with a Soden transmission could provide. The Soden transmission also received positive feedback in real life, as can be seen in this account – used by ZF for advertising purposes – from a customer in Dresden:

"I feel the need to share the following story with you, although it was not solicited: On March 26, [1924], I began a trip through Germany to Italy with my Otto automobile, which was equipped with a 100-horsepower Mercedes aircraft engine and a Soden transmission. I traveled through all of Italy with the car for seven weeks [...], and also through Sicily; in the process, [...] the vehicle was subjected to incredible ordeals [...]. I have driven a wide variety of other vehicles from first-rate brands, but the constant shifting on extreme inclines caused severe transmission malfunctions. With the Soden transmission, on the other hand, I did not experience even the smallest issue on my entire 4,225-mile drive. I did not even have to adjust the Bowden cable once."[8]

Better, but not cheaper

Despite its undisputed technological advantages, the Soden transmission remained a niche-market product.[9] Several thousand Soden transmissions were sold, but the unit did not meet the company's expectations in terms of market penetration. Many smaller manufacturers offered the transmission as an option, but at an additional cost. The Soden transmission was never included in a volume-produced model – apparently for reasons of cost and availability. The use of special versions of the transmission in trucks or the engine cars of German Reichsbahn railway trains was also quite limited. When the German economy experienced a temporary recovery in the mid-1920s, ZF launched a standard transmission of its own – a more affordable alternative to the Soden transmission. The Soden transmission became technologically obsolete in 1929, when the Aphon transmission was introduced. Because the three higher gears in this transmission included synchronization, the shifting process was easy, even without gear preselection. Like so many innovative ideas from the early days of the automobile, the Soden transmission was eventually forgotten in the mists of time. The idea of selecting a gear on the steering wheel in combination with a partially automatic transmission finally experienced a comeback years later, in the form of the paddle shifter that can be found in many of today's sports cars.

ALFRED COLSMAN

(1873 – 1955)

Alfred Colsman, managing director of Luftschiffbau Zeppelin GmbH (LZ) from 1908 to 1929, was one of the key figures in the early history of ZF. Colsman conducted the negotiations with Swiss engineer Max Maag that led to the founding of Zahnradfabrik in 1915, and in 1921, he was the driving force behind the conversion of the company into a stock corporation. In the opinion of his successor and future member of the ZF supervisory board Julius Oesterle, Colsman was responsible for nothing less than ensuring the company's survival:

"The support that Zahnradfabrik – still in its early stages at that point – received was exclusively thanks to Mr. Colsman, as Dr. Eckener [a Member of the Board of Management at the Zeppelin Foundation and Director of DELAG, the German Airship Travel Corporation] was only ever interested in airships. During those years, Dr. Eckener was essentially opposed to the idea of incorpora-

tion, because he believed that companies should divest themselves of participating interests in order to invest that money in airship manufacturing and travel."[1]

This assessment is extremely surprising, because in retrospect, Colsman never placed any particular emphasis on his commitment to ZF.[2] Despite the fact that the manufacturing of gears and transmissions for cars was never something especially close to Colsman's heart – rather, his greatest dream was to establish a fleet of airships that would operate worldwide – he recognized Zahnradfabrik's long-term financial potential, perhaps due in part to his background.

Son of an entrepreneur from Sauerland

While Hugo Eckener, a scholar of the humanities by background, served as editor-in-chief of the "Flensburger Nachrichten" newspaper before inheriting Count Zeppelin's legacy, Colsman had

*I would also like to stress that "Friedrichshafen"
is not a business; it is a calling.*

ALFRED COLSMAN ON HIS WORK FOR THE LZ CORPORATION, 1928

always been a man of industry. The son of an aluminum factory owner was born on May 7, 1873 in Werdohl, in the Sauerland region of Germany. After completing his studies at the Charlottenburg Technical College in Berlin (today known as the Technical University Berlin), he traveled abroad, visiting countries such as Russia, Sweden, and Turkey. He was first exposed to airship manufacturing in Friedrichshafen after meeting the woman who would later become his wife: Helene Berg of Lüdenscheid, the daughter of an industrialist. Helene's father Carl Berg also owned an aluminum processing company; he was a fervent supporter of Count Zeppelin and supplied materials for the first Zeppelin airship's aluminum frame. Alfred Colsman described his first encounter with the giants of the skies – still under construction at that point – and their creator:

"I first met [...] Count Zeppelin during my honeymoon at the Inselhotel in Constance in 1899. The Count paid us a visit to invite us to view this airship, the framework of which was complete, at a floating wooden hall in Manzell. [...] During my visit to see the airship, I had difficulty keeping up with the agile Count – already in his sixties – as I followed him up the ladders and onto the wobbling planks over the back of the ship."[3]

Commitment to airship manufacturing

When Colsman's father-in-law Carl Berg passed away in 1906, Colsman met Count Zeppelin at the funeral. At that point, Colsman was also already on the supervisory board at the Berg company, where he pushed for a resumption of the partnership with Zeppelin in fall 1907. He traveled to Friedrichshafen alongside his brother-in-law Rudolf Berg:

"Zeppelin was in a difficult financial position during this period; he had nearly used up the last of his reserves. He was thrilled to receive us, because he hoped that we would help him. His fervent belief in the future of the airship quickly won us over as well. We hadn't the slightest idea of the difficulties still plaguing the development of airship travel."[4]

Colsman quickly became aware that the considerable funds required for airship manufacturing would have to come from external investors. He managed to convince the top managers at the Berg and Krupp companies to participate in volume production of airships. An agreement regarding the fundamental contractual issues had already been made when the War Ministry in Berlin canceled the planned purchase of at least two airships, despite all of Colsman's arguments in favor of the sale. In order to test the effectiveness of the system, the War Ministry requested a 24-hour test flight. The company decided to fulfill this request with a flight from Friedrichshafen to Mainz on the LZ 4 airship. However, this trip unfortunately ended in a crash in Echterdingen on August 5, 1908; after the LZ 4 landed, it was swept up in a gust of wind and ultimately burned to a crisp. It was a miracle that no one was killed. But in one of the many ironies of history, it was exactly this catastrophe that allowed the airship manufacturing industry to acquire the solid financial foundation it needed. The Zeppelinspende des deutschen Volkes, a donation campaign that arose as a result of public sympathy following the tragic crash of the LZ 4, collected more than six million marks to

Postcard in remembrance of the Zeppelin disaster in Echterdingen in 1908.

support the company. Berlin was now also willing to provide the funding it had promised. This was the bedrock upon which Colsman would build up the Zeppelin corporation in the years that followed. The establishment of Zahnradfabrik, too, was largely funded by this public donation campaign.

Establishing the Zeppelin corporation

However, Colsman was still unaware of the kind of financial leeway he would soon have. On the morning of August 5, before he had been informed of the accident, Colsman had written a letter to Count Zeppelin in which he declared his willingness to continue to support the Count in setting up an airship manufacturing facility. Shortly thereafter, the two met in Friedrichshafen; the Count was still in shock after what had occurred in Echterdingen. Zeppelin asked if Colsman would be willing to serve as the director of a new airship company. Colsman immediately agreed.

After moving to the Lake Constance region, Colsman was involved in the founding of nearly all the companies that were part of the new Zeppelin corporation. Luftschiffbau Zeppelin GmbH (LZ) was established on September 8, 1908. On December 30 of the same year, the Zeppelin Foundation was created using funds from the public donation campaign. Almost all of LZ's share capital – 2.7 million marks, 300,000 marks of which remained the property of the Zeppelin family – was then transferred to the foundation. The corporation's first subsidiaries, Maybach-Motorenbau GmbH (initially founded as Luftfahrzeug-Motorenbau-GmbH) and Deutsche Luftschiffahrts-AG (DELAG, the world's first airline), came into existence in 1909. Colsman also founded a balloon hull factory, a warehouse construction company, and the Zeppelin Welfare Association. During the World War I three more companies followed: Zahnradfabrik, Zeppelin Werk Lindau GmbH (later Dornier-Werke), and Zeppelin-Werke Staaken

First newly constructed ZF factory in Friedrichshafen, 1919.

in Berlin, which constructed gigantic airplanes. Hugo Eckener, whom Colsman had appointed director of DELAG, is said to have criticized these "intermittent building fads."[5]

Split with Eckener and a lasting legacy

In fact, Colsman created a network of companies that rescued the still-unprofitable airship manufacturing industry from its dependence on donations and public subsidies. Additionally, the fact that Colsman had initiated the founding of all these companies had an unexpected but extremely important side effect: by investing in material assets such as property and production machines, the company managed to protect at least part of the assets it had acquired through the public donation program from the hyperinflation of 1923. However, this achievement was largely forgotten in 1924, when the media heralded Hugo Eckener as the savior of the German airship manufacturing industry after he delivered the ZR III airship to the United States as part of Germany's war reparations to that country. Colsman had previously expressed serious concern regarding this risky deal, which now put him at a strategic disadvantage. The tensions between the two equally charismatic and strong-willed captains of industry continued to intensify in the years that followed.

In 1929, Colsman ultimately left Luftschiffbau Zeppelin GmbH and returned to his hometown of Werdohl, where he took over the management of his father's factory. He spent his time researching local history and writing his memoirs of the founding years of the Zeppelin corporation. He refrained from making any critical remarks about Eckener, however. In the end, it was the airplane, not the airship, that made Colsman's dream of global commercial air travel a reality.[6] Airship manufacturing in Friedrichshafen came to a tentative end in 1939, but the subsidiaries that Colsman had founded continued to exist. Alfred Colsman passed away on January 9, 1955.

A risky deal succeeds:
The LZ 126 airship as a payment
of war reparations

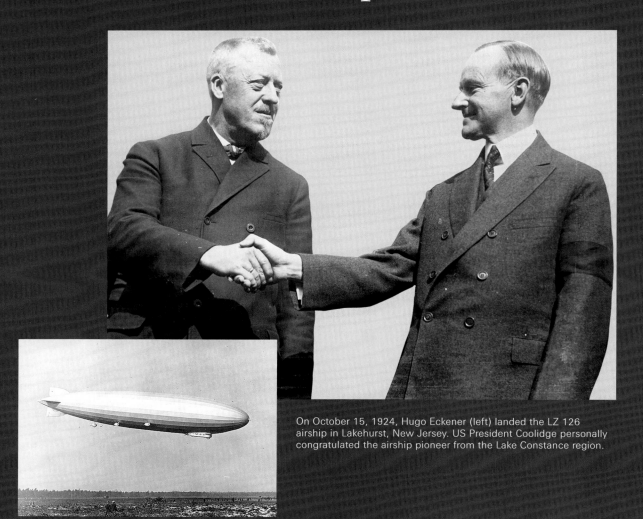

On October 15, 1924, Hugo Eckener (left) landed the LZ 126 airship in Lakehurst, New Jersey. US President Coolidge personally congratulated the airship pioneer from the Lake Constance region.

Hugo Eckener had reached his goal. After 81 hours of traveling, the director of DELAG – the German Airship Travel Corporation – disembarked from the gondola of the LZ 126 in Lakehurst, New Jersey on October 15, 1924.[1] The successful delivery of this airship to the United States as a war reparation payment from Germany was marked with wild celebrations on both sides of the Atlantic. US President Calvin Coolidge personally praised Eckener in a telegram: "I congratulate you upon the successful completion of the trans-Atlantic voyage of the great dirigible which you have brought from Germany to the United States. [...] It is an epochal achievement because it demonstrates as never before the feasibility of long distance flight by lighter than air craft and their ability to carry significant tonnages in passengers or cargo. The skill and efficiency of the German technicians in building such a wonderful aircraft and your skill in successfully navigating it without stop and without mishap from Friedrichshafen, Germany, to Lakehurst, N. J., is an event of world-wide interest. It is a matter of great satisfaction to me and to the people of the United States that the peaceful relations between Germany and America have been fully re-established and that this great airship has inaugurated the first direct air flight between Germany and America."[2]

Savior of the airship manufacturing industry

The Allied victors of World War I had originally planned to raze the airship production facilities on Lake Constance, but that idea was off the table – there was a future for the Zeppelins now. In that sense, Eckener's transatlantic voyage was more than just a feat of navigation; it was also stroke of public relations genius. Obviously, it would be unrealistic to say that the improvement in the political and economic climate between the USA and Germany was entirely due to Eckener's flight. Signs were already pointing to détente by that time, as both countries had a

vested interest in improving relations. Still, the media coverage of the record-breaking flight served as a catalyst. Eckener, an experienced journalist, had the opportunity to share his vision for transatlantic airship travel with US Secretary of the Navy Curtis D. Wilbur and the National Advisory Committee for Aeronautics, NASA's predecessor, in great detail.[3] According to his plan, the US would play a key role in commercializing the airship, as it was already clear that competing with the railroads and airlines for travel within Europe would be nearly impossible. While Eckener's American partners did not share his boundless optimism regarding commercial airship travel, they were pleased with his ideas. With his successful voyage, Eckener – dubbed the "Magellan of the skies" – became a hero overnight. In 1932, he was still so popular that he was considered as a potential candidate for the presidency of Germany.

Success proves Eckener right

In all the excitement surrounding the successful voyage of the LZ 126, the risks of the trip were forgotten. Indeed, if Eckener had crashed during the nearly 5,000-mile journey across the Atlantic, it would have inevitably led to the end of LZ and, consequently, Zahnradfabrik as well. Before the flight, the German government refused to accept any liability for the airship, which was valued at approximately 3.5 million reichsmarks, should it be lost. On the other side of the ocean, the Americans

only agreed to officially accept the LZ 126 once it had successfully completed the crossing. Eckener had such blind faith in his project that he put up all of the company's assets as collateral in exchange for the funds that the German government provided for him to construct the airship. And yet, he was more aware than anyone of the risks associated with an ocean crossing, especially since he was still piloting a ship that contained highly flammable hydrogen in its nearly 700-foot-long tail end. Julius Oesterle, who would later become director of Luftschiffbau Zeppelin GmbH, believed that it was Eckener's idealism as an aviation pioneer that made him throw caution to the wind:

"Dr. Eckener [...] was of the belief that Luftschiffbau Zeppelin had a calling: to develop and promote airship travel. He also felt that for this reason, it was wholly acceptable to [...] risk everything to achieve these goals."[4]

It is often said that history is written by the winners. The LZ 126 crossing the Atlantic is a good example of the veracity of that statement. A slight technical malfunction or an incorrect assessment of the weather conditions would have been enough to turn the flight into a fiasco, just like the Echterdingen accident in 1908 or the Hindenburg disaster in Lakehurst in 1937. But the voyage was a success, the US received its airship as war reparations, and Eckener went down in the history books as LZ's savior, rather than the man who dug the company's grave.

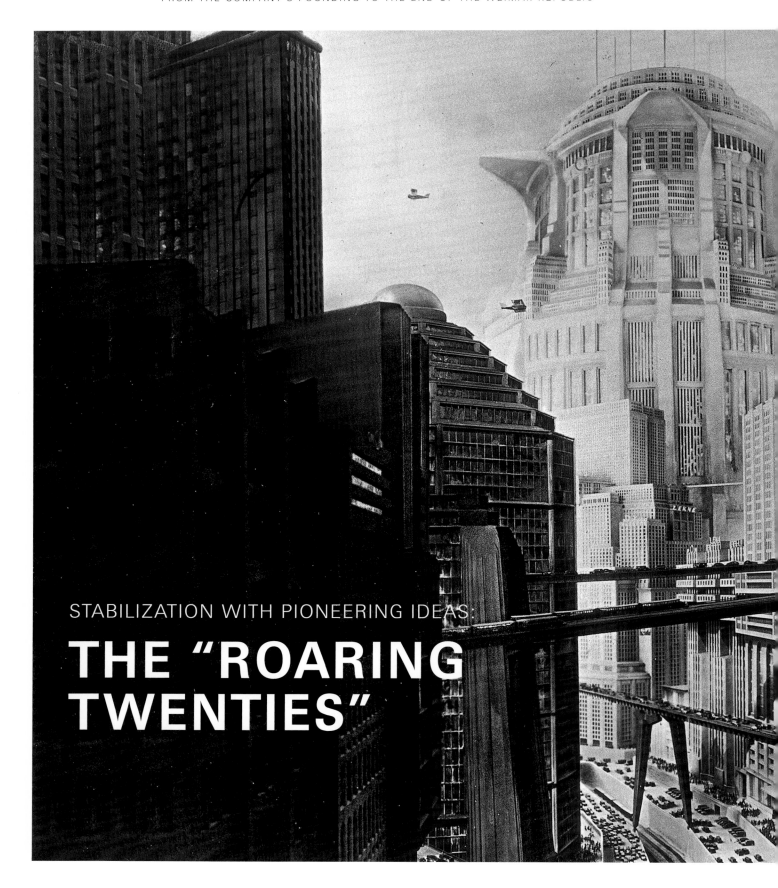

STABILIZATION WITH PIONEERING IDEAS:

THE "ROARING TWENTIES"

Many people in the 1920s imagined an urban future just like the one portrayed in the silent movie "Metropolis" (1925/26) from German director Fritz Lang. The film was shot in the LZ airship hangar in Staaken, near Berlin.

Between the hyperinflation of 1923 and the Great Depression that began in 1929, Germany's Weimar Republic experienced a period of economic recovery, due in no small part to the billions of marks in American loans that flowed into the country thanks to the Dawes Plan. Now that they no longer had to worry about their immediate survival, many Germans set their sights on the pleasures of culture and consumption. Movies and sporting events developed a mainstream following, and new technologies such as the radio and telephone became increasingly common. In the big cities – particularly Berlin – people began to enjoy a liberal lifestyle that stood in marked contrast to the conservative attitude that had characterized the fallen German Empire. The art and fashion of the era was innovative and often unconventional.

For the German automobile manufacturing industry, the "Roaring Twenties" brought about significant growth in sales, accompanied by a consolidation process. What had once been a scattered collection of smaller manufacturers that produced and sold customized vehicles as luxury products gradually developed into group of larger companies producing in greater volume. Daimler-Benz arose through the merger of Daimler-Motoren-Gesellschaft of Untertürkheim and Benz & Cie of Mannheim in June 1926 – and that's just one example. Like the rest of German society, the automobile industry was taking its cues from the USA. In 1914, Ford had already started manufacturing its famous Model T on the assembly line. The vehicle, which was tailored to the mass market, cost 370 dollars (in 1914 – equivalent to about 7,000 euros today) – far less than what traditional manufacturing companies could offer. Now that growing numbers of people in the Weimar Republic could afford a car, Ford decided to set up a facility for his modern production system right on the European manufacturers' doorstep. In April 1926, Ford's company began assembling the Tin Lizzy – or "Blechliesel," as Germans called the Model T – on the BEHALA premises at Berlin's Westhafen port.

A transmission for everyone

This development also presented a challenge for ZF. While the company did have superior manufacturing technology (the Maag process) and an innovative product (the patented Soden transmission), so far, these advantages had not translated into greater financial success. Albert Maier, who joined ZF in 1922 as a young engineer and later became technical director, described the situation in the mid-1920s as follows:

"Our borders were open to the import of mass-produced American products. Initially, our industry offered nothing that could compete with this influx of goods. American cars and trucks put a great deal of pressure on the market for German products. ZF was only able to counteract this development by interrupting its pioneering design work on the Soden transmission. Batch production (if not mass production) of conventional, low-price transmissions became the priority."[1]

In fact, Zahnradfabrik reacted relatively quickly to these changes in the market. While many automobile manufacturers were still focused on maximizing vertical integration and customization – Maybach, for example, manufactured the bodies of its luxury cars according to individual customer specifications and developed the transmissions itself – ZF created what was known as the standard transmission. It was made of simple, standardized parts and constructed in such a way that it could be installed in a range of different vehicle types without being altered. Various "off-the-rack sizes" were available for a variety of engines. However, even in higher performance classes, the standard transmission was extremely compact. A small group of engineers from the Technisches Büro Handelsübliche Getriebe (Technical Bureau for Conventional Transmissions, TBH), which was founded in 1923, developed the transmission in close cooperation with Alfred von Soden from the ZF Board of Management, as well as with the company's production management under Hermann Dolt, who would later be named director. At that point, ZF's customer MAN sent

the company a test vehicle to see how well the new design worked. "When the enormous MAN chassis rolled up to the testing garage," wrote Albert Meier, "the other new employees and I felt very anxious. Would the transmission live up to what we'd promised? During the first test drive to Blitzenreute [about 20 miles north of Friedrichshafen], however, our hearts only beat a little bit faster on the steepest inclines. The transmission held up, just like the 160,000 transmissions of the same type that were produced in the following years. It was a strong start, and we were in good spirits as we headed off to the Berlin Automobile Show with the transmission."[2]

The standard transmission at the IAA

The International Automobile Show (IAA), which was still held in Berlin at that time, was the most important industry trade fair in Germany. With the slogan Zahnradfabrik used for this event in 1926, "Einheit statt Vielheit" ("Unity, not Plurality"), the company appealed to people's economic sense as well as to the national conscience of the company's primarily German customers at the time. The clever concept paid off, and the standard transmission became ZF's first product to achieve large-scale success. In addition to MAN, ZF soon gained successful truck manufacturers like Dürkopp, Komnick, Mannesmann-MULAG, and Büssing as customers. However, the standard transmission for passenger cars did not become commercially relevant until the second half of the 1920s, when mid-sized cars were produced in greater quantities. During that period, the transmissions underwent a constant process of improvement.

With its standard transmission, Zahnradfabrik had responded to the desire for standardization among many manufacturers, so it was no coincidence that ZF representatives also pushed for the implementation of official standards in the German automobile industry. As the head of the design department at the time, Walter Ehrlenspiel, recounted, this campaign for standardization resulted in a partnership between Zahnradfabrik

Presentation of the standard transmission at the Berlin Automobile Show, 1926.
Below: Albert Maier (center) at the ZF design department, 1924.

and Schweinfurt-based company Fichtel & Sachs (part of ZF since 2001):

"At the standardization meetings taking place during that time [...] I met Mr. Binder from Fichtel & Sachs. He mentioned that his company was thinking of getting involved in clutch manufacturing. I immediately encouraged him in this endeavor and recommended that he base his designs on American single-disc clutches [...]. He and I immediately laid out internal standards for the connecting shafts of our transmission, because the German Standards Committee was progressing much too slowly. This strategy proved highly successful during the implementation of both the standard transmission and the modern clutch. [...]."[3]

ZF Berlin emerges

In order to improve its relationships with customers in the northern regions of Germany, ZF opened a branch on Gerichtstrasse in Berlin's Wedding district in October 1925. The branch was equipped with its own production machines, but its primary purpose was customer service and sales. In the beginning, the location was unable to cover its expenses through manufacturing as a result of the higher overhead costs in the German capital and the branch's small size. Internal audit reports from 1926 to 1931 indicated that the branch was operating at a loss, but ZF's management continued to invest in its machinery. In 1932 – the climax of the Great Depression, of all times – it seemed as though the strategy was finally paying off. ZF posted a modest profit of 14,500 reichsmarks.[4]

However, the figures gloss over the fact that ZF's Berlin branch was actually relevant to the company's manufacturing processes from an early stage. Even in 1925, the year the branch was established, four profile grinding machines were set up at the location. They operated according to the Minerva process;[5] ZF had purchased a license for this process from Minerva Motors S.A. in Antwerp in February of that year. Using this technology, the company was able to grind large-volume batches of helical gears for the first time. Compared to the straight-cut gears that had previously been in use, the Minerva gears offered a decisive advantage: they made transmissions much quieter. It took a long time to develop a functional prototype, however, and ZF was initially unable to achieve satisfying results with the new machines.

Aphon transmission on ZF's test bench, 1931.

The dream: a silent transmission

Luxury car manufacturers, in particular, were extremely interested in quiet alternatives to the "singing" transmissions that were the standard at the time. The trend toward closed vehicle bodies in Germany – an idea that came out of the USA – further increased the industry's interest in decreasing transmission noise, which had previously been drowned out by the wind and other sounds from outside the car while it was in motion. In their desperation, manufacturers like Maybach even dreamed of automobiles without transmissions; Maybach was working to develop engines with dramatically improved performance and resilience – so much so that they would make transmissions unnecessary. However, Maybach's attempts were unsuccessful, which meant that the market for a "silent" transmission was wide open, and would be a lucrative one for the company that finally made the technological breakthrough.

Zahnradfabrik had worked with several different approaches to this technology; its experience stretched back to 1921, when the company used a process it had developed called "A-gearing" to manufacture gears that Alfred von Soden called "completely silent and noiseless."[6] However, in practical terms, this technology was almost impossible to use. Silent transmissions required gear teeth so precise that they were extremely difficult to mass-produce on the machines of the time. Additionally, normal wear and tear reduced the gears' precision so quickly after they were installed in a transmission that it didn't take long before they were no longer noiseless.

As an alternative to manufacturing quiet transmissions, ZF engineers considered using helical gears. However, with the machines of the era, these gears could only be milled, not ground. The Maag company even stated at the time that grinding helical gears was impossible. But thanks to its license from Minerva, Zahnradfabrik made this "impossible" technology a reality by the end of 1925. In the meantime, however, the competition had not been idle – several different manufacturers from the USA presented prototype transmissions with internal gearing, as Walter Ehrlenspiel recalled:

"The Americans had taken a wrong turn on the road to developing a quiet transmission. It was a known fact that internally toothed gears were the quietest during operation [...] So some clever man invented [...] a 'ring-gear transmission.' It was a very complicated design, but company after company [...] copied it. [...] [These] companies ultimately changed course when they realized that quieter transmissions could actually be produced using our process."[7]

The Aphon transmission in volume production

Development of the first volume production-ready transmission that took advantage of the benefits offered by Minerva helical gearing was not complete until June 1929. The second, third, and fourth gears of the transmission, which was referred to internally as the G25 or the "quiet gear transmission," were equipped with helical gears, while first gear and reverse still employed conventional straight-cut gears. Albert Maier, who played a major role in designing the unit, described the result as "outstanding for the time, both in terms of shifting and smoothness during operation."[8] Maier also reported that commercial director Hans Cappus had the idea of holding a contest among the employees – the person who came up with the best name to advertise the new product would win. With exports in mind, company management selected the name "Aphon transmission" (a loose translation from Greek: "without sound") from among the many submissions; back then, it was safe to assume that the educated population in other countries would understand the name.

This demonstrates that Zahnradfabrik was increasingly looking for sales markets outside of Germany. Indeed, the company was in desperate need of new markets, as the German automobile industry also came under increased pressure during the Great Depression, which began in fall 1929.

ZAHNRADFABRIK DURING THE GREAT DEPRESSION:

INNOVATION ON THE BRINK OF THE ECONOMIC ABYSS

In 1929, Germany was caught up in the maelstrom of the Great Depression. Shown here: unemployed people in Berlin (circa 1929), stamping an unemployment card (1930).

We hope that through our strong financial management, excellent manufacturing facilities, and – last but not least – our innovative designs, we have provided our company with such a solid financial footing that it will be resilient enough to withstand another economic slump, and that it will maintain its value for our shareholders and continue to offer employment to our staff. However, this may not be possible if the overall economic situation continues to develop in a consistently negative way."[1]

The sober, succinct phrasing in the 1931 annual report barely hints at the momentous tasks that ZF faced in the final years of the Weimar Republic. The global economy had been in a state of deep crisis since 1929. The source of this economic collapse – the Great Depression – was the USA, where the troubles first began. Even today, experts are still divided on the exact cause. But one thing is certain: a stock market bubble and the fact that the country's currency was tied to existing gold reserves (known as the "gold standard") were major contributing factors. Additionally, consumer demand could not keep up with the steadily growing supply of consumer goods, which led to a collapse in prices. The Wall Street crash in late October 1929 was the straw that broke the camel's back.

Because the USA was one of the most important trade partners and lenders for many companies in Germany, the German stock market also experienced the aftershocks of the crash. However, the crisis did not begin in earnest for the German economy until the government – and a majority of voters – played their part in escalating the situation. While the German government under Chancellor Heinrich Brüning exacerbated the issues by slashing salaries and wages in the public sector and putting a moratorium on all state-sponsored construction projects, the right-wing National Socialist party (the Nazi party, or NSDAP) began to garner growing numbers of votes. The party of Adolf Hitler, with its aggressive nationalist and anti-Semitic slogans, had a strong showing in the Reichstag parliament elections of 1930

(18.3 percent) and 1932 (37.3 percent) – which, in turn, caused most foreign investors to rescind the credit they had extended to German companies. Bank loans were nearly impossible to come by. Countless companies lost their liquidity and were forced to declare bankruptcy. During the Great Depression, industrial production in Germany declined by more than 40 percent, and by 1932, the unemployment rate had surpassed 30 percent.

ZF bucks the trend

Considering the severity of the situation, it is both surprising and impressive that ZF avoided falling victim to the general trend. After its employee numbers dropped by 12 percent between 1928 and 1929, the company managed to stabilize its workforce at approximately 530 employees between 1930 and 1932. Only once during the entire economic crisis did Zahnradfabrik have to report a loss: in 1931. This was the result of a legally mandated reassessment of the company's inventory and was therefore not connected to its operational business; in fact, sales at ZF actually increased by approximately 10 percent in 1931. So why was Zahnradfabrik able to survive the Great Depression relatively unscathed?

Some of the company's success can be attributed to its efficient manufacturing and its technological expertise. As an audit report from 1929 indicates, the 212 production machines at the Berlin and Friedrichshafen sites were relatively modern.[2] The Board of Management emphasized in its 1929 annual report that the company had regularly purchased machines "with its own funds," so ZF did not depend on loans. Additionally, the company was working on "systematically improving its operating methods."[3] With licenses from Maag and Minerva, ZF had access to the best manufacturing technologies of the era for straight-cut and helical gears, and the company itself had distinguished inventors among its ranks. Chief designer Albert Maier alone registered more than 20 patents in his name during the period between 1925 and 1932[4] – more than even technical director Alfred von

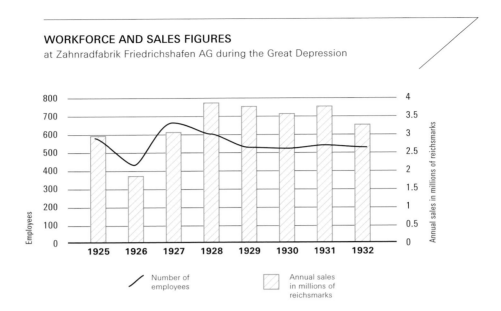

WORKFORCE AND SALES FIGURES
at Zahnradfabrik Friedrichshafen AG during the Great Depression

Soden, who also held a number of very important patents and intellectual property rights.

ZF's management was well aware that buyers' credit-worthiness was declining, so the company made a concerted effort to ensure outstanding debts were paid by the end of the ongoing fiscal year.[5] What's more, ZF had an efficient accounting department: beginning in 1929, the department began using a punch card machine – the first precursor to modern IT systems. This early model did not yet provide printouts, so all computed results had to be copied into the payroll sheets by hand. By 1932 – as the Great Depression was still ongoing – ZF consequently upgraded its equipment again, this time opting to rent a "self-printing" model.[6]

Sales success at home and abroad

It would be a mistake to attribute ZF's relatively positive development to its organizational foundation alone, however. The commercial success of the standard and Aphon transmissions was the primary reason behind ZF's survival. Members of the Board of Management Alfred von Soden and Hans Cappus elaborated on this in the 1929 annual report:

"The automobile transmission known as the 'ZF standard transmission' is in constant use in nearly all German and many foreign trucks. We expanded production volumes by consolidating the requirements of multiple customers whenever possible, which allowed us to systematically reduce prices and contribute to lowering the cost of German trucks in a significant way. The automobile manufacturing industry, too, is gradually freeing itself from the belief that individual companies must manufacture everything themselves; the trend is heading toward the cost-effective procurement of prefabricated transmissions. The new Aphon transmission that we recently launched – a four-gear transmission with three quiet gears – offers a particular incentive in favor of purchasing prefabricated units."[7]

Looking for new market opportunities abroad was the right choice for ZF, despite the fact that the political situation at the time was less than conducive to brisk, fair international trade, to say the least. In 1931, Swedish company Scania-Vabis and Czech company ASAP Škoda purchased transmissions from ZF, and Zahnradfabrik generated approximately 262,000 reichsmarks in busi-

A shot of the ZF accounting department in 1929. The proportion of women working in administration was high, while females were the exception in manufacturing and management positions.

Shifting gets easier

The units ZF sold were cutting-edge at the time, but they did have a number of characteristic disadvantages. The standard transmission was affordable, but it could be very loud, especially during faster drives. The pricey Aphon transmission was quiet in the higher gears, but that made its weaknesses all the more obvious: "Spoiled by the quiet operation of the vehicle," said Albert Maier, "drivers grew increasingly unhappy with the sound produced by clumsy shifting."[9] Transmis-

ness with the Soviet trade mission in Berlin – more than the company made from its business with Daimler-Benz.[8]

sion designs at the time required double clutching and intermediate application of the throttle while shifting in order to bring the gears up to the correct number of revolutions per minute. This idiosyncrasy exasperated inexperienced drivers and could turn a relaxing Sunday drive into a hectic affair. The solution to the problem was synchronization: a process that automatically adjusted the number of revolutions per minute when the driver shifted gears. When the Aphon transmission went into volume production in 1929, some American manufacturers were already offering synchronization in a number of transmission models. The solutions available at the time required too much installation space for the Aphon transmission, however. ZF consequently developed space-saving multi-disc synchronizers that could be integrated into the Aphon transmission's design, although initially, this simplified shifting was only available for the highest three gears.

The road to the "fully synchronized transmission"

All of these efforts to create partially synchronized or partially quiet transmissions were only temporary solutions, however. Ultimately, any solution that was to achieve commercial success would take all gears into account, and would be simultaneously compact and cost-effective to manufacture. Given the company's previous experience with this technology, the idea seemed like trying to fit a square peg in a round hole. And yet, Zahnradfabrik came ever closer to achieving this ideal during the economically troubled years between 1929 and 1932. In mid-1931, ZF regis-

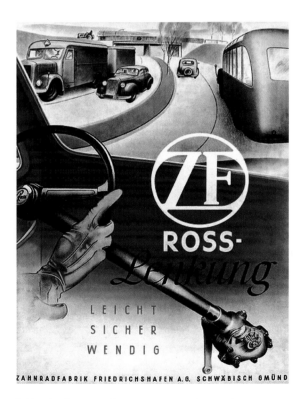

Ad for the Ross steering system, manufactured by ZF under license, 1932.

tered a patent for a freewheel. This unit was installed between the transmission and the axle being powered; it made shifting in all gears much easier, and it even saved fuel. Like modern bicycles, however, vehicles equipped with a freewheel could only be slowed through wheel braking. The "engine brake" no longer existed. This made driving on mountain inclines or in stop-and-go traffic uncomfortable and dangerous, and the freewheel was only manufactured for a short time, despite the fact that ZF designers had actually hoped that it would replace the much more complicated synchronizers as a method for facilitating shifting.

Steering system production begins

Generally speaking, mistakes like this one were nothing out of the ordinary. No developer could reasonably expect to lay the foundation for a successful product with every single patent. And yet, Members of the Board of Management Cappus and von Soden had to consider the potential risks of betting on the "wrong" technology for too long. Because Zahnradfabrik focused almost exclusively on developing and manufacturing transmissions, a single wrong decision could lead to financial ruin – especially considering that the Great Depression had significantly limited companies' economic leeway. It may have been deliberations such as these that led Alfred von Soden to suggest that in addition to transmissions, ZF should produce steering systems in the future.[10] Of course, the fact that German automobile manufacturers were increasingly working to optimize steering systems at that time likely also played a role in this decision; the company's 1932 annual report emphasized that "important components of the automobile, such as the engine, transmission, and axles, have been rapidly approaching perfection in recent years." [11]

As ZF had no real experience in this field, the company began searching for a partner with a technologically superior production process – just as it had done when entering the gear manufac-

*A new area of business is the
manufacturing of automobile steering systems.*

FROM THE 1932 ANNUAL REPORT

turing business – and found what it was looking for in Ross Gear and Tool Company, which was founded in 1906 and headquartered in Lafayette, Indiana. The company was known for its "one-pin steering system" – a simple design that operated smoothly, precisely, and relatively vibration-free. In 1932, ZF was granted an exclusive five-year license to manufacture and sell Ross steering systems in Germany and other European countries. ZF was required to purchase the steering worm, one of the core components of the system, from Ross in the USA. The licensing fees for manufacturing the steering system were included in the per-unit price.[12] ZF initially assembled the systems in Friedrichshafen, although steering fingers were supplied by SKF in Schweinfurt.[13] Wanderer-Werke in Chemnitz – at that time under the umbrella of state-owned company Auto Union AG – was the company's first customer for this product. The sales generated in the first few months after production began raised hopes of a profitable business in the future.

From the Great Depression to the Third Reich

In the second half of 1932, it seemed as though the economic tides were finally turning, albeit gradually. The unemployment rate began to decline slowly but steadily, and beginning in August of that year, the German stock index started to show signs of monthly growth. In late 1932 and early 1933, however, this progressive economy recovery was overshadowed by political events. The Nazis seized power on January 30, 1933, which was met with a less-than-euphoric response from the management of Zahnradfabrik. Staunch Catholic Alfred von Soden and supervisory board

chairman Hugo Eckener – a well-known supporter of America – certainly disapproved of the paramilitary attitude and open racism of Hitler's squads of thugs. During his denazification process, Eckener claimed that he had openly opposed the Nazi party before 1933:

"In 1932, I gave a radio address at the request of Chancellor Brüning, wherein I opposed the nationalistic activities surrounding the National Socialist ideology and the 'Stahlhelm' [paramilitary organization]. As a result of this address, after Hitler seized power, he wanted to put me in a concentration camp. It was only the intervention of [Paul von] Hindenburg that prevented him from doing so."[14]

And yet, Zahnradfabrik's Board of Management and Supervisory Board acted as willing helpers during the twelve years that Hitler's "Thousand-Year Reich" existed, aiding the dictator by supplying the government with armaments. Of course, they were also acting in Zahnradfabrik's financial interest, as the company's workforce and sales figures increased tenfold during that period; the company accepted the fact that the tanks and military vehicles equipped with ZF technology served a criminal regime. As captains of industry and Zahnradfabrik's managers, Hugo Eckener and Alfred von Soden, Hans Cappus and Hermann Dolt simultaneously contributed to making Friedrichshafen such a powerful center of armaments production that the Allies ultimately bombed it into dust. However, in late 1932, no one could have predicted how the company's strategy would end. Management was focused on Zahnradfabrik's financial survival.

1933
–
1945

ZF during the Nazi era

A boom in the automobile market and a growing need for military equipment result in soaring demand for ZF transmissions. However, growth comes at a terrible price.

DANGEROUS SUCCESS:

A MILITARY BUILDUP YIELDS GROWTH

ZF's trade fair stand at the Berlin Automobile Show, 1938.

The newly constructed train station at the port in Friedrichshafen seemed like the perfect staging ground: on the day of the inauguration ceremony for the station, March 7, 1933, members of the local branch of the Nazi party (NSDAP) hoisted the swastika flag on the tower of the new building. Regional station director Bihl-meyer had protested the action and insisted that the black, red, and gold German flag – the symbol of Weimar Republic democracy – be raised instead.[1] His argument was supported by the political numbers: the NSDAP held just two of the twenty seats on the city council. During the national parliament elections on March 5, the Nazis earned significantly more votes in Friedrichshafen, but even with 32 percent of the vote, they were still behind the Center Party (38 percent), which had deep roots in the region. However, supporters of Adolf Hitler – who had been named German Chancellor on January 30, 1933 by President Hindenburg – had the overall German election results in their favor; the NSDAP was the clear winner there by a wide margin. With marches and open displays of brutality, the Nazis had long since tightened their grip on Friedrichshafen as well. On March 8, they draped the swastika flag across the façade of Friedrichshafen's city hall. People continued to display their resistance publicly, albeit increasingly cautiously. The mayor of Friedrichshafen at the time, Hans Schnitzler, had held office since 1920; he declared that he would not enter city hall as long as that flag was hanging from the gables. However, Schnitzler avoided an open clash by holding appointments outside of the building until the Nazis removed their flag on March 11.

Isolation and forced coordination

In the meantime, border controls on the shores of Lake Constance had become much stricter.[2] After that point, very few opponents of the regime managed to escape to Switzerland on ferries. This growing isolation from the outside world went hand in hand with a policy of forced coordination within Germany. The goal of the new regime was to forcibly bring all areas of government and society into line with Nazi ideology; pluralism and regional independence fell victim to this centralized Nazi dictatorship. Two laws formed the basis for the Nazis' seizure of power: the Reichstag Fire Decree of February 28, 1933, which suspended important civil liberties, and the Enabling Act of March 24 of that same year, which allowed Hitler's cabinet to pass laws without the approval of the parliament. The Center Party, which held power in Friedrichshafen, actually voted in favor of the latter law in the national parliament in Berlin. Subsequently, the Nazis were able to pass a plethora of laws and regulations that put their people into key positions of power in government and public institutions. In May 1933, the memberships of state parliaments and local councils were "adjusted" in proportion to the majorities in the German national parliament – which meant that seven city councilmen from the NSDAP joined the local parliament in Friedrichshafen. Mayor Schnitzler, an open critic of the Nazi regime, was forced into retirement in November 1933, at the age of 59. Walter Bärlin, a native of Bietigheim who had joined the NSDAP in 1933, took his place the following year. Communists were fiercely persecuted throughout Germany's territory; many members of the KPD, Germany's communist party, were among the first to be sent to the newly established concentration camps. The SPD, Germany's center-left social democratic party, was also banned in June 1933. The Nuremberg Laws of September 1935 officially codified the anti-Semitism that was an integral element of Hitler's political beliefs. The state-sponsored violence against Jews escalated rapidly in the years that followed, ultimately resulting in the Holocaust – the policy of extermination that ended the lives of between 5.6 and 6.3 million people.

Economic boom in the Reich

In the months before the NSDAP seized power in 1933, even Hitler's most vehement opponents could not have fathomed the magnitude of the regime's future crimes. In fact, Germany's business leaders and intelligentsia vacillated between excitement at the energy behind the Nazi movement and disgust at the fact that the party attracted fanatical, violent thugs. However, as it became clear that the Nazis had apparently kept their promise of combating unemployment and guiding Germany out of the Great Depression, it grew increasingly easier for the German populace to accept Hitler and his (primarily petty bourgeois) followers. German industry began to do brisk business once again.

Compared to many other companies, ZF had survived the downturn of the global markets between 1929 and 1932 relatively unscathed. By late 1932, the company was receiving a significantly higher number of orders, thanks in part to international contracts with Ford and Citroen.[3] However, the boom in the market for automobile transmissions that began in spring 1933 exceeded all expectations. On April 10, 1933, the German government decided to temporarily lift the tax on motor vehicles – and as Hitler and his advisors expected, this move gave the automobile industry an enormous boost. In June 1934, when the ZF supervisory board looked back on the previous fiscal year, Director Hans Cappus determined "that the tax exemption had an unexpectedly significant positive impact on the market for passenger cars, and that this measure sparked a whole new level of demand where consumers had once been restrained. The trend is the same in truck manufacturing [...]. The Ross steering system also sold very well – 10,000 units in 1933."[4]

The numbers spoke for themselves: during the first year of Nazi rule, sales at ZF increased from 3.2 million reichsmarks (1932) to 5.6 million reichsmarks. With results like that, it hardly mattered that profits from international business were down by approximately 37 percent during this period. ZF's workforce doubled within a year as well: from 533 employees in early 1933 to 1,082 by the end of the same year. Production went from two to three shifts, and workers racked up countless overtime hours. Given the steady demand for ZF's products,

it seemed like a rapid expansion of the company's production facilities was in order. In mid-1933, the Board of Management and supervisory board approved 300,000 reichsmarks for the purchase of machinery and the expansion of the production area in Friedrichshafen. For its Berlin branch; ZF purchased a nearly three-acre property – a vacant ball-bearing factory – in the district of Wittenau. ZF Berlin moved into its new home in spring 1934, and the period that followed was marked by constant expansion of the branch's production capacities until the war broke out several years later.

Employee rights are curtailed

Given the declining unemployment rate and the palpable economic boom that was boosting all areas of business, the majority of German employees accepted the fact that they would lose many of their labor rights – all in service of their "ethnic community" of course. The German Labor Front (DAF), which was founded on May 10, 1933, took the place of the various labor unions that had previously represented the workers – and it also swallowed up their assets. The right to strike was abolished. Despite the fact that the DAF also officially represented Germany's employers, companies were able to maintain their own interest group, which was known as the Reichsstand der Deutschen Industrie (or the Reichsgruppe Industrie beginning in January 1935).

Between 1935 and 1938, the Reich government introduced special work papers (known as the Arbeitsbuch) for workers in Germany. The purpose of these documents was to make it more difficult for employees to change jobs of their own accord – if they found a better-paid position, for example. The freedom of many workers was completely eliminated by the "Verordnung zur Sicherstellung des Kräftebedarfs für Aufgaben von besonderer staatspolitischer Bedeutung" ("Act on securing the labor force necessary for tasks of particular national importance"), which went into effect in July 1938. This law allowed the German government to conscript any German citizen to

Above: Construction of the new Hall 2 in Friedrichshafen, ca. 1934.
Left: Company fitness programs to ensure military readiness among employees were part of everyday working life (1936).

work at companies that were considered vital to the war effort. If citizens refused, they could be sent to a "labor education camp."

While works councils and unions were stripped of power, managers at most German companies were largely spared from government intervention. As long as business leaders accepted the new political line and weren't Jewish, the system allowed them to continue managing their companies as they had always done. A look at ZF's annual reports from the 1930s and 1940s reveals that Nazi rule had little to no practical impact on the company's upper management. Hugo Eckener remained Chairman of the Board, and Count von Brandenstein-Zeppelin and Georg Fischer (as a representative of Maag) held their seats on the Board of Management without interruption from

1932 to 1946. Eckener, at least, was permitted to keep his position despite – not because of – his critical attitude toward the ruling regime. For example, the Nazi shop steward at LZ sent a report to the party's district business manager indicating that Eckener was "not national socialist-minded" and "only reluctantly" acquiesced to the Nazis' demands – and yet, Eckener faced no consequences.[5] Employee representatives, on the other hand, had already lost their rights in 1933, as Hansjörg Dach, son of the works council chairman at the time, recalled:

"My father, Valentin Dach, started working at ZF in 1926. He was considered a dedicated member of the labor union, and he was the chairman of the local Social Democratic Party association in Friedrichshafen. Shortly after the Nazis came to

Meeting of ZF's management, 1939.

power, he was forced to resign as works council chairman; however, he stayed at ZF, despite the fact that he frequently butted heads with Nazi shop steward and employee representative Franz Ade. In my opinion, this is proof that even during the Nazi dictatorship, ZF maintained a certain degree of political tolerance. At another company, my father might have been imprisoned for his political beliefs."[6]

Alfred von Soden and Hans Cappus continued to manage the business from their positions on the Board of Management even after the Nazis seized power. When von Soden died in 1944, former Vice Chairman Hermann Dolt took his place.[7] Dolt had served as an authorized representative at the company since 1921; in other

words, von Soden was not replaced by a "political" appointment from outside ZF.

Technology transfer for military projects

The Nazis' seizure of power only had an effect on the technology Zahnradfabrik produced insofar as the company had to adapt its existing processes and systems to new political priorities. ZF engineers supported the military buildup in Germany by adapting civilian transmission designs to military purposes. As early as 1933, ZF partnered with Friedrich Krupp AG; the companies were tasked with developing a light armored combat vehicle ("Panzer I"). Because the Treaty of Versailles prohibited Germany from manufacturing combat vehicles, the Panzer I was developed as an "agricultural tractor." As part of this project, ZF supplied a total of 477 five-gear FG35 transmissions that were largely based on the Aphon transmission for large automobiles.[8] In 1935, ZF and Maybach developed a higher-performance version of the vehicle that was equipped with the ZF FG31 Aphon transmission. More than 2,700 of these vehicles were produced by 1939 – and that was just a preview of what was to come in the years ahead.

Initially, ZF still generated the majority of its sales with civilian manufacturing. The trend toward motorized vehicles affected many industries and aspects of life, which meant new markets for Zahnradfabrik – specialized transmissions for fire trucks and dump trucks were among the products the company advertised during those years.[9] When it came to automobiles, mass production was slowly becoming the established method. Daimler-Benz, for instance, produced the AKS 15 partially synchronized transmission under license from ZF and began installing it in the Mercedes 170 V in 1936. A total of 80,000 vehicles were equipped with this particular unit by 1942.[10]

The accelerated expansion of the Autobahn system in the Reich posed new challenges for the designers at ZF. The transmissions the company had designed in the late 1920s were never intended to regularly operate at speeds of 50 mph or faster for extended periods of time. The short transmission ratio and the fact that the transmissions were limited to three or four gears meant that reaching these speeds required a very high number of revolutions per minute. This, in turn, consumed more fuel and increased wear and tear; it was not unusual for engines and transmissions to fail. To compensate for the fact that highway driving was becoming increasingly common, the designers at ZF – rather than developing an entirely new model – came up with a separate "Autobahn distance gear" that was mounted to the AK4S fully synchronized transmission. This meant that volume production of the AK4S models, which had launched in 1933 at great expense, could continue.

In 1937, ZF presented its first test vehicle with an "electric transmission" at the Berlin Automobile Show.[11] This unit included a magnetically powered clutch; to alternate between the six gears, the driver merely had to operate a simple shifter on the steering wheel. Like the Soden transmission before it, this product was so far ahead of its time that it seemed highly unlikely that the company would be able to turn a profit by installing it in passenger cars. For tanks, on the other hand, an electromagnetic clutch was a promising concept – shifting was extremely difficult with those large transmissions. In 1937, ZF began conducting tests with the "Panzer II" developed by MAN, which had previously utilized a non-synchronized six-gear manual transmission built by ZF. Electromagnetic shifting systems came under consideration a number of times – such as in 1942, when the heavy combat tank "Tiger" was being developed – but in the end, even for military applications, ZF opted for simpler mechanical designs instead.

Branches in Schwäbisch Gmünd

As Germany's military buildup continued, it increasingly began to shape ZF's development. By the time the company opened two plants in Schwäbisch Gmünd in 1937/38, it was already fully compliant with the Nazis' military agenda. Planning for the new plants began in summer 1936, after Hermann Göring's undersecretary General Erhard Milch indicated "that we have bigger plans for Z.F."[12] In a memo from October of the same year, the situation is explained as follows:

"The company ZF has been tasked – by both the Reich Ministry of Aviation and the Army Ordinance Office – with planning a new factory to supply the Wehrmacht. [...] At the behest and recommendation of Defense Economy Inspection V [...] and the Ministry of Economics in Württemberg [...] the city of Schwäbisch Gmünd, which has an available pool of workers due to the decline of the silver industry, comes highly recommended as a location for this planned Zahnradfabrik site.[13]

Construction on two additional plants at the Schwäbisch Gmünd site began in 1937.

The company had its eye on an undeveloped property in the district of Schiesstal. There, ZF would set up a subsidiary – Schwäbische Zahnradwerke GmbH – that would primarily produce gears for the Luftwaffe. At the same time, the company established a completely separate production facility in the Ziegelberg area of Schwäbisch Gmünd; this factory would supply the army. By 1938, the facility was already producing locking differentials. While the property in the Schiesstal district was being prepared for the construction of the factory, the Reich Ministry of Aviation and ZF were squabbling over the distribution of costs. ZF only wanted to provide its new subsidiary with the lowest possible amount of share capital; it would actually be financed by government loans. The ministry countered that proposal by suggesting

that ZF should invest share capital of one million reichsmarks in setting up the factory. The two parties eventually came to an agreement: they would reduce production planning for the plant by about a third, ZF agreed to provide the new company with 600,000 reichsmarks in start-up share capital, and the Reich Ministry of Aviation provided the same amount as a loan.[14]

Zahnradfabrik on the rise

While Hitler's regime consolidated its power through compulsory measures, social welfare, and propaganda, ZF was experiencing an unparalleled boom thanks to large-scale car ownership and the arms race. Between 1933 and 1938, the company's sales increased by 559 percent, and its workforce more than tripled. In that respect,

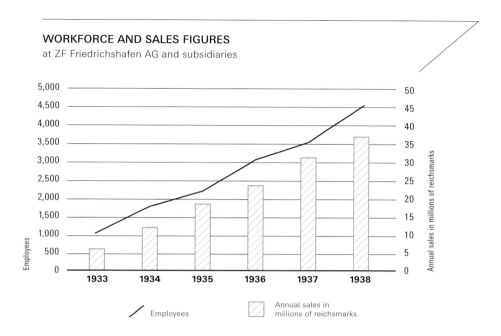

WORKFORCE AND SALES FIGURES
at ZF Friedrichshafen AG and subsidiaries

Employees

Annual sales in millions of reichsmarks

1933 1934 1935 1936 1937 1938

Employees

Annual sales in millions of reichsmarks

Zahnradfabrik was growing at a much faster rate than overall gross national product in Germany, which rose by 72 percent during the same period. In the 1938 annual report, Members of the Board of Management von Soden, Cappus, and Dolt (the last of whom was mentioned as a deputy for the first time) attempted to come up with an explanation for the sales boom that went beyond merely pointing to the overwhelming demand:

"As the largest transmission producer, we are very involved in the ongoing reorganization of the automobile industry. Many years ago, we conducted significant preliminary work to limit the number of transmission models for automobile manufacturing. We would refer the reader to our earlier reports, where we explained that using the same transmission in many different vehicle types would encourage the manufacturing of large volumes and reduce the price of the final product considerably."[15]

In fact, the Nazis' policy of military buildup facilitated the very standardization process that ZF had been promoting since the standard transmission was introduced in 1925. While other manufacturers struggled to manage enormous, wildly diverse portfolios of products and technology and were only brought into line by government regulations restricting the number of different models available, ZF had long since streamlined its product range. The company's motives for doing so were purely financial and had nothing to do with Hitler's preparations for war – but now, both ZF and the regime profited from the company's early focus on large-batch manufacturing. ZF management in Friedrichshafen must have been aware that the company had gradually taken on a pivotal role within the German military equipment industry – as evidenced by the "Regional Certificate for Excellent Performance" that the German Labor Front presented to ZF in 1937, among other things. The company would go on to receive this award three more times in the years that followed. On the eve of the Second World War, however, ZF's strategic importance to the war effort was only hinted at in writing. As the Board of Management wrote in June 1939, "with four state-of-the-art plants, we should be up to the task of meeting the ever-increasing requirements being placed on us."[17]

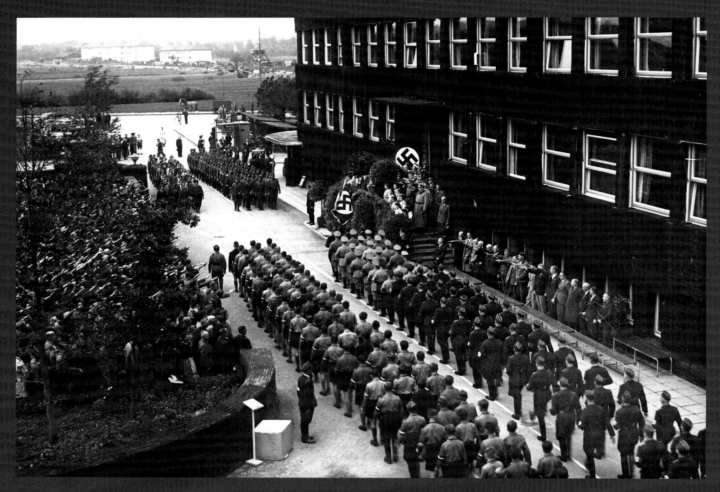

Company roll call to mark ZF's 25th anniversary, 1940.

25 Years of ZF: "In grave times"

On September 28, 1940 – the day of Zahnradfabrik's anniversary – the company reflected on the new sales records it had set during the previous fiscal year. ZF now employed more than 5,000 people, and all of the plants were operating at capacity. And yet, Alfred von Soden, co-founder and Member of the Board of Management at Zahnradfabrik, did his best to temper the euphoria of the moment: "We shall not mark the day of our anniversary with a festive, joyous celebration [...] rather, it shall be a solemn, quiet, and brief occasion."[1] In light of the ongoing

*Our duties do not permit us to hold a raucous celebration today,
nor do they allow us much room for pause.*

ALFRED VON SODEN IN THE FOREWORD TO ZF'S ANNIVERSARY PUBLICATION, 1940.

war, the Board of Management and supervisory board had decided to forgo a raucous party. Instead, the employees gathered for roll call – a necessary ritual during that time. Commercial director Hans Cappus had the pleasure of announcing that employees would be receiving anniversary bonuses of between 10 and 30 percent of their monthly wages, depending on how long they had worked for the company. In October 1940, the company paid out a total of around 286,000 reichsmarks.[2]

The anniversary festivities continued as a small number of guests were invited to the Buchhorner Hof Hotel, and then to the Kurgarten Hotel. Alfred von Soden was showered with tributes; at the employee roll call, he had received a portrait of himself painted in oils, and now, the dean of the mechanical engineering department at the Technical University of Stuttgart presented him with an honorary doctorate. After that, Mayor of Friedrichshafen Walter Bärlin named the Count an honorary citizen of the city. Government representatives, customers, and industry organizations also congratulated von Soden and the company he co-founded and helped to lead.

Unpopular alliance:
ZF and the Nazi regime

ZF had the Nazi regime and its steady military buildup to thank for the largest sales boom in the company's history. As staunch patriots, Alfred von Soden and chairman of the supervisory board Hugo Eckener felt that they had a moral obligation to the German troops in the field, as well as to the ruling authorities. However, as educated men of the world, they were also opposed to the racism and populism promoted by the Nazis. By the same token, the regime depended on Zahnradfabrik; the company's technology was vital to most of the vehicles used by the Wehrmacht. A representative of the Army High Command attending the ceremony, Colonel Philipps, emphasized in his speech that there was "likely not a single soldier in the motorized troop units [...] who was unfamiliar with the name ZF."[3] Ideologically and personally, however, the Nazi leadership and the upper echelons at ZF kept their distance from each other. Klara Schultheiß, who took a job as a secretary in the ZF executive office in April 1940, recalls the situation at the time:

"Hitler once wanted to hold a Nazi rally at one of LZ's airship hangars. Dr. Eckener, who was not a Hitler supporter, would not consent to allowing the hangar to be used in this way. After that, the 'Führer' ostracized Friedrichshafen in a way – he never visited the city."[4]

The ambivalent relationship between the Friedrichshafen-based military supplier and the Nazi leadership was also reflected in the events and speeches surrounding ZF's anniversary. For example, the Wehrmacht only sent officers who held the rank of Colonel, despite the fact that higher-ranking officers would've been more appropriate to the vital role that ZF's transmissions played in the war effort. Nazi district manager for Stuttgart, Wilhelm Murr sent his head of propaganda in his place. Alfred von Soden, who headed one of the most important military supply companies in the Reich, received the War Merit Cross Second Class – a medal that was presented 2.7 million times during the Nazi era. Von Soden got his revenge by hardly mentioning Hitler or the ruling Nazi party during his speeches; he only ever addressed the fact that the regime promoted car ownership by scrapping the motor vehicle tax in April 1933 – a move which he praised as "the Führer's first great feat."[5] Rather than extolling "German virtues" in his anniversary speech, the Member of the ZF Board emphasized how important the (Swiss) Maag gearing process and the (American) Ross steering system were to ZF's development. Above all, however, he spoke of the mutual understanding between the employees and management at ZF, and the loyalty of the company's workforce. "Our first workers and salaried employees are still with us here at ZF, and we are proud of that."

ZF AS A MILITARY SUPPLIER:

SUPPORTING VICTORY AT HOME

On the "home front:" iron storage facility at ZF, 1942.

We are well aware of the fact that you have a lot of work to do back home, because we are consuming endless amounts of material. [...] When the machines race by above us, we can also claim credit for that effort. Today, I tell people: that's the work of my comrades, who are laboring alongside us day and night for victory."[1]

Alfons Vetter, a salaried employee at ZF in Schwäbisch Gmünd, was serving as a military engineer, constructing bunkers on the eastern front, when he wrote this letter. By that point, in fall 1942, a large number of ZF's employees had been called up for military service. Approximately one-ninth of all workers and salaried employees from ZF Friedrichshafen AG were serving in the military at that time.[2] In the east, the Battle of Stalingrad was raging; it would result in the annihilation of the Wehrmacht's 6th Army a few months later. Alfons Vetter's description only gives us an inkling of the brutality of the battles being fought – specifically, when he mentions the "endless" need for military equipment. Because this letter from the field left no doubt that Hitler's forces would be victorious, LZ's plant magazine, which was controlled by the German Labor Front, printed it as a reflection of the mood on the battlefield. The hope was that letters like these would boost morale on the home front.

At the same time, all of ZF's factories were operating at full tilt. Sales figures and employee numbers consistently reached new highs; regular weekly working hours increased from 57.5 (standard for LZ at the time) to 60 (late 1943) and finally to 74 hours (with the implementation of the Emergency Fighter Program in 1944). ZF employees who were sent to the front were increasingly being replaced back home by women and foreign workers. Zahnradfabrik had to hope for preferential treatment when it came to the distribution of raw materials, which were growing ever scarcer. And yet, the company's importance to German troop readiness could not be overstated: approximately 92 percent of all transmissions installed in German tanks –

over 40,000 units in total, plus replacement parts – came from ZF's factories.[3] The remaining eight percent were manufactured by Maybach Motorenbau GmbH – also a subsidiary of LZ – which additionally supplied 100 percent of the tank engines used by the Wehrmacht. In other words, without engines and transmissions from these two affiliated companies – Maybach and ZF – German tanks would have gone absolutely nowhere.

Maybach competes with ZF

The development process for ZF transmissions between 1939 and 1945 reflects not only the necessities of war, but also the rivalry that emerged between Maybach and ZF regarding the principles of transmission manufacturing. Engine manufacturer Karl Maybach is quoted as saying that a transmission can never be too complicated, as long as it

As a result of its contributions to the war effort, ZF was named a „model wartime plant" in 1943.

Transmissions for the German "Tiger" combat tanks were primarily produced at ZF. Shown here: loading in Kassel (above, ca. 1942), maintenance at the eastern front (right, 1944), and a destroyed "Tiger" tank in France (below, 1944).

functions safely and makes shifting easier for the driver.[4] For a producer of luxury automobiles, this would seem like a logical approach. Maybach also applied this philosophy to the tank transmissions produced by his company. The units were state of the art at the time: during the first years of the war, a number of German tanks employed Variorex transmissions, which had either seven forward and three reverse gears, or as many as ten forward and four reverse gears. The vacuum generated by the engine helped the driver shift.

However, the transmission proved rather unreliable, and it began to reach the limits of its capacity as vehicles grew heavier – which was certainly the trend for German tanks. An important trigger for

this development was the Wehrmacht's unexpected confrontation with the Russian T-34 tank in summer 1941; it put the German weaponry systems of the time to shame. The T-34 was fast and maneuverable, it had immense firepower and strong armor plating – and what's more, it was manufactured in large batches. German military high command now ordered the development of a heavy tank that could stand up to the Russians. The result was the "Tiger," which was assembled beginning in 1942 by the company Henschel near the German city of Kassel, and the "Panther," which went into production in 1943. Maybach Motorenbau developed the Olvar transmission for the "Tiger;" it had a total of twelve gears, which, like in the Soden transmission, could be engaged semi-automatically with gear preselection and subsequent clutch actuation. The unit weighed around 1,430 pounds and had hydraulic shifting support and a highly complex control system. To compete with Maybach, ZF engineers came up with different versions of the "SMG transmission" (Sonder-Mehrgruppengetriebe, "special multi-combination transmission"), which was heavily based on the design of the Olvar transmission, but which differed in a number of details. Both designs were theoretically very promising, but for wartime products, they were extremely complicated. On the Panzerwiese ("Tank Meadow") – a testing ground near Gehrenberg Mountain in Markdorf, a city about eight miles north of Friedrichshafen – Karl Maybach is said to have presented the Olvar transmission to Albert Speer, Minister of Armaments and War Production since February 1942, with whom he had an excellent relationship.[5] Speer subsequently awarded Maybach the contract to produce transmissions for the "Tiger."

A simpler form of transmission manufacturing

ZF was less than pleased with this development, and not just because its designers were suffering from wounded pride. LZ had already decided back in 1937 that the tank transmission developed by Maybach would mainly be manufactured at Zahnradfabrik's plants. So in 1942, members of the Board of Management von Soden and Cappus faced the challenge of coming up with a method for mass-producing the Olvar transmission – an incredibly complex unit consisting of a vast number of individual components that had to be of the highest quality. The Maybach unit required rolling bearings made of highly alloyed steel; these were particularly difficult to come by. Additionally, ZF and Maybach had been pursuing very different design philosophies since before the war; ZF's was rooted in the standard transmission. Albert Maier, who was head of development at ZF during the war, described this contrast as follows:

"In 1942 [...] Count von Soden recorded his ideas on constructing transmissions for tanks, requiring that ZF designs be based on the simplest possible construction. It is only natural that a company that [...] itself was a manufacturer for many years would learn to avoid using any unnecessary parts in the process. The fact that the [German army ordinance office, which made decisions regarding the development of new weapons systems] endorsed a different course of action was not a condemnation of ZF's approach. German industry's ability to meet these demands depended on the respective manufacturing options. [...] In 1940/41/42, however, there were two distinct camps in the ordinance office: on the one side was the industry, which was in favor of simplified production (and consequently, larger batches), and on the other were the defenders of the more complicated method."[6]

In a speech Albert Maier held in 1944, he promised that in a purely mechanical sense, it was possible for even very heavy vehicles to shift gears without shifting assistance, as long as the manual transmissions were appropriately optimized. Additionally, the transmissions would require sufficiently high-performance engines in order to make do with a smaller number of gears. As Maier indicated here, this insight was gradually implemented at ZF as the company gained experience with volume production. The SFG and SSF transmissions ("Sonder-Fünfgang-Getriebe" – special five-gear transmission – and "Sonder-Sechsgang-Getriebe" – special six-gear transmission) constructed for use in the German tanks Panzer III and IV between 1935 and 1942 were structured very differently than the Aphon transmission for passenger cars, on which the first military drafts for the FG transmission in 1934 and 1935 were based. However, the units still included complex multi-disc synchronizers and rolling bearings, and given the ongoing raw materials shortages and lack of qualified workers, the design was nearly impossible to produce.

In 1942, when ZF was commissioned with developing a transmission for the medium-duty "Panther" tank – which was meant to serve as a direct counterpoint to the Soviet T-34 – the company con-

Count von Soden always required us to base our designs on the simplest possible construction.

ALBERT MAIER, 1944

sequently decided to work on a completely new design. Between February and August of that year, a ZF team under Albert Maier's leadership developed the AK7-200 seven-gear manual transmission; its structure was very similar to the truck transmissions of the time. It was relatively compact and contained a cost-effective cone synchronizer. From a technical point of view, the project was a gamble – up to that point, experts were unsure whether a tracked vehicle weighing nearly 50 tons and sporting a 700-horsepower engine could even handle manual shifting. Initial trials proved promising, however, and the German army ordinance office ordered 5,000 transmissions without conducting further tests. By the end of the war, more than 6,200 of these units had been manufactured; in addition to the "Panther," they were also installed in the "Tiger" heavy tank. In light of the extreme destruction German tank units caused during the second half of the war – during the Battle of the Bulge in 1944/45, for example – it is truly tragic that the transmissions ZF supplied to the Nazi forces functioned so reliably.[8]

The Waldwerke site in Passau

In order to meet the steadily rising demand for increased production, the Board of Management and supervisory board at ZF had been exploring potential new locations since 1941. In cooperation with the Army High Command, the company decided to establish a subsidiary in Passau that December; it was dubbed Waldwerke GmbH. After numerous scheduling delays, the company was officially founded on May 3, 1943, and the first Olvar transmission for the "Tiger" tank was shipped out of Passau in November of that year.

Despite the fact that ZF was the most important manufacturer of tank transmissions in the Reich between 1939 and 1945, the company also continued to produce transmissions and steering systems for civilian applications such as passenger cars, trucks, and tractors, albeit at much lower volumes than before the war. In practical terms, however, ZF made little progress on its civilian products during this time; the development process was overshadowed by demand from the military. An internal memo from October 31, 1944 made this very clear:

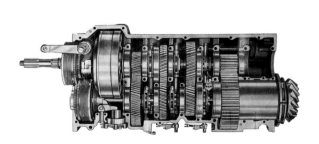
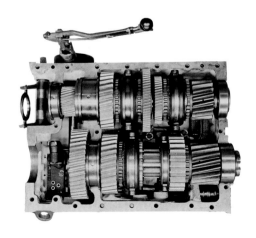

Comparison of a cross-section model of Maybach's Olvar transmission (left) and the AK7-200 (right) developed by ZF. The ZF design was much more compact and, more importantly, easier to manufacture.

Construction on
the Waldwerke
plant in Passau
started in 1943.

"Previously, ZF's transmission designs were divided into two categories: commercial transmissions and special transmissions, the latter being produced for the Wehrmacht [...]. However, as a result of the war, the entire field of commercial transmission manufacturing is now included under the heading of military production – and is strictly limited. Consequently, the company is, in practical terms, only producing transmissions of strategic importance to the war effort [...]."[9]

This conflation of civilian and military production had started long before the war began, however. Since the mid-1930s, the German automobile industry had been forced to begin standardizing its models. In

March 1939, the entire process was formalized with the introduction of the Schell Plan, which was named for Colonel Adolf von Schell, General Plenipotentiary for Motor Vehicles. ZF set the course here in a number of ways. For example, the "light standard automobile," which was based on civilian vehicles and was produced between 1936 and 1942 for use as an off-road commando vehicle, utilized the RW 1 five-gear constant-mesh transmission from the ZF plant in Berlin.[10] 30,000 units of this transmission were shipped out before the standard automobile was replaced by the VW military utility vehicle. However, even after this transmission was no longer in use, ZF continued to produce automobile transmissions – for the Mercedes 170 V and its military version, for instance. This vehicle utilized the AKS15 transmission, which ZF had introduced in 1932. In the commercial vehicle segment, ZF was extremely successful during the war, as Albert Maier points out: "We had captured nearly the entire market for truck transmission manufacturing."[11]

Outsourcing steering system manufacturing

With the incredible workload being placed on ZF, the company's steering system division – which was headquartered in Friedrichshafen – faced an enormous amount of pressure. In 1937, this division had been granted its own production facility, where it manufactured steering systems for axle loads of up to approximately seven tons for a range of different German companies. Zahnradfabrik desperately needed this production space for transmission manufacturing, so on the "recommendation" of the Stuttgart-based military supply command, ZF's management decided to partially relocate steering system production to Sélestat in the Alsace region after that territory had been conquered by the Nazis in 1940; the company would make use of the local workforce there. Franz Boll, who joined ZF in 1937 and would later go on to serve as head of production planning at the Schwäbisch Gmünd site for many years, recalled the situation at the time:

"So in 1941, ZF set up a production facility in Sélestat, which employed around 500 people once all the machines and equipment had been relocated. Production managers, supervisors, and foremen came from Friedrichshafen – although foremen only came in exceptional cases [...]. The folks from Friedrichshafen all brought their families along. They had a good relationship with the Alsatians, but our 'golden pheasants' [referring to the high-ranking Nazi party and military officials in light-colored uniforms, and Hermann Göring in particular] wanted to turn the [Alsatians] – who had been torn between France and Germany for a long time – into good Germans as quickly as possible. However, all they did was put everyone at loggerheads in the process."[12]

Even after the move, ZF continued manufacturing the Ross one-pin steering system that had been introduced in 1932; the company only optimized the design for the vehicle models dictated by the Schell Plan. However, for a brief period during the tenure of division head Werner Diedrich, the steering systems division was tasked with recreating a worm-and-roller steering system originally developed by US company Gemmer Manufacturing Co. to be installed in a light truck being constructed by Daimler-Benz under license from Opel. It was this design that ultimately replaced the Ross steering system at ZF in the 1950s.

Boats with airship technology

Another product segment that became more commercially relevant in the period after the war was directly connected to the military buildup during the Nazi era: the marine reversing gear division. Initial tests with the unit had been conducted back in 1928/29, but apparently did not produce satisfactory results.[13] However, a transfer of technology from the airship manufacturing segment in the mid-1930s proved successful: for the LZ 129 airship "Hindenburg," which was constructed in 1936, Daimler-Benz developed a diesel engine that performed at 1,200 hp and 1,600 rpm. The driveline utilized a propeller swivel transmission, which ZF had been manufacturing since 1932. According to the German Kriegsmarine's plans, the Daimler engine was supposed to work not only in the air, but also in the water, in speedboats. Engineer Eugen Hartmann, who had worked for Luftschiffbau Zeppelin since 1929, was subsequently tasked with converting the non-reversing bevel gear transmission for airships into a reversing marine gear.[14] He succeeded, and ultimately moved to ZF to continue working in this field. The transmission hit the market in 1935/36 under the name KS25; ZF constructed approximately 1,000 of these units before the end of the war. The Kriegsmarine was satisfied, and the design also attracted prospective customers from outside the Reich: on September 11, 1944, ZF granted the Imperial Japanese Department of the Navy the right to reproduce the KS25.[15] The company's decision was based on a German-Japanese treaty signed in March 1944, which stipulated that the Axis powers would make their

During the war, ZF employed growing numbers of women after many men were conscripted into the Wehrmacht. Shown here: the technical registry office, 1943.

technology and raw materials available to each other in order to improve their chances of winning the war.

Until the first Allied bombs fell on the shores of Lake Constance in June 1943, the employees at ZF's main plant barely felt the effects of the war – apart from the fact that they produced the endless stream of supplies that the war machine demanded every day. What little news arrived from the front was heavily censored, and few foreign press outlets were permitted to take a look beyond the factory gates. Klara Schultheiß, who was a secretary for the Board of Management at the time, recalled what working life was like back then:

"A Swiss newspaper was found in our office once; that was strictly forbidden. It caused a huge uproar. After all, in those days, you never knew who you could trust. The Gestapo was everywhere, and we were all constantly afraid that someone would inform on us."[16]

However, even in the face of the Nazis' propaganda and intimidation, employees at ZF were still aware of the fact that many people were dying in the war. It was impossible to ignore the growing numbers of foreign workers and forced laborers at the factory, or the fates of former colleagues who had joined the Wehrmacht. In its 1942 Christmas issue, the LZ plant magazine listed the names of ZF employees who had been killed at the front that year: 49 names, or more than one tenth of the ZF employees who had been conscripted. And given the military situation in the Reich at the time, it was clear that this was just the beginning.

FORCED LABOR DURING THE WAR:

THE DARKEST CHAPTER

Departure of French foreign laborers from the Gare du Nord train station in Paris on June 3, 1943

In late February 1943, young French engineer Jacques Desbois received a letter from the German military command in Paris.[1] He was instructed to report to the Gare de l'Est train station at 10:00 a.m. on March 11, 1943; from there, he would depart for Germany. Should he refuse to comply with this order, he would face "punitive measures."

Desbois was not alone in his fate; thousands of others in the territories occupied by the German Reich found themselves in similar circumstances. The Nazi regime was in desperate need of workers for its domestic economy – with every battle lost, more German men were called up for military service. For this reason, Fritz Sauckel – who had been appointed as Reich General Plenipotentiary for Labor Deployment in 1942 – instituted a policy of forcibly recruiting workers for the German agricultural and industrial sectors from all over Europe. The circumstances under which these foreign workers were "hired" varied greatly, as did their living conditions in Germany. The Belgians, Dutch, Danes, and French were known as Westarbeiter (western workers), and apart from the fact that they were forced into these jobs and faced the perpetual threat of punishment, they were otherwise treated comparatively well. In contrast, forced laborers from Poland and Russia were subjected to horrendous abuse – as were Italians, who were considered deserters after the ceasefire between Italy and the Allied Powers in September 1943. These workers were cared for only slightly better than concentration camp prisoners, who were also used as forced labor. Additionally, the situation of foreign workers depended greatly on their specific work environment and the attitude of their German supervisors.

As a military supplier, ZF was under constant pressure to increase production. At the same time, the company had to maintain a standard of quality that would allow their transmissions and steering systems to function reliably – and this required skilled workers. In that sense, the forced laborers at ZF had a degree of relative security compared to workers in other industries, such as mining.[2] The company needed highly trained foreign workers, so providing them with a basic level of care seemed reasonable; consequently, skilled laborers were generally guaranteed a certain minimum standard of care and recreation. On the other hand, however, discrimination against foreigners was legally mandated. The Ostarbeiter (eastern workers) from the Soviet Union, for instance, were required to wear a badge with the word "OST" sewn onto their clothing at all times. Members of this group were treated with extreme harshness. Polish workers (who were required to wear a "P" badge) and other workers from Eastern Europe suffered much the same fate. In most cases, treatment of the workers was left to the discretion of their German supervisors – they could distinguish themselves as agents of the regime by dealing with the laborers harshly, or, if they possessed a modicum of moral courage, they could treat their subordinates like human beings, regardless of their origin.

Hungry for labor

The earliest foreign laborers who began working in Friedrichshafen during the Nazi era actually came willingly. They first arrived at ZF in appreciable numbers in 1940.[3] During this fiscal year, 83 foreign workers were recorded at the Friedrichshafen plant, including 51 from Belgium and 22 from Yugoslavia. In 1941, the number of foreign workers at this plant rose to 283; Belgians and Yugoslavs still comprised the vast majority of this group. At the same time, women from branches of industry that

DURING THE WAR the proportion of foreign laborers in the ZF workforce steadily increased. In 1943/44, it reached its peak:

34%

were considered "not essential to the war effort" were also required to work at ZF.[4] From 1941 to 1942, the proportion of women in the company's workforce rose from 8.7 to 13.4 percent.

In 1942, Hitler and his military advisers realized that the war against the Soviet Union would not end in a quick victory. While the Wehrmacht prepared to face another winter on the eastern front, Hitler decided to lift the ban on using the labor of "Bolsheviks" – who were hated and feared in equal measure – in German companies, clearing the way for mass deportations of Russian laborers to Germany. This development was also reflected in the structure of the workforce at ZF. Between 1941 and 1942, the number of foreign workers at ZF increased from 311 to 1,456; the proportion of foreign workers in the overall workforce (ZF Friedrichshafen AG and subsidiaries) rose from 5.3 to 22.6 percent as a result of this influx. The number of Ostarbeiter at the company also increased drastically, from 15 to 812, while the total of foreign laborers employed at the company ultimately reached its peak in 1943 and 1944. With 34 percent of its workforce coming from foreign countries, ZF Friedrichshafen AG was above the average (around 30 percent) in the German metal industry.[5] At the company's plant in Berlin and its subsidiaries, Schwäbische Zahnradwerke Gmünd GmbH and Waldwerke Passau GmbH, foreign workers and forced laborers actually comprised more than half of the workforce in 1944.[6] Including a relatively small number of prisoners of war, more than 2,800 forced laborers were employed at ZF Friedrichshafen AG during the war.[7] An internal list from May 1943 indicates that the members of the ZF workforce at the time came from 15 different countries; Germans and "stateless persons" were counted separately. The largest groups originated in the Soviet Union, France, the Netherlands, and Belgium. In Friedrichshafen, the foreign workers at ZF during the war (1939 – 1945) comprised approximately 18.8 percent of the total number of forced laborers working at all industrial companies in the region. Maybach, Luftschiffbau Zeppelin, Rostan (a construction company), Dorni-

A Russian forced laborer in a German arms factory, 1943. People from the Soviet Union had to wear a badge with the word "OST."

er, and the Reichsbahn (German state railway) made up the remaining 81.2 percent.[8]

Fenced in and underpaid

In order to employ foreign laborers, companies had to prove that they could offer suitable living quarters. For this reason, in March 1942, the city of Friedrichshafen, the German Labor Front, and the companies Luftschiffbau Zeppelin, Maybach Motorenbau, and ZF decided to build a large barracks complex for 2,500 residents in the Allmannsweiler district. Construction was carried out by local company Rostan, which employed Russian forced laborers on the project. The allotment of 950 beds reserved for ZF was dubbed Wiesenlager ("Camp Meadow"). A barbed wire fence

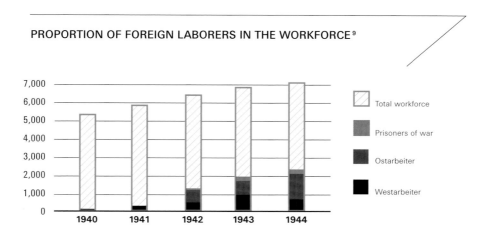

PROPORTION OF FOREIGN LABORERS IN THE WORKFORCE [9]

delineated the borders of the compound, but the area designated for prisoners of war was even more tightly secured. The barracks were divided into rooms of around 400 square feet each. Under normal circumstances, these rooms housed up to twelve people (or more, in the case of Ostarbeiter). Wooden beds with two or three bunks were set up for the residents to sleep on; they were equipped with a straw mattress and two blankets apiece – no bed linen.[9] In addition to these facilities, ZF also utilized a number of other communal and private residences that offered a higher standard of living. These were usually reserved for Westarbeiter.

On paper, wages for the work that Westarbeiter performed at the factory were the same as those paid to Germans. However, expenses for accommodation, board, and work clothes were withheld from their paychecks. Ostarbeiter were subject to special legislation that further reduced their pay, including an "Ostarbeiter tax" levied by the Reich regime. If they fell ill or were unable to work due to an air raid, the Eastern European workers at the plant didn't receive a single pfennig. The minimum daily net wage for regular work was set at 40 pfennigs, which would amount to about 1.50 euros today.10 What's more, the Ostarbeiter were only allowed to spend the pittance they earned in the camp's own canteen. In this way, the companies

responsible for maintaining the camp simply reabsorbed the meager funds they had paid the workers in the first place. Employing Ostarbeiter was profitable for these companies, as the workers were permitted no time off and only received cheap, poor-quality room and board. Many German industrial companies at the time expressed great interest in acquiring female workers from the Wehrmacht-occupied territories in Eastern Europe, as they were considered particularly reliable.

Concentration camp prisoners work in Passau

When the war returned to Germany in the form of squads of Allied bombers, the existing methods of procuring labor were no longer adequate to meet Hitler's increasingly unreasonable demands for armaments. In many areas, human labor was filling the gaps that the air raids had left in companies' machinery – as was the case at the ZF Waldwerke factory in Passau. Although it hadn't taken any damage from the bombings, the factory was suffering under a lack of tool shipments from Friedrichshafen. This may have been why the company now opted to implement a plan originally put forward by the Reich Ministry for Arms and Munitions in 1942 – the factory in Passau began using concentration camp labor.[12] Between March and October 1944, hundreds of prisoners from the concentration camp in Mauthausen

Above: Soviet women board a train, likely departing for labor deployment in the German Reich, 1943.
Below: Forced laborers at the army testing facility in Peenemünde, ca. 1943. Like many of the photos taken during the Nazi era, this is an idealized portrayal of the conditions these workers faced; the pristine work uniforms are one example.

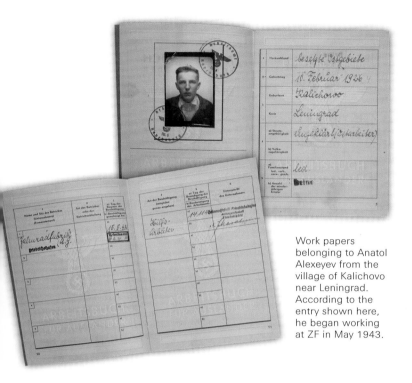

Work papers belonging to Anatol Alexeyev from the village of Kalichovo near Leningrad. According to the entry shown here, he began working at ZF in May 1943.

Ostarbeiter – which involved accommodation in camps, malnutrition, poor hygiene, and draconian punishments – raise the question as to how many of these forced laborers died of overexertion while working at ZF factories. Christa Tholander, who is recognized as a leading expert in the history of foreign labor in Friedrichshafen, explains that there is no simple answer to this reasonable question:

"The issue of casualties is the most difficult thing I've had to grapple with in my more than 20 years as a researcher. If we make comparisons based on the lists available in the city archives, it is safe to assume that approximately 1,000 people lost their lives in Friedrichshafen during the war. At least 316 of them were foreign laborers whose names were known; 163 of those laborers were killed in air raids. Forty infants were also among the dead. And there is no doubt that these figures are a very low estimate. For instance, many foreign workers who were injured in air raids later died in local hospitals. On April 28, 1944, a prisoner barracks in Löwental was completely destroyed by an aerial bomb; the numerous Russian prisoners of war who died in that overcrowded building are not recorded anywhere. There are also no figures regarding the terminally ill forced laborers who were deported to the death camp in Großsachsenheim, where they later passed away. Even the workers who died in the temporary factories set up after the destruction and de facto surrender of the city of Friedrichshafen in 1944/45 went unrecorded. Of the 42 prisoners from the Dachau concentration camp who died in Friedrichshafen, 22 were sent to the crematorium in Lindau. Of the rest, there is no trace; there isn't a single grave to be found anywhere in the city. After the war ended, the bodies of Ostarbeiter were exhumed from a mass grave in a field near the city cemetery and relocated to a grave of honor, together with numerous dead from southern Baden, southern Württemberg, and Lindau. Civilian Russian workers from the arms factories run by Luftschiffbau Zeppelin are buried under the numbers 1001 to 1543."[14]

were forced to work alongside the nearly 2,000 civilian employees at the Waldwerke factory. The highest recorded number of these prisoners working at one time was 334 (on 9/23/1944[13]); however, the actual size of the group was likely closer to one-and-a-half to two times this number, as many of the prisoner numbers were assigned to more than one person. Fluctuation among the prisoners was high, which indicates that the work was extremely arduous. The living conditions of the concentration camp inmates, prisoners of war, and

FOR A FULL DAY OF WORK Ostarbeiter employed in German companies received a legally mandated minimum wage of 40 pfennigs. Today, this would amount to approximately:

1.50 euros

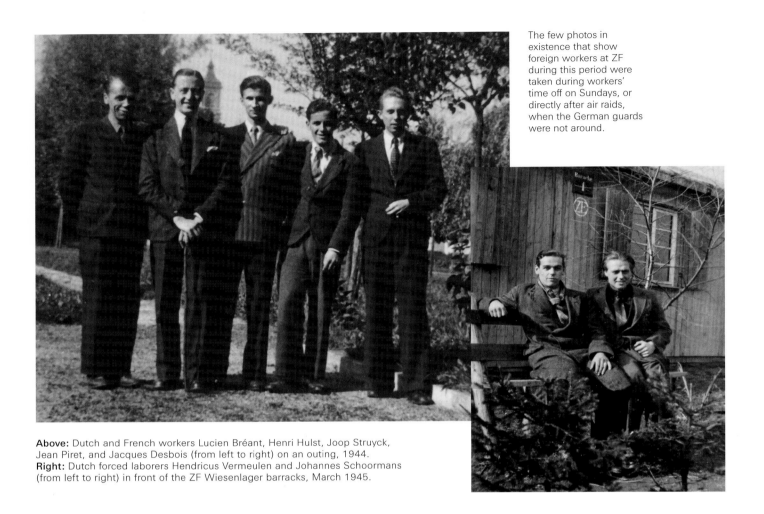

The few photos in existence that show foreign workers at ZF during this period were taken during workers' time off on Sundays, or directly after air raids, when the German guards were not around.

Above: Dutch and French workers Lucien Bréant, Henri Hulst, Joop Struyck, Jean Piret, and Jacques Desbois (from left to right) on an outing, 1944.
Right: Dutch forced laborers Hendricus Vermeulen and Johannes Schoormans (from left to right) in front of the ZF Wiesenlager barracks, March 1945.

FORMER FORCED LABORERS:

STORIES OF SURVIVAL

The number of forced laborers at ZF reached its peak in late 1944, with more than 2,800 foreign workers employed at the company. 1,2 Behind this figure are human beings, about whose fates and suffering we know very little. The records from the time are incomplete; they often contain little more than tables and lists. And most eyewitnesses have already passed away. Only a few foreign workers kept a record of their time at ZF during the war – one of them is Frenchman Jacques Desbois, whose friendship with ZF engineer Hansjörg Dach resulted in extensive correspondence by mail. Desbois describes his arrival in Friedrichshafen as follows:

"We were expected at the square in front of the train station; I was with my three colleagues in a small group of about ten people who were being sent to ZF. They then sent us to the camp in Allmannsweiler, to Barracks 14. The barracks consisted of one large bedroom with bunk beds and an oven for heating; the facilities were quite primitive.

[...]

Approximately ten days after we arrived, Mr. Wiedmann came to Lucien Bréant [who had also come from Paris] and me. He had decided to provide us with different accommodations, because every morning, we tracked the filth from the camp into the office, and he felt that this was unacceptable in the long term. We were then moved into the camp in Weissenau (Building F), where a comfortable room with two beds awaited us. It was a former psychiatric clinic."[3]

Desbois could not have known that other people paid a hefty price for his new living quarters. The 691 patients who had previously been housed in the Weissenau Psychiatric Sanatorium were sent to a death camp in Grafeneck in late 1940 as part of the "Action T4" forced euthanasia program. The Nazi regime considered mentally ill individuals "unworthy of life."

Seven ounces of bread per person, per day

While Westarbeiter like Desbois could eat a "standard meal" – a meatless meal available without ration stamps – at any of the neighboring restaurants, Ostarbeiter were fed at a canteen kitchen at Wiesenlager. Lilia Shinglinskaya, a Russian woman who was 13 at the time, recalls the conditions for Eastern European workers:

"We woke up at 5:00 a.m., and at 5:30, we all lined up for breakfast [...] with two policemen – one in the front and one in the back with the dog. [...] We wore these wooden shoes, and we always had blisters on our feet. Whenever anyone stopped, [a policeman named W.] would always hit them. In the canteen, breakfast was a quart of tea and a loaf of bread – a little more than two

pounds of bread for five people for the whole day. [...] At 12:00 p.m., we had to line up again for lunch. The food was very bad [...]. A few pieces of beet in a quart of water. Then we lined up to go back to work. [...] And for dinner, we had another quart of tea – without bread, because we'd already eaten the bread for breakfast."[4]

The conditions at Wiesenlager improved somewhat when ZF started running the camp canteen itself in fall 1943, in accordance with new official guidelines. Part of the improvement was due to the fact that food rations for Ostarbeiter increased slightly – as a result of longer working hours. However, provisions remained very poor. Children and teens were affected particularly badly; they were often sent to the camps with their mothers, but there was no real place for them within the Nazis' system of forced labor. Children of Ostarbeiter were either considered "dependents unfit for work" – in which case, the mother's income was further reduced – or, when they turned 10, they were labeled "fit for work" and were officially treated like adult factory workers. At least 23 children between the ages of 10 and 14 served as workers at ZF during the war; another 21 younger children were known to be living in the camps, but not working. Schooling was not provided. Dutch forced laborer Hendricus Vermeulen, who lived at Wiesenlager during that time, described the situation as follows: "The [older] children had to line up and march to the plant every day to work, and they came back the same way. The adults always stood on either side of them."[5]

Emotional numbness, extraordinary bravery

While the war raged abroad and the people on the "home front" still remained unaware of the crimes being committed at concentration camps, the foreign workers at German companies labored side-by-side with their German colleagues. Historian Ulrich Herbert, who has published the most extensive research on forced labor in the Third Reich, has his doubts about the Germans' actual willingness to help:

Above: Maria Vermeulen, from the Netherlands, with two Russian girls at the Wiesenlager camp, summer 1943.
Left: 14-year-old Ukrainian boy at a Wehrmacht repair plant in Berlin, January 1945.

In this painting, Dutch artist Pieter Portielje captured his room at the Maybach Motorenbau forced laborers' camp Seeblick I. The Zeppelin Museum acquired the painting in 2004.

And for dinner, another quart of tea –
without bread, because we'd already eaten
the bread for breakfast.

EYEWITNESS ACCOUNT FROM LILIA SHIGLINSKAYA

"If we look at the majority of individual cases, it seems as though most Germans were not particularly interested in the fate of foreign workers. They neither participated in mistreating them, nor did they sympathize with their plight. They were too focused on their own problems."[6]

And yet, some of the Westarbeiter who were employed at ZF at the time reported positive interactions with Germans. In his letters, Jacques Desbois mentions a designer named Kriegbaum – his direct supervisor at ZF – who made no secret of his distaste for the Nazis. But that sort of attitude was risky, even for Germans. One day, Kriegbaum received a postcard with a single phrase written on it: "Heil Hitler!" "He told me that this was a warning, and it was to be taken seriously," Desbois wrote.[7]

The growing destruction being wreaked on Friedrichshafen by Allied aerial bombardments was traumatic for locals and foreigners alike. In the face of such imminent danger, the restrictions set by the Nazi regime were sometimes violated, as Ukrainian Yevgeny Mavrenko, who was 17 at the time, recalls:

"And then we all had to protect ourselves somehow, so we ran into the forest. We were all there together, the German soldiers, the guards, and everyone just hid."[8]

BELATED AMENDS

For decades, the large-scale exploitation of forced labor in Nazi Germany during World War II was a subject largely ignored by the German public. It wasn't until the late 1990s that politicians and business leaders were prepared to negotiate with survivors' associations and international partners to provide compensation to the millions of foreigners who had been forced to work for Germany's war economy. The German federal government and an association of approximately 6,000 companies banded together in August 2000 to establish the foundation "Erinnerung, Verantwortung und Zukunft" ("Remembrance, Responsibility, and Future"); both parties contributed 5 billion deutschmarks each to finance the foundation. In April 2000, the Board of Management and supervisory board at ZF agreed that the company should join the foundation and contribute 25 million deutschmarks – this amount was based on the company's current sales figures, as was the case for all member companies. By June 2007, ZF had paid out approximately 4.5 billion euros in compensation to 1.66 million claimants.

ALLIED BOMBINGS AND LAST-DITCH ATTEMPTS
AT MILITARY BUILDUP:

THE WAR HITS HOME

Friedrichshafen after the devastating air raid on April 28, 1944.

On the weekends, we would often go on nice little outings with our manager – usually on a boat on Lake Constance [...] June 20, 1943 was another sunny Sunday, and we decided to take a trip to the 'Pfahlbauten' lake dwelling museum in Unteruhldingen. At that time, no one was expecting an air raid on a beautiful city like Friedrichshafen, and especially not at night. The other girls and I were still tired from our trip, and when the sirens went off, we crawled out of our beds pretty slowly. But the bombs started to fall fast, and so we ran, half-dressed, into the air-raid shelter. The camp supervisor ordered us to get on the ground, face-down, so that if a bomb went off nearby, it wouldn't tear our lungs. We were shocked when we finally left the shelter again after the all-clear."[1]

On the night of June 21, 1943, Friedrichshafen was bombed for the first time; it would be bombed ten more times by 1945. The primary target of these attacks was the military equipment industry, but the bombs also hit the city itself. The people of Friedrichshafen spent very little time in their basements and shelters in the early years of the war, but that first attack in June was followed by another in October, and the air raids became increasingly frequent in spring 1944. Alfred von Soden, co-founder and technical director of ZF, was already on his death bed in the clinic at the University of Tübingen by that point; his advanced leukemia could no longer be cured. Commercial director Hans Cappus informed von Soden of the current situation in a letter:

"The final days of last week were [...] extremely trying for Friedrichshafen and its people. [...] Once again, the plant was exceptionally lucky, for the most part; a large bomb went off between Halls IV and XI, but it caused relatively little damage. [...] However, the impact of the bomb did damage the cables, so we only had power in part of the facility on Monday.
[...]

Only a few of the machines caught fire, but we were always able to extinguish the flames right away. The training barracks burned down completely, however. [...] It is a miracle that the air raid shelter survived the attack unscathed, and that its occupants [...] were rescued. To the left and right, parts of the building were blown away by heavy bombs. The biggest problem for us at the moment is the fact that many of our workers are not reporting for their shifts because they are attempting to repair the bombing damage to their homes – in the cases where repairs are actually possible.

[...]

This is [...] a brief overview of the sad events of recent days. Most families fled Friedrichshafen in a hurry. The housing complexes are almost completely empty. [...] However, we should be prepared for further attacks as soon as the enemy discovers that not everything here has been destroyed yet."[2]

Destruction of Friedrichshafen

Cappus was right to worry about further attacks. The Allies had realized that Maybach and ZF, at least, were still producing at almost full capacity. On the night of April 28, 1944, Friedrichshafen was once again the target of an aerial assault by 309 Royal Air Force bombers. The purpose of the attack was to annihilate the local military supply industry, but in fact, the bombs struck the city – and changed its face forever.[3] This was in line with the Allied war strategy, however; the Area Bombing Directive, which defined the deployment framework for British bomber squadrons, stipulated that German cities should be destroyed to the greatest extent possible. The goal was to decrease morale at the local companies by inflicting targeted damage on the civilian population. Like the Ruhr region or the city of Hamburg before them, the people on the shores of Lake Constance now watched as their surroundings were reduced to rubble.

As usual in these situations, the attack came in waves. First, the bombers dropped a small number of explosive bombs on the populated areas of the city in order to destroy roofs and windows and provide a target for the next wave: a large number of firebombs. They also used bombs with timed detonators and executed further attacks after the first waves in order to make it more difficult for emergency and fire crews to do their jobs. In the narrow alleyways of old German city centers, the fires spontaneously intensified, and they consumed so much oxygen that even the people who made it to nearby shelters often did not survive. In the letter quoted above, Hans Cappus explains that the Allies used phosphorus bombs in Friedrichshafen; the hissing sound these bombs made could be heard from miles around, and it always caused a panic. The bombs contained a mixture of white phosphorus and rubber that ignited upon mere contact with oxygen and stuck to the skin. The reaction could be halted by quenching the mixture with water or sand, but there was always a risk that it could reignite. Additionally, the burning phosphorus gave off enormous amounts of white smoke – the source of the hissing noise Cappus described. Inhaling the fumes caused severe poisoning that resulted in death a few days later. Most of the city's residents had left by April 1944, but between 115 and 136 people still died during the attack on the 28th, and more than 200 more were injured.[4] Difficult times lay ahead for those who remained in Friedrichshafen.

Relocation of production

The ZF plant in Friedrichshafen also suffered severe damage in the bombing. The company's management had long since come to the conclusion that it would be pointless to rebuild the manufacturing facilities, as the city was under constant threat of further bombardment – and the Nazi government in Berlin agreed. On April 29, 1944 – one day after the devastating air raid on Friedrichshafen – Karl-Otto Saur, the undersecretary at the Ministry of Armaments and War Production responsible for relocating military supply production underground, flew to Friedrichshafen. One day later, Saur informed Hitler of the devastation inflicted on the city and reported on his meetings with ZF's management. The response from the Führer's headquarters reads as follows:

"The Führer approves the decisions that the Dornier and ZF plants will not be rebuilt as a result of the severe damage; rather, production for these companies will be relocated immediately. Because these facilities cannot be permanently housed underground, they will be temporarily moved to highly decentralized locations".[5]

In the period that followed, ZF began to tackle the task of distributing production among a number of small-town operations. It is known that the company moved some of its production facilities to Klingenstein near the city of Ulm, to Waldkirch in the Breisgau region, and to various locations in the Austrian region of Vorarlberg. In 1946, ZF could list 14 locations to which it had relocated production. In order to make it more difficult for the enemy to identify these production facilities, ZF used code names that sounded like textile companies or engineering firms, for example.[6] On May 24, 1944, Hans Cappus informed Alfred von Soden – who was hospitalized at the time – that all of the departments that had originally operated in Friedrichshafen had been relocated:

"Some of our departments, as you know, have already been moved; some relocations are still ongoing. As for the rest, decisions have just been made within the last few days. However, the relocation of these departments will also begin shortly. [...] The decisions regarding these types of projects are always protracted because the companies operating in these buildings often object to vacating them, and our appropriation of the facility is countermanded."[7]

Producing military equipment underground

In light of the extensive aerial bombardments, decentralizing production was only a stopgap

Friedrichshafen was the target of Allied bombardments many times. Shown here: Inspection of the damage caused on April 28, 1944, and a map drawn at the time showing bomb impacts between March and August 1944.

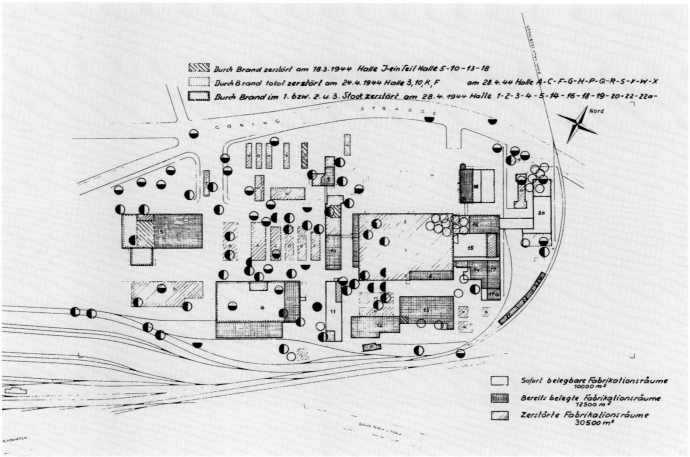

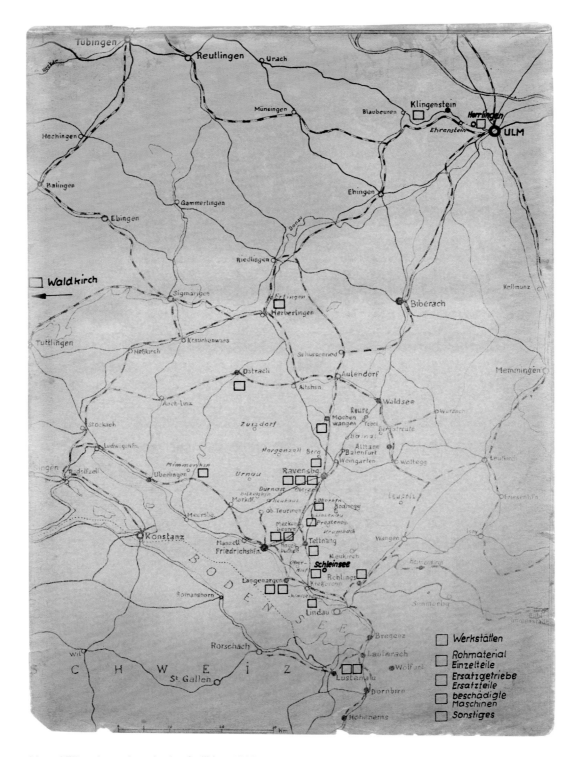

Map of ZF's relocated production facilities, 1944.

Most families fled Friedrichshafen in a hurry.
The housing complexes are almost completely empty.

HANS CAPPUS TO ALFRED VON SODEN, SPRING 1944

measure – so the company began working non-stop on moving production into underground caves and tunnels. One of these relocation projects was codenamed "Glaukonit AG" and involved setting up a ZF branch in the caverns of the Unterklien quarry near the small Austrian town of Hohenems. Since the same code name was also used for another plant in the town of Dornbirn, it is safe to assume that this project was what was known as U-Verlagerung: setting up a production facility underground, where it would be protected from air raids. Hans Cappus reported on this project to chairman of the supervisory board Hugo Eckener in September 1944:

"Currently, production [in Friedrichshafen] is only operating in the basement of Hall V. However, by the end of the year, this department is scheduled to be relocated to the caves you inspected. The relocation process has already begun. Additionally, our heat treatment plant in Friedrichshafen is still in service. [...] We plan to move the heat treatment plant to a newly discovered cave, near the cave previously mentioned. All other production facilities have already been moved out of Friedrichshafen. [...] In that regard, we have completed the task of relocating production [...], and any new attacks in the coming months will no longer cause us any appreciable damage."[8]

The Allies cross the Rhine

The optimism that Cappus displayed in this letter was unrealistic: the western front of the war was inching ever closer, and the relocated facilities had no defense against ground troops. This was particularly obvious in Sélestat in the Alsace region, where the company had moved its steering system production facilities. Franz Boll, who had worked at ZF since 1937, recalled the company's gradual retreat during the final months of the war:

"Despite the air raids that were already happening in the Reich [in 1943/44], [...] we felt safe, because we assumed that the Allies wouldn't bomb the Alsace region. [...] On June 6, 1944, Allied invasion troops landed in France. We were becoming increasingly worried about the fate of the steering systems production facility. In August, armaments command ordered us to once again relocate 60 percent of production back into territory held by the Reich before 1938. [...] Manufacturing of steel components was moved to Waldkirch [in the Breisgau region of Germany], and cast parts to Breisach [on the German-French border]. In both cases, we evicted textile companies in order to house our production facilities. Then in November, we received the order to relocate 100 percent of production.

[...]

The front loomed nearer, and Breisach was no longer a safe location for production. [...] The machines were moved to Hölzlebruck [in the Black Forest], and from there, they were supposed to be transported by train to Klingenstein, near Ulm. However, many of them got stuck at the freight depot in Ulm, because Ulm was hit hard by an air raid on December 19, 1944. The roof in Klingenstein had also collapsed on the machines that had been brought there from Friedrichshafen. Diedrich [head of ZF steering system production] then gave the order: everything was to be shipped on to Herbrechtingen [near Heidenheim]! At that point, Diedrich was already aware that the Allies would later divide Germany into occupation zones, and since it could be assumed that the Americans would be less likely to confiscate our property than the French, production facilities were once again relocated, from Waldkirch to Herbrechtingen."[9]

Digging tunnels in Überlingen

The hopeless military situation did not stop Hitler and his leadership from trying to achieve "ultimate victory" and stubbornly pushing ahead with military production. The construction of an enormous system of tunnels near the Westbahnhof train station in Überlingen was of particular importance to the companies that were part of the LZ Group. The system was codenamed "Magnesit," and in its unfinished state today, it has three lengthwise tunnels and 17 cross-tunnels, each of which is up to 82 feet wide and 32 feet high – the tunnels are more than two and a half miles long. Ultimately, the entire production space was supposed to be more than one million square feet, 130,000 square feet of which were reserved for ZF. Construction began in June 1944; the construction company, Butzer & Walther, and the consulting engineer, Arno Fischer, were both based in Munich, and a number of local contractors from the region around Überlingen also worked on the project. The majority of the grueling, dangerous tunnel excavation in the brittle molasse rock was carried out by prisoners from the Dachau concentration camp. The satellite camp in Überlingen that was set up for this purpose housed an average of 700 prisoners until it was dissolved in April 1945. At least 219 prisoners died during the construction of these tunnels.

Adam Puntschart, a communist from Carinthia, Austria, survived to share his story. He fought in the Spanish Civil War and was imprisoned at Dachau by the Gestapo in 1940. When he was sent to Überlingen to work on the tunnels in

October 1944, he spent months drilling holes in the mountain for detonations, until he and fellow prisoner Vassily Sklarenko from Russia managed to escape in March 1945. Puntschart recollects:

"The tragic thing was that the detonations were set off without ventilation in the tunnels, so all of the gasses stayed within the tunnel system. [...] People were also killed or injured by the detonations. The dead and injured were laid down until the shift was over, and then we would take them back to the camp. [...] Incidentally, people usually died as a result of malnutrition or exhaustion. [...] You could only ever think about one thing at a time: sometimes you'd think about going berserk, sometimes about having a full belly, sometimes about running away..."

Construction was originally scheduled to take 100 days – wishful thinking, considering the size of the project. Naturally, the deadline came and went. When the war ended for the people of the Lake Constance region in April 1945, there was little evidence left of any form of industrial production in the "Goldbacher Tunnels;" only a few abandoned machines remained. In any case, the poorly ventilated, damp, and extremely dusty tunnels would hardly have been a suitable location for manufacturing precision components. This fact makes it all the more absurd that so many people sacrificed their lives for this project – although such occurrences were typical for the final months of the "Thousand-Year Reich."

The final days

Unlike Friedrichshafen and some of the other relocated facilities, production initially continued with relatively few issues at Waldwerke in Passau, at the plants in Berlin, and at both plants in Schwäbisch Gmünd. These three locations escaped the bombings almost completely unscathed. In Passau, at least, we know that the facility's location on a hillside – with the corresponding updrafts – was decisive in

The end of the war in the capital city of the Reich, Berlin: a destroyed Reichstag parliament building, and a girl collecting firewood.

keeping it protected. It was nearly impossible to hit the factory complex with the bombs of the era.[11] The plant in Berlin did not suffer severe damage until spring 1945, when its equipment and buildings fell victim to the demolitions and looting that were rampant at the time. However, despite the fact that ZF still had some operational production facilities during the second half of the war, manufacturing came to a standstill before the Allied occupation began, in large part as a result of the disruption of transportation routes between the plants. The warehouse that stored raw materials, for instance, was still in Friedrichshafen, but the production facilities were scattered across the German-held territories – when Friedrichshafen was leveled, there was no way for the company to supply its factories. Additionally, the company's management – which had relocated to Langenargen in the meantime – could not keep a handle on the situation in the various plants. Despite all the morale-boosting slogans from the Nazi leadership, military production at ZF ended weeks – if not months – before the German Reich officially surrendered on May 8, 1945.

1945
–
1965

Occupation and the "economic miracle"

As a former military supplier, ZF expects to be liquidated – but that doesn't happen. Soon, the economic recovery in the wake of West Germany's founding also gives the company reason to be hopeful.

END OF THE WAR AND FRENCH OCCUPATION:
ON A
RAZOR'S EDGE

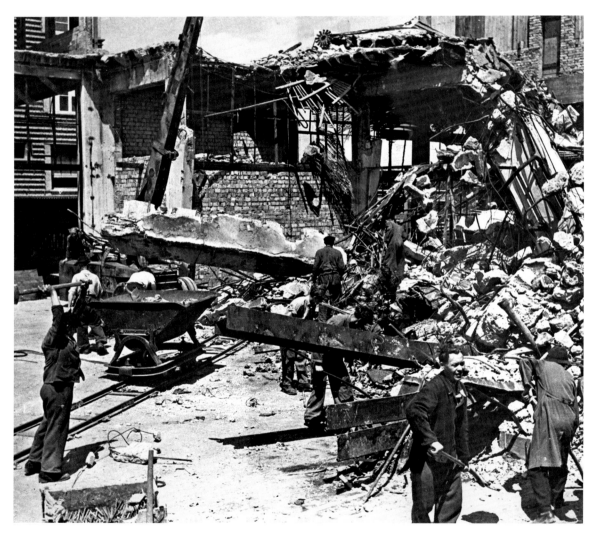

At the end of the war, the plant in Friedrichshafen was in ruins. Clean-up at many
of the buildings did not begin until 1947/48.

On April 29, 1945, the day the war ended in Friedrichshafen, the ruins of the ZF plant stood empty. The remnants of the company's production and (barely functional) administration facilities had long since been relocated to various satellite plants. Shortly before the last of the Wehrmacht troops made a hasty retreat, the soldiers of the "Première Armée Française" reached the gates of the plant compound.

Just a few hours prior, the city had been peacefully handed over to the advancing French troops by a civilian delegation headed by Mayor Walter Bärlin and Senior Health Officer Walter Gmelin. The only ZF employee remaining at the company's headquarters was Erich Maier, head of the on-call service. He recorded his memories of that Sunday in April which marked the end of the Second World War for ZF:

"Around 6:00 p.m., the factory doors were closed, and the lights in the courtyard turned on when night fell. At about 2:30 a.m., four men arrived in a tank and asked if there were any German soldiers here, and who was occupying the factory. Once I explained the situation – that there was only a single civilian here – the tank drove off

again without further incident. [...] Everything was quiet until Monday morning, 4/30/1945. Then, at about 8:00 a.m., six officers arrived in two cars; they occupied ZF [...]. It had been explained to the men that there was no one at ZF save a single man, and that the company's management was in Langenargen."[1]

While the French occupying forces were moving into Friedrichshafen, Adolf Hitler committed suicide in his bunker under the garden of the Reich Chancellery in Berlin. Approximately one week later, on May 8, 1945 at 11:01 p.m., the unconditional surrender of all German troops – as approved by Colonel-General Alfred Jodl – went into effect, ending the war in Europe. Hitler's "Thousand-Year Reich" had crumbled in just twelve years, but the carnage it had wreaked during that time was like nothing the world had ever seen before.[2] 50 million people died in the war, half of whom were civilians. The Nazis' policies of extermination claimed an additional 13 million victims, including six million Jews and three million Soviet prisoners of war. In Friedrichshafen, approximately two thirds of the buildings had been destroyed in air raids. The city's population of more than 28,000 (as of early 1944) had plummeted to under 8,000 by the end of the war – people died or were taken prisoner, and huge numbers of them fled from the bombs and the fighting. Additionally, many foreign workers and forced laborers left the city during that time. Most of Zahnradfabrik's buildings had been destroyed.

And yet, ZF remained extremely valuable to the Allies; they suspected that ZF and its neighboring companies Dornier, Luftschiffbau Zeppelin, and Maybach Motorenbau had blueprints for military equipment – for tank drivelines and V2 missile technology, in particular. Albert Maier, who would go on to become ZF's technical director, described the events as follows:

"Just four days after the troops took the city, a technical director from Chrysler Detroit, Mr. Pfeifer, stopped by to see us, accompanied by a man in an American military uniform; he came to

I collected the wooden beams and planks that were lying around and cobbled together something resembling a bed frame. My mattress was a piece of wire mesh from a fence that had collapsed.

HERMANN FERCHL

collect all the design drafts that the company had available, particularly the ones for the tank driveline [...]. A few days after that, an army engineer I knew from Vickers, England dropped by, just to pay a friendly visit. It wasn't until a number of weeks later that French army engineer Robin showed up at ZF. We knew him well, as we had previously cooperated with him on the "Robin van Roggen" transmission [...]. He was accompanied by General Molinier (Director of A.M.X. Sofen, Paris). Our negotiations resulted in our 12-person design department agreeing to develop a cutting-edge, 1,000-horsepower tank transmission for Molinier, free of charge."

Tank transmissions for France

ZF's management – still represented by directors Cappus and Dolt at that point – had very little choice but to agree to develop the transmission. After all, the company was under the control of the occupying military authorities, and all of the LZ Group's subsidiaries faced the threat that they would be completely dismantled if they failed to cooperate. While a group of Maybach engineers in Vernon, France were commissioned with designing a high-performance tank engine, ZF built on its work from the final years of the war and developed a transmission for the M 4 prototype (manufactured later under the name AMX-50). This unit was the first combination steering box and manual transmission ZF had ever constructed, as well as the first tank transmission designed for rear-wheel drive applications. The project never reached the point where it was ready to go into production, however, and it was eventually dis-

continued in the late 1950s – but ZF incorporated the experience it gained into the development of the German Leopard 1 combat tank.[3]

The company could not have foreseen these developments in the weeks immediately following Germany's surrender, however. Given the troubled economic situation at the time, it was much more important for the company to revive its civilian product portfolio.[4] Development on civilian products had essentially come to a standstill in the mid-1930s, while ZF was occupied with producing military equipment. In order to even be able to start manufacturing products again, ZF needed permission from the Allies for each of its sites – not to mention the severe damage from the war that would need to be repaired.[5] The plants in Schwäbisch Gmünd and Passau (the latter of which was not yet owned by ZF Friedrichshafen AG) were still intact for the most part, and the customer service department in Dortmund was still able to operate. The company's headquarters in Friedrichshafen, on the other hand, had been almost completely destroyed. The plant in Berlin was also in bad shape; first, it had been badly damaged during the air raids, and then in the months after the war, the Soviets dismantled it at a frantic pace. By now, ZF's Berlin plant was in the French zone of occupation – the district of Wittenau, where the plant was located, was under French control. Additionally, ZF's access to the customer service center in Vienna and the production facilities that had been relocated to Austria was cut off. On the whole, it was not an ideal situation in which to rebuild a company.

Numerous former ZF employees who returned

to the company in Friedrichshafen during the early days of the occupation had to be turned away. By that point, the French troops were calling the shots – and many of them had personally suffered at the hands of Germans during the war. The French were often wary of the locals, or even hostile toward them. Looting and abuse were rampant, despite the French officers' frequent calls for strict discipline. Hermann Ferchl, who had started an apprenticeship as a metal worker at the Friedrichshafen plant in 1938, had a very vivid memory of these first few weeks after the fall of the Nazi dictatorship. In May 1945, he fled from a prisoner-of-war camp and secretly returned to his hometown of Wasserburg, and to ZF:

"We were overcome with worry; it had been ten months since we'd had word from home. Luckily, while I was on the road, I happened to meet a former classmate who told me that half of my parents' apartment had been converted into a guardhouse. So I sneaked around the back of the house and crawled in through the kitchen window; the guards didn't see me. Two hours later, I had to leave the same way I came in, carrying fresh underwear that I'd borrowed from my father. I had no other possessions. Incidentally, one of the tools I'd made as part of my qualifying examination [at ZF] was causing problems for my mother. A soldier found the adjustable framing square in our things and claimed that it was a part from a French machine, and that her sons had stolen it in France.

I set off down the back roads once again, this time to Friedrichshafen. I was in luck; I spoke to the right people and was given accommodation at Director Dolt's demolished house. [...] I collected the wooden beams and planks that were lying around and cobbled together something resembling a bed frame. My mattress was a piece of wire mesh from a fence that had collapsed.

One of many volunteers: ZF employee Karl Flösser on work detail, cleaning up the rubble of Hall 1, 1947.

I shored up the loose, somewhat crooked partition wall next to my "bed," and once I patched up the main fuse in the house, I even had electricity. I went back to Mr. Schmäh. Yes, he said, they would definitely be able to find a place for me in the tool shop soon, but nothing was up and running yet. The biggest problem was registering with the local police. To do that, I needed discharge papers from an occupying power. And that was one thing I certainly didn't have. After endless explanations and excuses, I was finally given temporary papers and told to report to the Hecht construction company, where I would be assigned to a detail to help clean up the city. That's when I was given ration coupons, too."[6]

Unlike its parent company Luftschiffbau Zeppelin, ZF was not considered purely a military supply company,[7] which meant that it was able to resume operations relatively quickly. On May 14, 1945, two weeks after the Allies had marched into the city, Commander Lasnier – the French military officer responsible for the city – approved a clean-up detail of up to 100 people for the plant in Friedrichshafen. On June 6, he agreed to permit manufacturing of tractor transmissions. Production relaunched under extremely primitive conditions; ZF employees set up the few operational machines that remained in the basement of the former Hall V. To meet the immediate needs of the local population, the companies in the LZ Group initially also produced and repaired household appliances, including meat grinders and presses for making Spätzle (Swabian egg noodles).

The relaunch of the plant in Schwäbisch Gmünd, which was in the American zone of occupation, went off without a hitch. After a two-

Necessity is the mother of invention: vegetables were planted on the grounds of Plant 1 (1948) to feed ZF employees in Friedrichshafen.

and-a-half month occupation by the US Army, the plant was given the go-ahead to supply Opel in July 1945[8]; this permission was extended to all of ZF's (civilian) customers in the western zone of occupation in August. During the same year, ZF's management decided to relocate all of its steering system production processes to this plant – in large part because it was the only plant that was still completely operational.

Surviving the scarcity

All of the company's locations had a great deal of difficulty procuring raw materials and dealing with a lack of functional machinery. These factors may have been the main reason why ZF was unable to generate more than minimal sales revenue, even given the enormous demand for its products, especially spare parts. To put it in concrete figures: the company's sales[9] in the months from June to December 1945 amounted to less than 1.3 million reichsmarks, compared to approximately 76.6 million reichsmarks in 1943.

What little of ZF's equipment and resources had survived the war was by no means guaranteed to remain in the company's possession. The constant threat of complete dismantlement loomed large. The company's fate hung in the balance on May 6, 1946, when the district governor in Tettnang, Pierre Ulmer, told representatives of ZF about the Allies' plan to liquidate the company. The recently elected ZF works council, chaired by Georg Groner, intervened with Ulmer – and succeeded in rescuing the company.[10] Just a few days later, on May 9, the French military governor told the members of the works council that ZF could continue operating for the time being. However, the dismantling process did not stop. A handwritten note dated September 1946, which appears to have been penned by Herbert Greinert, member of ZF's extended management, addresses the issue of 537 machines that were handed over to the occupying authorities after the end of the war. 417 of them were sent to France, while the remaining 120 were rented out to Daimler-Benz in Gaggenau

on the orders of the occupying authorities.[11] 293 machines remained in Friedrichshafen.

In addition to the reparation payments that ZF had to make as a consequence of its participation in arming Germany during the war, the company was also burdened by the fact that many of its employees, from low-level foremen to the upper echelons of management, were tainted by their association with the Nazi regime. A list in the works council files dated December 14, 1945 names at least 46 former Nazi party members who were still working as salaried employees at ZF – approximately 20 percent of the total number of salaried employees at ZF at the time. Compared to the average number of Nazi party members in the rest of the population, this was a relatively large figure – possibly a result of the fact that party membership was often a prerequisite for those who wanted to hold management positions in German industrial companies during the Nazi era.[12] This assumption is supported by the fact that the overwhelming majority of the 46 people on the list did not join the Nazi party until the late 1930s or early 1940s, suggesting that opportunism and professional ambition likely played a larger role in their decision to join the Nazi party than ideological factors did. There are no comparative figures available for the wage laborers who made up the vast majority of the company's staff.

Above all, as part of the denazification process, employees who had drawn attention to themselves by informing on their colleagues, mistreating forced laborers, or holding a prominent position in the SA or SS (among other things) were supposed to be fired and possibly prosecuted. Like most German companies, however, ZF did not truly come to terms with its Nazi past during this period. The majority of employees and managers wanted to forget their personal and professional involvement with the Nazi system as quickly as possible and focus on rebuilding. The occupying authorities were generally satisfied if those who were primarily responsible for the crimes committed during the war were brought to

The Waldwerke factories in Passau suffered very little damage during the war. Zahnradfabrik Passau GmbH was founded at this location in 1946. ZF primarily produced transmissions for tractors here, including the successful A12. The 2,000th unit of this model was shipped out in 1949.

The only way to begin to reassure the salaried employees and wage laborers is to guarantee that former Nazis no longer hold management positions at ZF.

FROM A LETTER WRITTEN BY THE ZF WORKS COUNCIL ON JANUARY 25, 1946

justice and all visible traces of the Third Reich were eliminated. As a result of this combination of motives, many people who had, in fact, openly supported the Nazi regime were gradually declared "followers" or "exonerated persons" – in other words, they were never punished for aiding the Nazis.[13]

Hans Cappus comes under fire

After the French military government had enacted the necessary regulations on January 10, 1946, the works council and directors Hans Cappus and Hermann Dolt met on January 21 to discuss specific measures going forward. The membership of this committee raised questions, however, because Cappus and Dolt were former Wehrwirtschaftsführer ("defense economy leaders") and both held a War Merit Cross First Class, which meant that they were considered potential offenders in the denazification process (additionally, Cappus had been a member of the Nazi party since 1937). This new management board reported that thus far, 16 salaried employees had been let go for political reasons, and a few others had been demoted. Additionally, there were 15 cases of employees whom the works council felt should be dismissed immediately; these cases were under discussion. The employee representatives on the council primarily selected employees for dismissal who were considered political offenders, but who were also generally disliked on a personal level. Robert Pirker, who later joined the Board of Management, strongly criticized this combination of motives in a letter dated January 23. Ultimately, the works council up-

held the requests for dismissal in twelve of the cases.

Meanwhile, opposition to commercial director Hans Cappus, who had held his post since 1923, was growing. In a letter dated January 10, 1946, the works council only agreed to allow Cappus to remain in his position until April 1 of that year. Shortly before this term expired, on March 11, former ZF employee Fritz Kemmler provided a sworn statement in which he asserted that Cappus had informed on him to the Gestapo twice in a row because Kemmler had publicly criticized the inadequate air raid protection measures at the company's main plant. Kemmler, who was himself a member of the Nazi party, described Cappus' mindset as "purely capitalist" – according to him, Cappus was more interested in protecting the machines than ensuring that his employees were safe. The works council also began to express its own strong criticism of Cappus: while Cappus had refused to allow any wage laborers who had been members of the Nazi party to return to work at the company, he was happy to permit former managers who were known offenders to return to their previous posts. This discrimination and Cappus's autocratic management style led the works council to file a request for his dismissal with the state directorate for business in Tübingen, and on April 16, the works council stated in writing that it would refuse to continue working with Cappus. However, this conflict surrounding ZF's management was not finally resolved until July, when the occupying authorities also demanded that former "defense economy leaders" Cappus and Dolt be removed from office – otherwise, ZF would be forcibly shut down.

Stopgap solution and radical idea:
The subcompact car "Champion"

1946

CHAMPION

Albert Maier, head of the engineering department, drafted a design for a subcompact car for everyday driving. The idea for the Champion was born.

It was somewhere between a soapbox derby racer and a classic race car: the vehicle that Albert Maier, head of the engineering department at the time, sketched with a practiced hand on July 21, 1946 was extremely small, even by the standards of the time. It had a 4.6-foot wheel base, a teardrop-shaped, open vehicle body with freestanding wheels, two unupholstered seats, and an external rear-mounted engine with a tank installed above it. On the hood of the vehicle, Maier had written the name "CHAMPION"[2] in big letters.

But this was much more than just a sketch made by a talented designer, as Albert Maier made clear in a lecture to members of the union of technical and commercial employees in March 1947. The country was in dire straits, said Maier, and the passenger vehicles manufactured before the war – with their luxury features and top speeds of over 60 miles per hour – had become prohibitively expensive for most people. To make travel easier for the many people who had to commute from the countryside to the destroyed downtown areas of cities every day for work, Maier suggested a radical new design for a subcompact car with a daily cruising range of 2 to 30 miles. The core idea behind the vehicle involved limiting maximum speeds to 25 to 30 miles per hour in

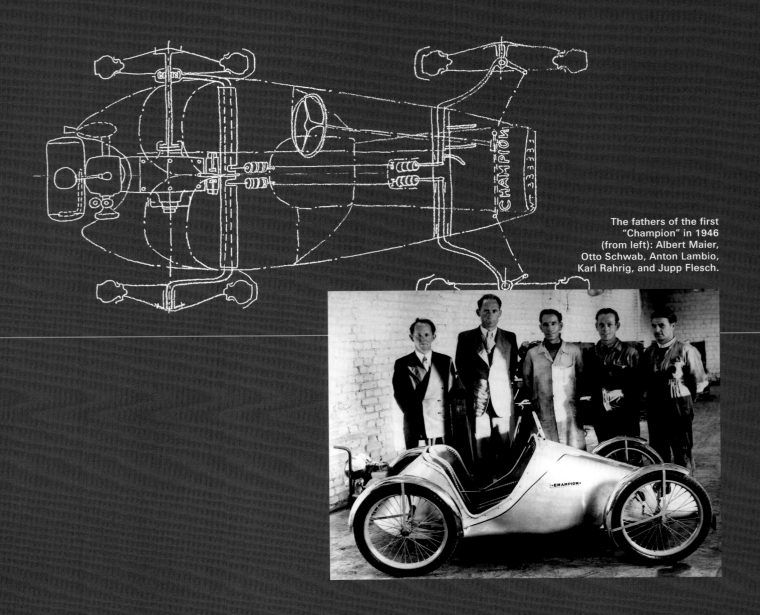

The fathers of the first "Champion" in 1946 (from left): Albert Maier, Otto Schwab, Anton Lambio, Karl Rahrig, and Jupp Flesch.

order to allow for a much more simplified design, with a compact engine and low fuel consumption; it would be cheap to manufacture. With this vehicle's performance specs and streamlined design, Maier was taking a conscious step backward in the era of the first automobiles. At the same time, however, this downsizing would be carried out with state-of-the-art production methods and materials. The car's own weight was to be reduced by approximately one third compared to the previous standard, while the payload would remain the same. The idea was that potential customers would assemble the car themselves, which would save them money. Designing the engine block as a single, removable unit was also an innovative concept; it could additionally be used as a driveline for machine tools, motorized lawnmowers, or boats.

While the audience listened to Maier's lecture with rapt attention, a first prototype of the Champion did laps in the courtyard of the ZF plant. For this prototype, the development team – which consisted of Maier, Otto Schwab (design/engineering), Anton Lambio (body design), Karl Rahrig (assembly), and Josef Flesch (test drives) – had combined a five-horsepower engine from Nuremberg-based motorcycle manufacturer Triumph with the ZF Mo1 two-

Removable rear-mounted engine, unupholstered seats, spoked wheels, and not much room: the first "Champion" was a spartan – but practical – vehicle.

gear lawnmower transmission. Since this driveline did not have a reverse gear, the driver – to avoid making a wide U-turn – had to pick up the car by its front wheels and turn it around by hand. This wasn't a problem, however, as the first generation of the Champion weighed just 364 pounds. At full load capacity with two adults and one child, the vehicle could travel 62 miles on one gallon of gasoline-oil mixture (at a constant speed of 15 mph).

By 1948, the developers had remedied some of the prototype's technical shortcomings. For example, a universal joint was installed to handle the power train between the transmission and the drive wheel (initially, the car only had single-wheel drive); it replaced an extremely error-prone shim construction. The engine could now be started electrically, and improved brakes were installed. French officer and designer Louis Lepoix, who was

stationed in Friedrichshafen at the time, designed a new, contoured body after Albert Maier provided him with a small workshop at the ZF plant; it was presented in 1949. During the same year, ZF tested a three-gear transmission that August Winter designed specifically for the Champion.

However, volume-producing the Champion was still outside the realm of possibility for ZF. After all, ZF's management and staff had their hands

1949

ZF sold the manufacturing license to an engineer named Hohlbein, who launched an improved version of the Champion.

The Champion in numbers

- **Weight:** approx. 364 pounds
- **Length:** 77 inches
- **Width:** approx. 51 inches
- **Engine performance:** 5 hp
- **Left rear-wheel drive, 2-gear shifting**
- **Fuel consumption with 330-pound load:** 62 miles per gallon at a constant speed of 15 mph

full just trying to meet the sharply rising demand in the company's core areas of business: namely, manufacturing transmissions and steering systems. Consequently, ZF sold the manufacturing license for the Champion to engineer Hermann Hohlbein in January 1949, but retained the right to produce small batches of the vehicle for its own employees. By 1951, Hohlbein had launched two new, improved versions of the Champion with enhanced engine performance, before focusing on the Champion 400 – a brand new design. The vehicle never earned him a penny, however.

Production was sold multiple times; new investors were constantly backing the project, but without success. In light of the rapidly increasing prosperity in West Germany, demand for high-performance mid-size cars with better features was returning much faster than anyone had initially expected, given the damage the country had suffered during the war. The Volkswagen Beetle and similar cars became symbolic of Germany's "economic miracle," and the Champion vanished from the automobile market in the mid-1950s. And yet, with his vision of a lightweight, affordable vehicle with low fuel consumption, Albert Maier had already anticipated the future of urban mobility in a number of important ways.

Above: The gate at Plant 1.
Left: enemies become partners. ZF technical director Albert Maier (left) accompanies representative of the French military administration Pierre Ulmer (center), along with Robert Pirker (right), on a tour of the plant, 1950.

CONFLICTS OF INTEREST IN THE POST-WAR ERA:

THE LONG ROAD TO STABILITY

Both sides had dug in their heels. Hans Cappus, still the company's commercial director, made very little effort to hide his anger at the fact that the occupying authorities had demanded that ZF hand over its machines to Daimler-Benz in Gaggenau. In a heated discussion on July 5, 1946, Cappus went so far as to threaten French Colonel Meffre, who supervised the automobile industry in the Lake Constance region from his post in Baden-Baden; Cappus said that Meffre was no longer safe from the rage of ZF employees.[1] This was the spark that finally ignited the simmering conflict between ZF's management and the occupying authorities.

The French military, including the aforementioned Colonel Meffre and Tettnang-based Commander Ulmer, requested meetings with the members of ZF's works council in Friedrichshafen on July 7 and 8, 1946. Meffre summarily stated that the Allied Control Council had decided to liquidate ZF. Ulmer added that this shutdown could only be prevented if Cappus and Dolt were removed from their posts and the company converted into a cooperative. The works council members immediately held a secret meeting with managers Alfred Häfele, Albert Maier, and Robert Pirker on July 8 to discuss a plan to force a change of leadership. It was the only way to ensure the company's continued existence.

The Zeppelin Group disintegrates

On July 11, a Group meeting was held at Luftschiffbau Zeppelin; during this meeting, the conflicts between the various groups on the German side erupted into the open. While Group director Hugo Eckener allied with Maybach director Jean Raebel in vehemently supporting the idea that all of the companies – Maybach, Luftschiffbau Zeppelin, and ZF – remain within the Group, representatives of ZF argued that the individual companies should be spun off into cooperatives. The talks ended in a rift between the ZF employees, who were fighting for their livelihood, and Eckener, who wanted to defend the integrity of the whole company against the French occupying authorities. According to Albert Maier's notes, towards the end of the meeting, Eckener stated that he would turn his back on Friedrichshafen: "I'm going to America; I have good friends everywhere." Eckener then left the meeting, "without saying goodbye, and leaving his hat behind."[2]

Uncertain future for ZF

This kicked off a long series of complex events, the ultimate result of which would determine nothing less than the future existence of ZF. It is difficult to disentangle the complex web of political, financial, and occasionally selfish interests that came into play here; the following account only attempts to reconstruct a general outline of the events that occurred between mid-1946 and late 1950. A letter dated July 19, 1946 sent by the members of the works council to SPD politician, state councilor for Tübingen, and future member of the upper house of the German parliament Carlo Schmid demonstrates just how serious the situation was for ZF:

"We are fighting for our very survival, which is why we are forced to take this unusual course of action [...] to exhaust our last possible option to safeguard our families. [...] The LZ Group has been served notice that it will be shut down. [...] The execution of this order, which Baden-Baden [referring to Col. Meffre] has now made three times, has so far been deferred by the intervention of district governor Commander Ulmer. We can only expect [...] to receive further assistance if ZF rids itself of the burden placed on it by the Group's reputation as a military supplier."[3]

The measures put forward in the rest of the letter were certainly radical, but by and large, they were in line with what had been discussed during the Group meeting: ZF was to be released from the Zeppelin Foundation and reestablished as a new company by the employees. Additionally, the military administration would loan the company the production equipment it needed, and the company would set up a new management structure composed of the works council and a number of long-time managers. The workforce would be reduced to around 300 employees over the long term, and the company would be restricted to producing agricultural machinery and spare parts.

Challenges for a new generation of managers

On July 23, 1946, Hans Cappus officially stepped down; one day later, Hugo Eckener informed the ZF works council that he was resigning as head of the Group, chairman of the ZF supervisory board, chairman of the Zeppelin Foundation, and chairman of the Board of Management at Luftschiffbau Zeppelin GmbH – however, none of this was official at that point. Rather, he informed district governor Ulmer that he would delay taking this step until the next shareholders' meeting, which he promised would be called soon. In fact, it did not take place until 1950. As a result, Eckener continued to act as chairman of the supervisory board at ZF from 1946 to 1950, while the company's management in Friedrichshafen assumed that the supervisory board was unable to act, partly as a result of Eckener's resignation. After making his proclamation in 1946, Eckener – who still had not officially stepped down as head of the Zeppelin Foundation either – attempted to transfer the foundation's assets to a new non-profit, "Buchhorner Foundation." He requested that he and his former colleague from the Board of Management, Ludwig Dürr, be put in charge of this new foundation – which resulted in a confrontation with district governor Ulmer. He categorically stated once again that he would not tolerate any former "defense economy leaders" (including Eckener and Dürr) serving as the heads of a foundation.

Ultimately, it was Count Zeppelin himself who resolved the conflict surrounding the foundation – in a manner of speaking, anyhow, since he had been dead for nearly 30 years at that point. The deed that he had signed on December 30, 1908 in order to establish the foundation made it crystal clear what was to occur if the foundation's original purpose – namely, the manufacturing of airships and the promotion of airship aviation – could no longer be fulfilled. In this case, Paragraph 15 of the document states, "the foundation's assets shall pass to the township of Friedrichshafen, which shall manage them separately under the name 'Zeppelin Foundation' and [...] use the proceeds for charitable purposes." Eckener and his supporters were familiar with this passage, but had previously quoted it to the authorities in such an abbreviated form that they remained unaware of its implications. It wasn't until mid-October 1946 that attorney Ernst Mühlhäuser of Ulm, who had been hired by the city of Friedrichshafen, officially assessed the documents and pointed out that the Zeppelin Foundation would have to devolve upon the local authorities. This took place on March 1, 1947 – which also meant that the plan of converting ZF into a cooperative was now off the table.

Luftschiffbau Zeppelin GmbH still held 82.5 percent of ZF's shares – but this company, now considered symbolic of Germany's wartime ambitions, was being forcibly ad-

ERNST MÜHLHÄUSER
(1911–1980)
The economist and native of Ulm
served as a consultant and legal
advisor to the Zeppelin Foundation
from 1946 to 1952.

ministered by the French occupying authorities. At that point, it was inevitable: Commander Jean Deudon, who had been appointed administrator of Luftschiffbau Zeppelin GmbH in September 1946, announced on July 11, 1947 that ZF was now also under his control. The company's management, which consisted of Robert Pirker, Albert Maier, and Konstantin Schmäh at the time, still had not been entered into the commercial register and was additionally saddled with an impotent supervisory board – for these three men, this announcement meant a loss of authority that made it even more difficult to run the company.

Reconciliation and new fronts

At the same time, the occupying authorities were increasingly attempting to overcome the rift between the French and the Germans, despite the crimes committed during the Nazi era. In addition to district governor Ulmer in Tettnang, former German teacher Albert Merglen – a native of the Alsace region – deserves particular mention here. He succeeded Ulmer in February 1947, and in April of the same year, he launched a noteworthy initiative: he sent letters to around 150 people living in the occupation zone and asked them to openly discuss their situation, their expectations, and any possible grievances they might have. One of these letters was sent to the recently elected chairman of the works council at ZF, Hermann Metzger. In his response, he bluntly outlined the situation at the time, particularly criticizing the ongoing dismantlement of companies and

the poor nutrition options and living conditions available to the local population.[6] Merglen did not react with irritation; rather, during the following three years that he served in his post, he used Metzger's criticisms as a jumping-off point to benefit both the city of Friedrichshafen and ZF. For example, in December 1947, he contributed significantly to the final editing process for the position paper drafted by Ernst Mühlhäuser to secure the foundation's assets and safeguard the integrity of the companies that were part of the foundation; this move preempted the eventual transfer of LZ's assets to the city. Merglen maintained his ties to the region even after leaving office in November 1950, and he developed a friendship with chairman of the ZF works council Hermann Metzger that is documented in numerous letters exchanged between the two.

While the company's relationship with the French authorities improved, it was actually former head of ZF Hugo Eckener who became a hindrance as the company was in the midst of the difficult rebuilding process. After returning from the USA in late 1947, he did his utmost to seize control of the company with the support of the Schwäbisch Gmünd plant. He apparently had very powerful contacts in the USA that he could rely on for help, and it didn't hurt that in official terms, he was still technically considered head of the supervisory board at ZF. What's more, he had formed an unusual alliance with the French administrator of ZF Friedrichshafen AG, Emile Knipper, who had succeeded Jean

HERMANN METZGER
(1911–1989)
After joining ZF as a machine fitter in 1936, Metzger served as chairman of the supervisory board between 1947 and 1963. He was also a member of the Friedrichshafen municipal council, representing the Social Democratic Party (SPD).

Deudon in this post in April 1948. Events began to unfold when Werner Diedrich, general manager of Zahnradfabrik Passau GmbH (founded in 1946)[7], asked his parent company in Friedrichshafen for a one million reichsmark loan. Knipper denied Diedrich's request, forcing him to try his luck with the plant in Schwäbisch Gmünd.

The steering system manufacturing business had been completely relocated to the ZF plant in Schwäbisch Gmünd in 1945, meaning that this plant now had an independent, profitable business segment. Additionally, like the plant in Passau, Schwäbisch Gmünd was in the American zone of occupation, had not been significantly damaged during the war, and was not at risk of dismantlement. Eckener and plant manager Erich Klug, who had held his post in Schwäbisch Gmünd since 1945, offered Diedrich the loan in exchange for 60 percent of the voting rights in ZF Passau. Diedrich declined.

But Eckener had no intention of giving up. He made Diedrich another offer: ZF Passau had received a number of machines for manufacturing truck transmissions from Friedrichshafen. Eckener demanded that these machines be transferred from Passau to Schwäbisch Gmünd, as collateral for the loan. Eckener even managed to have machines from the temporary factory in Klingenstein, which was also in the American zone, brought to Schwäbisch Gmünd. The French rejected Eckener as a military industrialist, but with the support of the Americans, he managed to become the "head trustee" for the plants in Klingenstein and Schwäbisch Gmünd.

The Robin Plan for a French ZF

While the former head of the LZ Group was attempting to drive a wedge between the ZF plants from his base in Schwäbisch Gmünd, ZF Friedrichshafen had come to an agreement with the French authorities; ZF was removed from the Allies' list of companies to be dismantled on July 30, 1948. However, the company paid a high price for this victory. At the beginning of this entire chain of events, Leo

Robin – a French engineer who had been in contact with ZF for a very long time, even before the military occupation – had made a plan to found a French Zahnradfabrik under the umbrella of transmission manufacturer SOFEN[8], which was headquartered in Paris. ZF was to lease the necessary machines to the new company, although the production equipment that the company had already sent to France in the form of reparation payments would be taken into account. Additionally, ZF was to support the new company with its business expertise and technological know-how. Although both sides insisted that this was an equal partnership, Zahnradfabrik did not agree to the project voluntarily. Robin knew that he had the support of the French government, and he also had two letters up his sleeve in which former board members Cappus and Dolt and (still technically current) supervisory board chairman Eckener expressed their support for the idea – if they were given a say in the project.[9] All that remained was for managers Maier, Pirker, and Schmäh to agree to Robin's "offer of negotiations."[10]

In the meantime, the western zones of occupation were preparing a currency reform to stop the collapse of the reichsmark, which was still in circulation. The plan was to introduce the deutschmark as the new currency on June 20, 1948. Immediately before that date, French administrator Emile Knipper attempted to secure a greater role in the future of Zahnradfabrik for a group of German and French investors that he supported. His idea was to sell 46 percent of the ZF shares that were part of the Luftschiffbau Zeppelin GmbH portfolio to an intermediary company: Schwäbische Zellstoff AG in Ehingen, Germany. However, because the intermediary company didn't have the necessary funds to purchase the shares, ZF was supposed to provide a loan. Julius Oesterle, who later chaired the supervisory board at ZF, recalls the situation:

"This move was supposed to be made on June 19, 1948, right before the currency reform was implemented. Two men from Zahnradfabrik had

As part of the currency reform, old reichsmark notes were exchanged for deutschmarks throughout the western zones of occupation in Germany on June 20, 1948.

We engineers are men of the world.

ALBERT MAIER

to go to the French administrator's office at midnight so that the check for approximately 4,000,000 reichsmarks could still be submitted to the state central bank on that same day. The state central bank had to keep its tellers' counter open for that reason only."[11]

The investors believed time was of the essence, because as part of the currency reform, debts were going to be converted at a ratio of 10:1. Assets, on the other hand, would be converted at 1:1. Consequently, this block of shares would be worth ten times more once the deutschmark was introduced. However, Knipper had overlooked the fact that any transactions conducted on June 19, 1948 already had to use the new currency – that was the law. As a result, the plan failed.

An unexpected turn of events

On July 24, 1948, ZF – represented by Emile Knipper as its administrator – signed the completed contract for leasing machines to SOFEN in France, which was represented by Leo Robin. The initial term of the contract was five years, and it stipulated that 304 machines in ZF's possession would be leased to SOFEN at an annual price of 150,000 deutschmarks.[12]

In September 1948, administrator Emile Knipper announced to ZF managers Maier, Pirker, and Schmäh that he had granted manager of the Schwäbisch Gmünd plant Erich Klug full power of attorney in all matters of business at ZF. With this move, he effectively placed full responsibility for all of ZF's commercial affairs with the Schwäbisch Gmünd plant. The fact that management in Friedrichshafen felt the situation was desperate was evident – the works council and general managers were actually willing to appoint director Hans

Cappus, who had been suspended in 1946, to the post of commercial director instead of Erich Klug if it was the only way to avoid a split with the plants in the American zone. In the end, however, things worked out differently: the French High Command in Baden-Baden released ZF from forced administration on September 30, 1948, ousting both Knipper and his chief representative Klug from their posts.

The French Zahnradfabrik that was supposed to be based on German ZF technology also never materialized. Instead, Leo Robin announced in September 1949 that SOFEN, the company he represented, had never paid the transportation fees for the machines it had leased from ZF, so the shipping companies had acquired a court order to sell 23 of the machines in order to pay the costs that had accrued. ZF investigated the situation further and discovered that the majority of the machines that it had leased out one year prior were still sitting unused in a temporary storage facility in the northern French city of St.-Étienne-du-Rouvray. A smaller number of machines were in use at various branches of French telecommunications and military supply company Sagem; ten machines had gone missing. It seemed that Robin's idea of founding a centralized French transmission company was still a long way from becoming a reality. Apparently, SOFEN had little actual capital to speak of. At the same time, the French High Commissioner for Germany, André François-Poncet, made it clear that he wanted to settle the matter in ZF's favor as quickly as possible. After all, ZF had ostensibly leased the machines to France as part of a purely private business transaction, of which the British, Americans, and Soviets had no knowledge. Poncet was naturally worried about the diplomatic implications; the transaction was in conflict with the reconstruction policies that the Americans were pressing for in the western zones of occupation. A series of difficult negotiations regarding the return of the machines and the defrayal of transportation costs followed. In the end, ZF received around 85 percent of its machines back by May 1950; the rest remained in France to satisfy various claims.

In retrospect, it seems obvious that both the initial idea and the eventual failure of the Robin Plan were historical strokes of luck for ZF, although the men in charge at the time might have disputed that assertion. The plan for a French Zahnradfabrik did more than just bring an end to the forced administration of ZF and ensure that the dismantlement of the plants stopped for good. It also prevented the group of managers including Robert Pirker, Albert Maier, and Konstantin Schmäh – who were extremely successful later on – from being removed from power by the group surrounding Hugo Eckener or the machinations of French administrator Emile Knipper. After Leo Robin's plan failed completely, ZF once again benefited from having the majority of its machines returned – much more so than if the dismantling had continued. At the same time, the failure of the plan meant that Zahnradfabrik was spared having to deal with a strong French competitor with a nearly identical product range.

New ownership structure

Additionally, the fact that ZF was so accommodating when it came to handling the consequences of the Robin Plan made the French occupying authorities more willing to provide the stable ownership conditions that the company had wanted for years. On August 17, 1950, the ZF shares held by Luftschiffbau Zeppelin were transferred to the city of Friedrichshafen and the Brandenstein-Zeppelin family in accordance with the previous ownership structure. The city of Friedrichshafen (in the form of the Zeppelin Foundation) became the majority shareholder, with 89.9 percent of the stock in the company. The Brandenstein-Zeppelin family also held 6.2 percent, while the Maag company held four percent. According to Max Mugler, who started a commercial apprenticeship at ZF in 1950 and had become a financial representative on the Board of Management by 1983, the resulting ownership structure was a significant factor in the company's success:

"Maintaining the original structure of the foundation was absolutely the right decision, and it was extremely beneficial to ZF. Rather than paying out high dividends on the capital market like other corporations, we were able to invest more in research and development – which was good for our future."

Merglen's departure

ZF's ownership structure was finally clarified, setting the company on sound footing and allowing it to begin to rebuild. A few months after later, Albert Merglen's departure drew near. The city government under Mayor Max Grünbeck was conspicuously indifferent to this event, but ZF opted to show its heartfelt appreciation for the outgoing district governor. In October 1965, Merglen returned to Friedrichshafen to mark ZF's 50th anniversary. Albert Maier took this opportunity to explain the importance of reconciliation between the French and Germans to his audience, and to demonstrate how it had helped the company successfully develop during the post-war period:

"The fact that former governor Merglen is joining us today and celebrating with us after his 15-year absence is decisive; back then, he was the first person to truly put the concept of German-French partnership into practice. [...] Today, there is no question as to whether we should foster the German-French relationship or not – it is thriving. We engineers are men of the world [...]. Do you see the vehicles out there, made by the major French factories? [...] You can also see many other vehicles, from many different countries. And we are proud of this partnership, in the spirit of a global engineering community."[13]

THE SCRAMBLE FOR QUALIFIED EMPLOYEES BEGINS:

SOCIAL PROGRAMS WORK IN ZF'S FAVOR

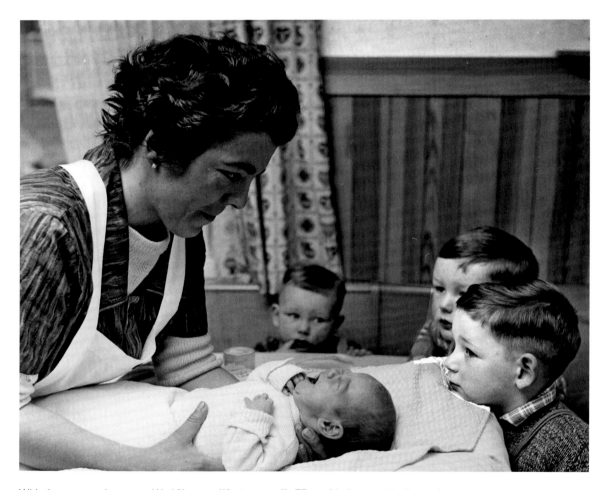

With the program known as Werkfürsorge ("factory care"), ZF provided support to its employees with large families by offering free child care and household help.

The incredible momentum of the economic recovery that began in the late in 1940s and continued unabated until 1966 was practically incomprehensible for people at the time. The "economic miracle," as the recovery was called in West Germany, earned that name because it seemed truly miraculous to those who lived through it. In hindsight, the economic boom – which benefited the automobile industry in particular – is easy to explain: The external conditions were put in place by the Marshall Plan (also known as the European Recovery Program and initiated by the USA), the currency reform of June 1948, the founding of the Federal Republic of Germany in May 1949, and the associated commitment to a social market economy. Additionally, the country's labor costs – which were relatively low compared to other countries' – played a role, as did the fact that the majority of Germany's infrastructure remained intact, despite the massive damage inflicted on the country during the war. Germans at the time also apparently repressed the traumatic events of 1933 to 1945, instead seeking salvation through work and consumption – factors that played an important role in driving the German economy. Passenger cars, once a luxury, now became a mass-market product – and a symbol of the rising levels of individual wealth in the country. Consequently, demand for transmissions and steering systems grew every year. Within five years, between 1949 and 1954, ZF's workforce had doubled, while its sales had more than tripled.

IN JULY 1954, the ZF Board of Management and works council agreed on a series of special benefits for employees, including spending money for the Seehasenfest festival held in Friedrichshafen every year:

20 deutschmarks

In West Germany, the economic boom resulted in full employment; the unemployment rate dropped to under two percent. A rate this low would likely be impossible today – it was due in part to the fact that women were largely excluded from the primary labor market. During the war, large numbers of women had worked in many different branches of industry, because the men who previously held these jobs had been called up for military service. Now, women were expected to return to the home, freeing up those jobs for the returning men. The following comment from Klara Schultheiß, who had served as Count Alfred von Soden's secretary at ZF since 1940 and who left the company in 1946, is representative of the situation that many women faced during the first few years after the war: "I was expecting a baby. [...] When you got pregnant, you handed in your notice." Gender even played a role during the denazification process. Female Nazi party members were more likely to be fired, while for most men, party membership was not generally considered grounds for dismissal.[1]

Full employment becomes a problem

At the same time, the lack of job hunters – highly qualified job hunters, in particular – was becoming increasingly problematic for ZF. In their 1953 annual report to the supervisory board, managers complained that the competition over the best minds in the German automobile industry had become extremely fierce:

"We discovered that some of our competitors were regularly attempting to poach our top specialists with particularly attractive offers. In terms of applicants and new hires, another issue to note is that highly qualified employees can earn much more money at other companies than they can with us, particularly in northern Germany. We are attempting to compensate for that deficit somewhat by offering voluntary social benefit programs [...]."[2]

In fact, nearly every important event in a ZF employee's life was marked by a bonus from the company:[3] a wedding or a silver wedding anniver-

A peaceful place and the first vacation many had taken since the end of the war: the ZF vacation resort "Jägerwinkel" in the Allgäu region of Bavaria.

sary, a child's birth or first communion, the death of a relative, the company's anniversary, or the employee's 60th birthday. Employees even received a special vacation day for their parents' golden wedding anniversary. From 1951 to 1957, employees received something called Seehasengeld: a bonus that marked the Seehasenfest festival held in Friedrichshafen every year. In 1957, this bonus was replaced with vacation pay. Christ-

mas bonuses were paid out for the first time in 1950, and end-of-the-year bonuses, which allowed employees to participate in the company's financial success, started to be handed out in 1953. The fact that the latter bonus steadily increased is evidence of ZF's rising profitability during those years. In 1953, employees received an additional 1.2 percent of their annual gross salary as an end-of-the-year bonus; by 1962, that figure had risen to 6.6 percent.

The relaunch of the ZF company health insurance plan in 1949 was also a very significant event for employees, as Walter Schmalzigaug, a long-standing employee of the testing department, explains: "Before that, most employees were members of the local health insurance fund – and the dues were relatively high. The company health insurance plan saved us a great deal of money." The Zeppelin Pension Fund, which had been established in 1938, was replaced in 1951 by the first ZF pension plan; it was available to all employees of the LZ Group. This program also offered above-average services.

In June 1952, ZF opened the "Jägerwinkel" vacation resort in the Allgäu region of Bavaria. During the first year that the facility was open, as many as 1,105 employees – more than a quarter of the workforce – spent at least a few days there, often with their families. It was the first vacation many of them had enjoyed since the end of the war. The company covered travel costs and subsidized accommodation and meals. When an employee had been with the company for 25 years, he or she received an entire week of special vacation time at the facility, all expenses paid – including spending money. Because the resort was also open to employees from outside of the main plant, time spent at "Jägerwinkel" often helped to build bridges between ZF's various locations, as the following story from the employee newspaper "ZF-Ring" demonstrates: "Only a few of us knew each other before our arrival; we were an interesting mix of people. But from the very first day, we came together as a cheerful community. We Friedrichshafeners formed a very close relationship with our colleagues from Schwäbisch Gmünd and their families."[4]

Intense competitive pressure for employers

As broad and diverse as ZF's range of social benefit programs was, it wasn't always enough to convince highly qualified professionals to take a job at the company. After all, other industrial companies also provided their employees with comprehensive benefits. Wedding bonuses or company-owned vacation resorts were typical of the corporate culture in the early days of the social market economy; at the time, it was not unusual for companies to provide for their employees in an almost parental way. And like Hermann Stahl, who retired in 1994 after 40 years of service to the company, many long-time employees of ZF reported that other companies in Friedrichshafen enjoyed higher levels of prestige:

"In Friedrichshafen, there was the railway repair workshop, which was a coveted employer; there was also Maybach (known as MTU today) and Dornier – both of those were big names, as well. On the other hand, a job at ZF was considered very secure, and I earned a comparatively good salary."

This statement also makes it clear that by the standards of the region, ZF paid reasonably well; the wage gap that the company's management described in its report only existed when pay was compared on a national basis, and was primarily a problem for highly qualified employees. What's more, wages and salaries at ZF were constantly increasing during this period. For example, the average hourly wage at the Friedrichshafen plant rose from 1.42 deutschmarks to 2.94 deutschmarks between 1950 and 1960 – an increase of approximately 107 percent. During the same period, industrial wages at the national level "only" rose by 94 percent.[5] Consequently, if ZF was having trouble attracting qualified employees to its various locations, the reasons likely had nothing to do with the pay.

THE AVERAGE hourly wage at the ZF plant in Friedrichshafen rose from 1.42 deutschmarks to 2.94 deutschmarks between 1950 and 1960: an increase of

107%

CHALLENGES IN THE MIDST OF RECOVERY:

OUTPACED
BY SUCCESS

Thanks to the "economic miracle" in West Germany, ZF was operating at full capacity and was able to construct new buildings, like the "Count von Soden Cafeteria," which was built in 1954. **Below:** Quality control, 1950s.

By 1960, ZF's workforce had nearly tripled compared to ten years earlier. In total, 12,074 people worked for Zahnradfabrik; the Friedrichshafen location alone employed 5,117 people. Housing shortages had been a problem in the city on the shores of Lake Constance since the industrial era began there, and the issue became all the more obvious during this period. Even back in 1920, Count Alfred von Soden had recognized that building more housing would be vital if the company wanted to acquire qualified employees:

"Given our extremely complex manufacturing processes and the very high standards of precision demanded of us, we can only hire diligent, highly trained employees for most positions. In order to ensure the long-term availability of a larger group of such employees in Friedrichshafen, the local authorities or the companies here in the region will need to significantly improve the availability of housing in Friedrichshafen. Given the poor financial situation in which we have previously found ourselves, we have been unable to provide support for the construction of housing in the way that other local companies have largely done. However, we are now aware of the fact that sooner or later, we will have to allocate some level of funding so that we can also support the construction of housing."[1]

Combating the housing shortage

The company began to make good on this promise after ZF Friedrichshafen AG was founded in 1921. Numerous private and public construction projects were sponsored, brokered mainly by the Zeppelin Welfare Association. The housing construction program in the region near ZF, which was supposed to be a tool to help people, reached a tragic low point during the Second World War: although between 1940 and 1943, more than 300 homes were built in the district of "Mühlösch" which the Zeppelin Group had purchased, they were predominantly constructed by prisoners of war who faced horrendous working conditions.[2] Additionally, between 1943 and 1945, Allied air raids nullified all of the company's previous efforts to construct housing, and the shortage in Friedrichshafen became more pressing than ever before.

After the end of the war, ZF initially launched a modest project to build affordable housing for its own workforce, and as the company's profits increased, so did the scope of its efforts. In 1949, the company purchased a building on Georgstrasse 1 with two housing units.[3] ZF began issuing low-interest loans for the construction of rental apartments to cooperatives and the Zeppelin Foundation in 1950. ZF's commercial director, Robert Pirker, calculated that between the currency reform in June 1948 and the end of the 1955 fiscal year, ZF granted a total of approximately 3.2 million deutschmarks' worth of loans to employees and cooperatives.[4] Reliable figures regarding the number of projects sponsored are only available for the cooperatives: during the period previously mentioned, the cooperatives who received loans built 169 apartments and eight single-family homes.[5] Given the average number of employees at the company during these years, this meant that at least one out of every twenty-five employees had the opportunity to live in one of these subsidized homes. In this way, ZF complemented the local government housing subsidy programs, which played the most important role in the reconstruction of Friedrichshafen.[6] Between the mid-1960s and the early 1980s, ZF continuously expanded its own housing subsidy program.

A crisis in steering systems production

Initially, however, the company was confronted with challenges that seemed more pressing than a lack of affordable housing. In addition to the need for enormous investments in production facilities, ZF's steering systems division was undergoing a crisis. The stumbling block was the steering systems production method that was modeled on a concept developed by the Ross Gear and Tool Company headquartered in Lafayette, Indiana. ZF had been manufacturing one-pin steering systems

under license from Ross since 1932. The license agreement had expired in 1942, but the company had continued to produce steering systems in the meantime – production had been relocated to Schwäbisch Gmünd in 1945. The conflict that emerged in 1950 once again centered on the antagonism between management in Friedrichshafen and the supporters of Hugo Eckener and Erich Klug in Schwäbisch Gmünd. The latter group not only acknowledged the tacit extension of the license agreement and the necessity of making back payments to Ross; it also delayed the end of American control over the assets of the Schwäbisch Gmünd plant and attempted to make Ross the majority shareholder of that site. The licensing dispute was meant to provide Eckener and Klug with the leverage they required to spin off Schwäbisch Gmünd. However, when the Americans relinquished control of that plant's assets on February 28, 1951, management of the site reverted to Friedrichshafen. Ross held firm to its demand for back payments from ZF and filed suit in 1951. After a difficult negotiation process, in November of that year, Robert Pirker, Ekart von Soden[7], and Werner Diedrich reached an amicable agreement with Ross regarding the amount to be repaid. Additionally, the men managed to talk Ross out of buying shares in ZF – instead, they signed a new license agreement.

In the years that followed, however, ZF produced fewer Ross-licensed products – partly because in August 1953, ZF also signed a license agreement with Ross's Detroit-based competitor Gemmer Manufacturing. The Gemmer steering system, also known as a worm-and-roller steering system, was more durable than the Ross system and offered a wider steering angle. Additionally, it was available in a hydraulic version, which was easy to operate, even in very heavy vehicles. While the Gemmer steering system gradually began to replace the Ross system in ZF's product range, the steering systems division's output also rose sharply – it had been completely relocated to the plant in Schiesstal, a district in Schwäbisch Gmünd, in

In 1945, steering systems production was relocated to the Schwäbisch Gmünd plant.

Even in the 1950s, ZF's vocational training program enjoyed an excellent reputation. **Left:** A plant ID belonging to apprentice and future vocational trainer Georg Federle.

1953. The worm-and-nut power steering system for vehicles with particularly high axle loads, which was introduced in 1956, was the first proprietary product to come out of Schwäbisch Gmünd – and was the reason steering systems first became an important pillar of ZF's product portfolio.

Customers become copycats

At around the same time, the major German automobile manufacturers began moving in a direction that ZF's management found extremely unsettling:

"Despite [significant investments], we had to survive a serious crisis [in 1955] that was triggered by the booming economy. The most renowned companies among our clientele in the automobile industry threatened to start manufacturing their own transmissions – transmissions that they had previously purchased from us. We had to use all our influence with the management boards of these companies to put a stop to these plans and avoid the consequences, which would have been catastrophic for us. For now, we have succeeded, but we can only prevent this development on a more permanent basis if we make a supreme effort to bring our capacities completely into line with the increased needs of our most important customers."[8]

In order to capitalize on its technological edge in the areas of transmissions and steering systems, ZF had to be able to compete with its own customers in terms of cost-effectiveness and delivery capability. The risk that the big automobile manufacturers would attempt to reverse engineer the company's products – a key problem for any supplier – was something that continued to worry the Board of Management in Friedrichshafen in the years that followed. A lack of production space and qualified employees made it more difficult for the company to produce the volumes needed to meet demand, as the following report that Robert Pirker made to the supervisory board in 1959 indicates:

"All of the plants lack a sufficient number of workers; in Friedrichshafen alone, we are short

250 people, and we will not be able to avoid hiring women to work at the plant. We do not have enough space at the plant or in the offices – 'We are stuck in a suit that is several sizes too small and is threatening to burst at the seams.'"[9]

Newly constructed buildings eased the lack of space for offices and manufacturing. In Friedrichshafen, Schwäbisch Gmünd, and Passau, new production facilities were built in 1960 – and in Schwäbisch Gmünd, an additional building was constructed for the company's customer service department. Some of the administrators from the headquarters in Friedrichshafen were relocated to rented spaces, and the company purchased numerous new machines. Expanding ZF's workforce proved much more difficult, however.

Dramatic changes in vocational training

Because the labor market was short on qualified employees, vocational training and further education became the company's focus. Previously, the apprentices that ZF hired often had relatives who already worked at there; that practice was gradually abandoned in favor of an open application process. The vocational training program at ZF already had a good reputation in the 1950s. However, the content and environment of the program at the time were very different than standards would require today. Georg Federle, who completed an apprenticeship at ZF between 1951 and 1955 and worked as a vocational trainer himself for many years after that, commented:

"In the past, the main focus was on teaching basic technical skills and helping to shape apprentices' character so that they could succeed in life. For example, we wanted to teach young people to stick with a task, even if it was tedious. Like many people my age, I still remember how we had to spend hours filing down components by hand. Despite the blisters I got from that work, I learned a great deal from it."[10]

The vocational training program of the 1950s was characterized by strict hierarchies and a great deal of rigor. Julius Maier, nephew of technical director Albert Maier, recalled his experience:

"My uncle might have been part of the company's management, but I didn't get anything handed to me during my apprenticeship. The supervisors were the ones in charge – there was no getting around them. Some of our trainers consistently impressed me with their practical knowledge, as well as their honest intention to start a dialogue with us apprentices. But beatings were still considered an effective teaching tool back then. I learned that the hard way after a few unsuccessful attempts at using the lathe."

In fact, most of the vocational trainers who were also part of the company's operational business did not have a background in education, and they meted out discipline at their own discretion.

On occasion, the works council and Board of Management were forced to take action against certain supervisors for their physical attacks or arbitrary conduct. Adam Beisert, who came to Friedrichshafen from northern Germany in the early 1950s and was hired by ZF thanks to his ties with a local union representative, initially had a difficult time standing up to his supervisor:

"On my first day, I was met at the gates of the plant by a man who didn't even say hello. It turned out that he was the supervisor responsible for my apprenticeship. When we arrived in the production area, he asked about my profession. I told him I was a mechanical engineer. He responded: 'Then I don't need to explain anything to you. Here's your work station.' I was pretty baffled, and I just stood there until another supervisor came

Busy and crowded: assembling transmissions in Friedrichshafen, 1955.

up to me, introduced himself properly, and explained the situation: my dour new supervisor was a butcher by profession and didn't like 'experts.' Our relationship didn't improve when on my first payday, a Friday, I sent an errand boy to go get me some rolls, milk, and sausage. I had just started eating when my supervisor came up to me in a fury, shouting at me in the local dialect. It took a while before I understood him: no one was permitted to eat meat on Fridays in his department. He didn't care that I was a Protestant and didn't adhere to this dietary rule."[11]

Cultural shift

In the mid-1950s, the vocational training program at ZF began to change. In 1956, the training workshop in Friedrichshafen reopened in its traditional location above the tool shop. Since the air raids of 1943, it had been housed in a number of different temporary buildings, jumping from location to location – but now it had a permanent home again. In 1958, the Chamber of Industry and Commerce began holding seminars for ZF's trainers on issues of education, technology, and the workplace. The first seminar in April 1958 was titled "Youth Psychology," and the following year, the focus was on "Leadership and Human Interaction."[12] At the same time, many veteran supervisors retired in the late 1950s. With a new generation taking the reins, more of the mid-level management positions were granted to employees with stronger professional qualifications.

While the quality of the vocational training program improved, ZF was still having trouble attracting enough young people to meet its enormous need for new employees. In the 1950s, the number of employees at the Friedrichshafen site grew by an average of 288 per year, but only about 48 apprentices were accepted into the training program annually. The growth that ZF was able to generate at its established sites was not keeping pace with the development of the market, so the Board of Management and the company's employees were forced to explore new horizons – literally.

Roman artifacts under the cafeteria

The dining hall in the "Count von Soden Cafeteria," which was inaugurated in February 1955, could hold up to 2,500 people. The size and features of the new building far outstripped the wooden barracks that had served as a temporary cafeteria since the end of the war. It was the first new building not directly related to manufacturing that had been constructed since 1945; it was simultaneously a gift to the employees in Friedrichshafen and a symbol of what ZF had achieved in recent years. However, deep beneath the building's foundation, relics of an age long past were slumbering. When construction began in summer 1953, workers stumbled upon artifacts from an ancient civilization; teacher and historian Ulrich Paret identified them as part of a system of Roman baths.[13] In the years that followed, further excavations on the campus of Plant 1 brought more Roman artifacts to light. All signs pointed to the fact that the ruins of an ancient Roman estate were buried beneath the facility – possibly the biggest one in the Lake Constance region. However, today, archaeologists can only speculate about how important the complex might have been and who exactly lived there.[14]

Above: On April 13, 1959, nine ZF employees and their families wait to depart for Brazil. **Left:** The ZF branch in São Caetano do Sul, Brazil in 1966.

GLOBALIZATION FROM THE LATE 1950S ONWARDS:

BEYOND THE SHORES OF LAKE CONSTANCE

On the morning of April 13, 1959, the loading ramp of the chassis manufacturing facility was a strange sight to behold. Nine ZF employees stood there with large suitcases, surrounded by their wives and children; many of them were even accompanied by other relatives. Growing numbers of their colleagues began to gather around the group, including representatives of management and the works council; these employees were facing an hours-long bus ride and 14 days at sea.[1] Their destination: São Caetano do Sul,

southwest of São Paulo, approximately 45 miles inland from Brazil's Atlantic coast. ZF was establishing a branch in Brazil – its first overseas production facility. Max Mugler, who played an important role in setting up the site, explained how the Brazilian subsidiary came into being:

"The founding of our first foreign site was tied to our business relationship with Daimler-Benz. The Stuttgart-based company already had a plant in Brazil and wanted to procure its transmissions locally as well. It was only logical that we would follow our customer. The head of our foreign sales department, Bert Greinert – a real genius at foreign languages, incidentally – was sent to Brazil in spring 1957 to test the waters in the new location. At the same time, the plan had to be explained to the Friedrichshafen municipal council and its chairman, Mayor Grünbeck, because the city – via the foundation – was supposed to have a major say in any strategic decisions the company made. Mr. Pirker, who was Chairman of the Board of Management at the time, faced a number of problems in this regard."[2]

In late October 1957, members of the ZF Board of Management Pirker and Maier visited the Mercedes-Benz plant in São Paulo, accompanied by mayor and chairman of the supervisory board Grünbeck and head of sales Greinert. Louis Winckler, the general manager of the Mercedes-Benz plant in Brazil, explained the background of the partnership offer to the ZF delegation, as the following report from their visit indicates:

"Like all automobile factories, Mercedes-Benz do Brasil is [...] required to produce or procure 90 percent of every vehicle's weight within Brazil by June 30, 1960, and must use Brazilian materials in the process. Mr. Winckler repeatedly assured us that the company was not intending to set up its own gear or transmission department [...]. For this reason, his company is extremely interested in having ZF establish a branch in Brazil."[3]

The report also mentions that the major advantage of ZF transmissions is their durability, which is vital in Brazil. From the outset, ZF was to be a neutral supplier – meaning that in addition to Daimler-Benz, ZF could also supply other companies that were planning to open a branch in Brazil as a result of the latest political and economic developments.

ZF do Brasil: the early years

After more than two years of preparation, the day finally arrived: on July 13, 1959, ZF and the holding company Spartasul (owned by Friedrich Flick K.G. of Düsseldorf) founded ZF Fábrica de Engre-

nagens S. A. as a joint stock company under Brazilian law. ZF provided 70 percent of the total share capital of 260 million cruzeiros (not more than 600,000 deutschmarks at the exchange rate of the time). However, the company name had already existed in Brazil since August 15, 1958, when the company Industrias Sant'Anna S.A., which belonged to Spartasul, was renamed. In 1960, ZF bought all of that company's remaining shares, making ZF do Brasil a wholly owned subsidiary of ZF. Manufacturing began the same year.

Information about the early days of ZF's business in Brazil is scarce, but obviously, the process of setting up a factory under completely unfamiliar environmental, political, societal, and business conditions was not without its bumps in the road. The Board of Management's 1959 annual report to the supervisory board makes vague mention of "teething problems;" once these were overcome, the report stated, "a rich and rewarding field of work" would await. Max Mugler went into greater detail in conversation:

"In the beginning, we generated a lot of sales in Brazil, but we weren't earning anything. Our profits and costs hadn't been properly recorded in the books, and in 1960, we were shocked to discover that our financial reserves had run out. Mr. Pirker immediately sent my colleague from the accounting department, Mr. Vetter, and me to Brazil to clear things up. I was 30 years old, and this was my first big trip overseas – with layovers in Geneva, Lisbon, Dakar, and Rio, we were traveling for about 45 hours. Each of us had brought several suitcases full of special tools, and after three or four hours of negotiating with the Brazilian authorities – there were a few moments where we really though we were going to land in jail – we finally made it through Brazilian customs. The following six weeks flew by as we spent most of our time on cost accounting. In the process, I had to collect receipts from the desk drawers of each of the individual supervisors. By the end of our trip, the Brazilian and German accounting systems were finally synchronized to the point where we could advise our colleagues in Brazil from our home base in Friedrichshafen."[4]

The first annual report for ZF do Brasil was published in 1961. Surprisingly, Daimler-Benz was not the most important buyer for the Brazilian subsidiary's transmissions and components; in fact, it was Brazilian company Veículos e Máquinas Agrícolas S.A. (Vemag) – by a wide margin. This company manufactured vehicles under license from DKW. Volkswagen was actually ranked second in ZF do Brasil's customer statistics. However, considering the orders that had been placed at that point, it was already clear that ZF do Brasil would be shipping many more products to Daimler-Benz in the future. While there was talk of increased sales, no specific information is actually available on the company's profits and losses for this period. The minutes of the supervisory board's meetings from the mid-1960s primarily mention ZF do Brasil in the context of cost aspects. Chairman of the supervisory board Max Grünbeck was also very obviously concerned that ZF do Brasil might cause the company to incur financial losses. Despite the difficult situation in Brazil, which was exacerbated by high inflation and constant, radical shifts in economic policy, the Board of Management held firm in its commitment to the Brazilian site – and in so doing, laid the foundation for ZF to become a global company.

Multi-cultural approach at the German plants

ZF's expansion to Brazil was complemented at home by the hiring of foreign workers for its German plants. The Board of Management was pushing to expand the search for qualified applicants beyond Germany's borders, because the pressure on Germany's labor and education market was not expected to ease anytime soon. ZF benefited from the groundwork done by the German government here: in 1955, West Germany had signed a "recruitment agreement" with Italy that was intended to attract foreign workers to German agricultural and industrial companies. Similar agreements with Spain and Greece followed in 1960,

and an agreement with Turkey was signed in 1961. Germany's southern European partners primarily viewed these bilateral agreements as a way to bring the rampant unemployment in their own countries under control. In addition to the obvious goal of reversing its labor shortage, West Germany also hoped to foster markets for the export of German products and to improve its reputation abroad.

Foreign workers at ZF are mentioned for the first time in the Board of Management's report to the supervisory board for the 1960 fiscal year. The 362 foreign workers comprised less than three percent of the entire workforce at ZF during that time, but that number would increase drastically in the years that followed. In 1969, foreign employees made up more than 18 percent of the workforce at ZF's German sites. The first and initially largest group came from Italy, followed by workers from Spain, Greece, Yugoslavia, Austria, and France; beginning in the late 1960s, many colleagues from Turkey began to join their ranks. There were also individual employees from a wide range of other countries; reports from the time mention more than 20 nations. Foreign workers were usually housed in special company-owned dormitories. In this way, ZF counteracted the aforementioned housing shortage in Friedrichshafen while simultaneously making it clear

Native of Italy Gregorio Remo with shift supervisor Klaiber at the factory in Friedrichshafen, 1961.

that hiring foreigners – like women – was meant to be a temporary measure only. In fact, however, many first-generation "guest workers," as they were known, ultimately spent their entire careers at ZF.

Slowly but surely building a global team

The transition from a majority local workforce to the global ZF family with more than 300 locations that we know today was a long process that took many years. Contact with "foreigners" in the workplace was something that older employees were familiar with from the years during World War II. Officially, fraternization was prohibited back then, but there were times when Germans and foreign workers or forced laborers had contact with one another – although these interactions were generally characterized by extreme inequality. While Germany was occupied by the Allies, ZF took in many people who had been expelled from Germany's former eastern territories. In 1953, this group accounted for 15 percent of the entire workforce; in Schwäbisch Gmünd, this number was as high as 30 percent.[5] However, at that point, almost everyone on staff at ZF spoke German. With the arrival of the first "guest workers," things at ZF suddenly became much more international, and the transition wasn't without its problems. ZF was in desperate need of new employees, but the immigrants often came from agricultural backgrounds – the day they arrived at ZF was generally the first time they'd ever been inside an industrial plant. Back then, the locals and the new arrivals were much less likely to speak a foreign language than they would be today – and when employees couldn't understand one another, prejudices filled the gap. But very gradually, the new workers became colleagues, and sometimes even friends. Otto Gillhausen reflects on that time:

"I was responsible for assembly, and our primary task was to avoid errors while putting together the final product. It seemed as though we could only achieve this goal by working with trained fit-

"Guest worker" at the dormitory for unmarried employees in the Friedrichshafen district of Allmannsweiler.

ters. But since our foreign colleagues didn't have that kind of training in the beginning, most of them were paid as 'unskilled laborers.' We quickly replaced this 'premium pay' system with a performance-based payment scheme that reflected the fact that every worker played a part in creating the final product.

The 'unskilled workers' became 'plant assistants,' and the discriminatory distinctions made between them and employees with more formal qualifications were eliminated. Increasingly, foreign workers who had taken part in programs to earn additional qualifications were also taking on roles with greater responsibility. Some of them were promoted to management positions and were very successful there as well. It was important for us to overcome our initial prejudices; this cleared the way for us to establish a working environment where friendly relationships between employees of different backgrounds could flourish. Mutual tolerance also grew – for example, non-Muslim employees helped ensure that their Muslim colleagues could adhere to their prayer times without disrupting the work schedule."

STREAMLINING AND INNOVATION TO COMBAT COST PRESSURE:

THE LIMITS OF GROWTH

Managing success: the purchasing department (above), the Hollerith department (lower left), and the patent office (lower right). Photos from 1959.

In 1959, ZF's sales increased by 29 percent as compared to the previous year. And the company's workforce was growing almost as rapidly – from 7,999 employees in January to 10,317 in October. This growth was the result of an enormous surge in demand. In 1956, German Federal Minister of Transportation Hans-Christoph Seebohm (of Germany's Christian Democratic Union party) had introduced restrictions on the dimensions and payload of trucks – which, among other things, led to a slump in demand in the heavy truck manufacturing segment. It was subsequently announced that these restrictions would be eased in July 1960, and shipping and logistics companies began to order large trucks in greater numbers again. An economic boom followed; it was additionally fueled by the public sector. Because ZF was also receiving many more orders in both its passenger car segment and, to a lesser extent, its agricultural machinery segment, the plants were operating at full capacity, often for months at a time. The company constantly had to integrate new employees into the ongoing production process.

Oddly, it was precisely these extremely positive market dynamics that posed unexpected social and fiscal challenges for ZF. Despite the company's rising sales, productivity declined. Labor, machines, and material grew increasingly expensive; price hikes were fueled by the booming economy. The Board of Management's annual report to the supervisory board for the 1960 fiscal year included some very dramatic numbers:

"Now that we have finalized the latest agreements [with our customers], our own prices are approximately 30 percent higher than they were in 1950. However, the prices we pay for materials are more than 100 percent higher in some cases; on average, machine tools are 52 percent more expensive, and standard wages have risen by 107 percent since 1950."[1]

The members of the Board of Management also complained about the "extremely protracted and very difficult negotiations" with their own customers. Apparently, ZF was unable to pass these increased costs on to the automobile manufacturers, because the manufacturers always had a fallback argument: they could manufacture the transmissions and steering systems themselves. As a result, ZF's only option was to become more productive. Streamlining became the order of the day.

Unauthorized strike in Friedrichshafen

The average workers on the shop floor remained unaware of these financial problems, however. On the contrary: the workers consistently put in overtime, and new employees were being hired at a rapid pace, so they were convinced that ZF's transmissions and steering systems were generating a veritable flood of sales. As a result, many employees understandably reacted with incomprehension and anger when management once again delayed a wage adjustment based on an "analytical assessment of working hours" that was originally supposed to come into effect in 1959. In reality, as part of this wage adjustment process, ZF representatives and the labor unions were struggling with an extremely complex catalog of criteria that required each task carried out at the ZF plants to be categorized according to how physically and mentally demanding it was, the scope of responsibility it necessitated, and the working conditions in which it was executed. However, many of the younger and newer employees at ZF felt that this postponement was merely a delay tactic – that ZF was attempting to avoid instituting long-overdue pay raises.

On October 12, 1959, when the IG Metall labor union called the wage adjustment into question yet again – after the issue had supposedly been settled – the situation escalated. Unauthorized strikes were held at the ZF plants in Friedrichshafen, as well as at other companies in the metal industry, such as Siemens and Karmann. According to a report by German news magazine Der Spiegel, the plants affected by the strikes exclusively offered "high wages and excellent social benefits."[2] Participating in these strikes involved practically no risk for employees, the report con-

131

tinued, because "today, these [employees] – unlike in the past – either do not get fired, or can sign an employment contract at another company before even entering the plant gates." Up to 3,000 ZF employees participated in the walkouts. Chaotic scenes occasionally occurred when supporters and opponents of the strikes clashed, as the following account from Otto Schwab – head of the ZF testing department at the time – shows:

"The striking workers [...] attempted to convince the employees of the testing department to walk out by shouting, threatening [them] with raised fists, etc. They just kept getting louder, and they tried to open the plant's locked iron gates by force. [...] The people in [the] testing department, salaried employees and hourly wage earners, immediately lunged at the intruders and attempted [...] to force them back. [...] When it became clear that we would only be able to hold out for a little while, our last resort was to use the paint spraying

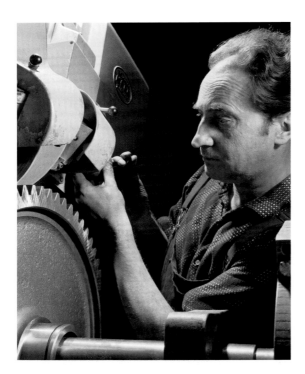

In the late 1950s, ZF was one of the most popular employers in the Lake Constance region, but the company faced a brief strike in 1959. Shown here: setting up a Maag machine from the early days of the company, 1958.

gun hanging next to the gate; I held it up to the opening in the gate and pointed it at the intruders. This only resulted in momentary relief, however, because they immediately began hitting the gun with wooden planks. The lid came off the paint pot, and the contents (red nitro lacquer) spilled all over Karl Digel, the testing department employee standing next to me. To the people watching us through the windows from outside, it must have looked like someone was badly injured. [...] Seeing this apparently severely wounded person [...] suddenly brought the strikers back to their senses, and [they] abandoned their plan to force their way into [the] testing department."[3]

While the unrest might seem like a flash in the pan in retrospect, ZF's management made a concession to the strikers by increasing hourly wages by four to ten pfennigs. Other employers were also extremely lenient, despite the fact that even the labor unions felt that the companies were officially in the right in this situation. It was an indicator of just how strained the labor market actually was.[4] Things soon calmed down at ZF, and apart from another strike in 1963 – this time sanctioned by the unions – which temporarily shut down the Schwäbisch Gmünd plant, the company was spared further walkouts in the years that followed.

Cashless and computerized

Now that the relationship between ZF's management and its workforce had stabilized, the company was finally able to tackle the process of streamlining its manufacturing and administration. Cashless paychecks were introduced for salaried employees in Friedrichshafen in January 1960, and for the rest of the company shortly thereafter. ZF was one of the first companies in Baden-Württemberg to make the cultural shift from paying wages or salaries with an envelope full of cash to paying by bank transfer, as Max Mugler, who was responsible for this transition, recalled: "In the 1950s, wages were paid every two weeks in cash. We prepared the pay envelopes in the accounting department; the supervisors then picked them up and distributed them to their employees. By lunchtime on payday, the employees' wives were usually already waiting at the plant gates or the popular restaurant 'Zum Klosterwirt' to take charge of the money – or most of it, anyway. It took a lot of hard work to convince employees that cashless salary payments were a good thing.

Once we received approval from the works council, we chose the local savings and loan [Sparkasse] as our correspondent bank. The bank was then responsible for distributing the money to our employees' accounts."[5]

Another aspect of the streamlining process at ZF was the use of computers in development and administration. Electronic data processing – or IT, as it is more commonly known today – was still enshrouded in an aura of mystery in the early 1960s, because it was a field understood by only a small number of specialists. Punch cards were the primary data storage medium; data output via printer was standard back then, as the early systems didn't have monitors. For ZF, the computer age[6] began in 1962 with the installation of an IBM 1401 – a compact system by the standards of the time, with dimensions roughly equivalent to a kitchenette. The computer was used for accounting purposes until 1970, as well as for financial planning and the management of manufacturing processes. The computer was capable of performing a maximum of 193,300 operations per minute – a fraction of what an average smartphone can do today. Compared to the mechanical punch-card computers known as "Hollerith machines" that ZF had been using since 1929, however, the 1401 was lightning-fast. What's more, it could be programmed to handle any number of different tasks. The development department, where mathematical computations were the primary focus, had theoretically considered using computers starting back in 1958. Since 1959, ZF had been using a mainframe computer at IBM in Böblingen to calculate the complex variables required to produce functional spur gears; Daimler-Benz, MAN, and Dornier also shared this machine. In 1963, a computer designed to handle technical

tasks – the IBM 1620 – was installed at ZF's Friedrichshafen site. It even included a plotter, which graphically displayed calculation results. It would take a few more years until the first workstations with monitors would arrive at the company's offices. When they did finally appear in 1972, ZF was still ahead of the game – many other industrial companies did not have workstations with monitors until much later.

Automatic transmissions for passenger cars

Computer technology was just one tool that ZF used in the early 1960s in an effort to increase its productivity over the long term. In hindsight, the company's decision to enter a new market segment was equally important – despite initial skepticism, automatic transmissions would eventually become one of the most important pillars of ZF's product range. Hansjörg Dach, who developed the automatic passenger car transmission for ZF, explained the background:

"The head of the testing department, Otto Schwab, knew that automatic transmissions had been prevalent in the USA since the late 1940s, and he was convinced that there was also a huge potential market for these transmissions in Europe. However, the American transmissions wouldn't work in European cars – they were too big, and they required engines with significant piston displacement and torque. So our goal was to develop a more compact version. We also came up with some new details of our own that set us apart from our American competitors, such as using multidisc clutches instead of brake bands that were prone to wear and tear."[7]

ZF's first fully automatic passenger car transmission was completed in 1958 and went by the model name 2HP14. Although the transmission never went into volume production, it was part of a promising test drive that took Opel and Chevrolet vehicles across the Alps to Italy, as Hansjörg Dach reported:

"We had no problem crossing the Stelvio Pass at an elevation of more than 9,000 feet above sea level. A small inn was still open at the top of the pass. We sat outside in the sun and enjoyed some snacks and red wine. The weather was beautiful, and these two days were a great experience for us – especially since the transmission worked perfectly."[8]

However, for city traffic and especially for lower-performance engines, the transmission with just two gears seemed somewhat impractical. Consequently, by June 1961, Dach had developed the 3HP12 three-gear automatic transmission that was installed in the Ford Taunus 17M P3 – a mid-size sedan that was very successful in Europe – on a trial basis. The tests were again promising, but the planned partnership with Opel and Ford never materialized; parent companies General Motors and Ford Motor Company decided to install their own automatic transmissions instead. In the meantime, though, other manufacturers had taken notice of ZF's automatic transmission, which made shifting comparatively easy. BMW announced that it wanted to use the 3HP12 in its new mid-size 1800 and 2000 series models. After a long testing phase using a Ford-based test vehicle, Peugeot also opted to work with ZF. The company had head of design at the Souchaux plant Jacques Desbois to thank for this latter partnership; he had been a forced laborer at ZF from 1943 to 1945. Desbois knew both technical director Albert Maier and head of testing Otto Schwab from the years during the war, and he always emphasized that despite the circumstances, they had always treated him well. Manufacturing of the first ZF automatic passenger car transmission to be produced in large volumes began in Friedrichshafen in 1965. In the beginning, sales were modest – so much so that the company's management apparently held heated discussions regarding whether or not to even continue manufacturing automatic passenger car transmissions, which were extremely complicated to develop. The end-of-the-year supervisory board report for 1965 includes a statement on the subject from commercial director Robert Pirker:

"Regarding the passenger car segment, ZF must decide whether it will become heavily in-volved in the automatic transmission business, or abandon it completely from now on. In the former case, however, an investment totaling 10 million deutschmarks would be required. In 10 years, the automatic transmission for passenger cars will have the same market share in West Germany as it does in the USA."[9]

ZF as a symbol of the "economic miracle"

While Pirker's prediction regarding the popularity of the automatic passenger car transmission in Germany was far too optimistic (it had a market share of up to 90 percent in the USA), the decision to keep developing the automatic planetary transmission was vital in determining the company's trajectory after 1945. Even recently developed products like the 8HP and 9HP are based on ZF's many years of experience in this field. When ZF celebrated its 50th anniversary on October 29, 1965, the company's technical director at the time, Albert Maier, anticipated the importance of this approach:

Using an IBM 1401 computer in ZF's administrative department, 1961.

"We are at the beginning of a new era of transmission manufacturing. It is the advent of an age when the automobile of the future – so we hope – will use an automatic transmission from Friedrichshafen."[10]

Past its peak?

The official ceremony was held on the shop floor of Plant II and included more than 700 guests. In addition to representatives of the former French military government, the Minister-President of Baden-Württemberg Kurt Georg Kiesinger – a friend of supervisory board chairman and mayor of Friedrichshafen Max Grünbeck[11] – was in attendance. As Kiesinger emphasized in his ceremonial address, ZF's anniversary coincided with "a high point in the development of the economy" in West Germany; wages and salaries for industrial workers and salaried employees were "among the highest in the free world."[12] ZF embodied the West German economy's rapid recovery during the 20 years after the end of the war like no other company. With more than 14,000 employees in 1965, the year of the company's anniversary, Zahnradfabrik became "the largest European company specializing in gears, transmissions, and steering systems," as commercial director Robert Pirker observed.[13]

Kurt Georg Kiesinger, who would soon become Chancellor of West Germany, unintentionally touched on an uncomfortable truth when he lauded the state of the economy in 1965 as a "high point." It was becoming increasingly evident that the economic boom West Germany had been experiencing since its founding would soon come to an end. "The age of the 'economic miracle' seems to have come to an end," said Robert Pirker during a supervisory board meeting on July 25, 1966. "It is becoming apparent that the pent-up demand has been satisfied and reconstruction is largely complete."[14] In order for ZF to stay in business, he added, the company would need to expand its international horizons even farther and develop more innovative products than ever before.

ZF Berlin – walled in

The construction of the Berlin Wall – which began when East German police and border troops cordoned off the sector borders on the night of August 12 and into the morning of August 13, 1961 – was one of the key events of the Cold War. Overnight, the approximately 2.2 million residents of West Berlin were not only cut off from East Berlin, but also from the entire surrounding area – essentially, West Berlin was an island within East German territory. ZF's Berlin plant – which had been founded in 1925 and was the largest gear factory in the Berlin area – was inside this enclave. It was located in the district of Berlin-Wittenau, in the French sector. The building of the Berlin Wall primarily affected employees who had, up until that fateful day, commuted to Wittenau from the eastern sector of the city. Once the Wall was up, it was nearly impossible for them to return to work at ZF.[15] The company's sales department also faced serious logistical problems, as nearly one third of the products the plant produced were intended for export to Friedrichshafen and Schwäbisch Gmünd. When the members of ZF's works council met in Berlin in September 1961, however, they found that things at the plant were almost unsettlingly normal. "Sober and realistic" were the words a report in the employee newspaper, "ZF-Ring," used to describe the way the (West) Berliners were handling the extremely difficult situation.[16] Apparently, no one at the plant believed that the division of the city, now set in cement, would end any time soon.

World record holder Jim Clark in the 1965 Formula 1 Lotus. Clark signed this picture to express his thanks: "With thanks and Best Wishes, to all at Z.F."

ZF WINS THE FORMULA 1 WITH JIM CLARK:

RACING FEVER

On September 8, 1963, former farmer Jim Clark won the Italian Grand Prix: his first championship title in Formula 1 racing. Just a few days later, Clark's record-breaking race car, a green Lotus 25, was presented in the courtyard of the ZF factory in Friedrichshafen. There was a good reason behind this gesture by the British racing team: the 1,000-pound race car had a ZF 5DS10 transmission under its hood.

ZF developed the transmission especially for Jim Clark in 1961; it was commissioned by Lotus founder and head designer Colin Chapman. Clark, a native of Scotland, had a fondness for 5-gear transmissions, which ZF took into account – other drivers generally preferred to have six gears. The

gearshift and differential were directly integrated into the transmission block. Additionally, according to technical director Albert Maier, the 5DS10 delivered precisely the advantages that mattered most during a race under extreme conditions: "A high level of mechanical efficiency, low weight, fast shifting, effective gear ratios, and durability." The ZF design and numerous other technological innovations in the Lotus 25 – such as the monocoque chassis, which was used here for the first time – helped Jim Clark win a series of victories that are still considered legendary today. His first win was at the French Grand Prix de Pau on April 3, 1961, where he took first place. In the years that followed, Clark won more than 50 races. In 1965, he earned his second world champion title in Formula 1 racing, and on May 31 of the same year, he also earned first place at the legendary Indy 500. One day later, a telegram arrived in Friedrichshafen:

"Jimmy Clark and Colin Chapman were absolutely thrilled with your transmissions at the 1965 Indy 500. Team Lotus sends you its sincerest congratulations."[2]

These numerous victories attracted other racing teams to the high-performance transmissions from Friedrichshafen. In the 1967 Indy 500, for example, two of the drivers on the winners' podium had used ZF transmissions: Anthony Joseph Foyt (1st place) and Joe Leonard (3rd place). Both of their cars had the ZF 2DS20 transmission under the hood; this unit was well suited to the particular demands of the circular racetrack, as it had only two gears. During the same year, Belgian Jacky Ickx won the Circuit de Spa-Francorchamps, an extremely fast 620-mile race – his car featured a ZF transmission as well.

ZF racing suffered a tragic setback in 1968, when Jim Clark lost his life in an accident on the Hockenheimring circuit on April 7; it was the result of a damaged tire. His teammate Mike Spence died exactly one month later during a test lap in Indianapolis. Many ZF employees had shared in the thrill of the Lotus Team's numerous victories, and losing both of these exceptional drivers came as a great shock.

ZF racing in the post-Clark era

ZF's involvement in the world of motor sports did not end with these tragedies, but it did take a backseat to other projects. ZF's most successful transmission during the 1970s was the 5DS25. Maurice Kelijian, who had repaired countless numbers of these units since the founding of ZF France in 1973, reflects on the machine:

"The 5DS25 was installed in luxury sports cars and race cars. One special feature of the design was the self-locking differential, which prevented individual wheels from spinning and allowed the vehicle to take the curves at higher speeds, for example. Additionally, a mechanic could change the transmission ratio to suit any upcoming race. I became familiar with this transmission back during my apprenticeship in 1971; today, I'm one of the few people who still has practical experience with the unit."

Gradually, ZF began to withdraw from manufacturing transmissions for motor sports, but sporty manual transmissions like the S6-80, which was installed in the Chevrolet Corvette during the 1980s, remained part of the company's product range. Lately, however, ZF has started to get involved in long-distance racing once again: the BMW M235i Racing features an 8hp automatic transmission. While ZF was making a name for itself in motor sports, Fichtel & Sachs (which was named Mannesmann Sachs when ZF acquired it in 2001) was doing the same. Today, SACHS-brand shock absorbers and clutches can be found in both rally cars and Formula 1 vehicles.

1965
—
1990

Expansion and globalization
The years of unfettered economic growth are now a thing of the past. In order to survive in the cutthroat market environment, ZF needs new ideas and new markets – and is forced to become more competitive.

ZF BETWEEN 1965 AND 1972:

A BOOM-AND-BUST CYCLE

Above:
The ZF plant soccer team in 1974.
Below:
Manufacturing the first automatic passenger car transmission 3HP12, 1971.

Zahnradfabrik Friedrichshafen AG broke its sales record once again in 1966; the company generated approximately 456 million deutschmarks that year, or 18.1 percent more than in 1965.[1] And yet, for the first time since the founding of the Federal Republic of Germany, dark clouds were gathering on the economic horizon. When members of the Board of Management Pirker and Maier presented their report on the past fiscal year to the supervisory board in early 1967, they were under no illusions as to the severity of the situation: "The business segments in which our customers operate performed particularly poorly."[2]

In fact, the domestic market for capital goods – including the agricultural machinery, construction vehicle, and truck sectors, which were vital to ZF – had reached the point of saturation. Demand for commercial vehicles continued to decline after September 1967, when Federal Minister of Transportation Georg Leber introduced a platform of policies that would shift most cargo transportation traffic to the railways. The "Leber Plan" became a stumbling block for the automobile industry, and ZF felt that it hindered economic growth. Speculation about the end of Germany's "economic miracle" additionally led German consumers to refrain from purchasing passenger cars for personal use – or to buy cheaper foreign brands instead. The decline in ZF's transmission and steering systems business was a direct result of these domestic developments; after all, in the mid-1960s, exports made up less than one fifth of the company's total sales.[3] And as if that weren't enough, competitors like US company Allison Transmission, Inc. were elbowing their way into the German market and drawing away consumers with their low prices. At the same time, some of ZF's most important customers, including Daimler-Benz, Hanomag, Klöckner-Humboldt-Deutz, and MAN, were investing a great deal in developing their own transmissions. If the largest manufacturers started producing their own products while the smaller automakers either went out of business or opted for cheaper imports, how would ZF survive in the long term?

Many of the plant's long-time employees expected an answer to this question when Chairman of the ZF Board of Management Erwin Ziebart stepped up to the podium at a workers and staff meeting in Friedrichshafen on November 16, 1967. Ziebart had recently succeeded legendary technical director Albert Maier, which was no easy task. There was a distinct air of unease in the meeting room; during the past fiscal year, ZF had been forced to cut jobs. "Double earners" (the wives of male ZF employees) and employees with fixed-term contracts were laid off, and employees who retired were not replaced. The company planned to reduce its workforce by 786 employees (or 5.7 percent) by the end of the year. Ziebart, the new man in charge at ZF, attempted to prepare the employees for a long and arduous reform process:

"We will [...] need to drive innovation in the areas where it seems like we have the best opportunities

ERWIN ZIEBART
(1921–2007)
Ziebart, who was born in Arzys (in modern-day Ukraine), joined ZF in 1967 from Munich-based Krauss-Maffei AG. He served as spokesman for the Board of Management until 1984, while simultaneously volunteering as a professor at the Technical University of Munich.

for the future. We also have to keep an eye out for new products. [...] However, all of this also means avoiding any expenses that are not absolutely necessary, as well as any activities that [...] do not benefit the company to a great enough extent. Redundant work, misunderstandings, and insufficient communication are the sorts of issues I feel compelled to mention here [...]."[4]

Ziebart's speech clearly laid out the areas that needed work, and the company's management had already begun to take action. Volume production of automatic transmissions, which began in 1965, marked ZF's entry into a promising new product segment – even though German consumers, unlike Americans, still vastly preferred manual transmissions. And moves such as issuing production licenses to companies in foreign countries (like Japan, India, or Switzerland) or bolstering international sales were meant to reduce the company's dependence on its domestic business.

ZF discovers continuous improvement

In late 1966, when ZF was still being managed by Albert Maier and Robert Pirker, the company initiated what was known as an "efficiency campaign." As part of this initiative, numerous employees were surveyed and directly asked to provide suggestions for improvement. Approximately 80 specific ideas were put into practice at the company by April 1968.[5] For example, the

The early days of the IT department: design meeting in the early 1970s.

roads between the production halls were resurfaced to avoid the damage that potholes sometimes caused to products during transport. Telexes now had to be written in a brief telegram style; lengthy messages were taboo, as each individual character made the transmission more expensive. Allowances for night shift and overtime work were partially replaced by quality bonuses, which rewarded meticulous work. Despite the obvious successes that the streamlining program achieved, many employees were still reluctant to accept it. Ottmar Dichtl, who had worked at the Passau plant since 1947, explains why:

"In the late 1960s, a new, better machine was set up in Hall 7. The technical plant manager at the time, Willy Futscher, cheerfully informed us that this new technology could take the place of thirteen or fourteen employees. We, however, would've been happier to have more work instead of the best machines."[6]

It was precisely because of these reservations among the employees that the Board of Management depended on the cooperation of employee representatives. The situation was rife with potential for conflict, particularly since spokesman for the Board of Management Erwin Ziebart was facing off against chairman of the works council Frithjof Reizner, a cantankerous, old-school metalworker. Reizner was raised in Tettnang, on the shores of Lake Constance, and joined ZF as an apprentice in 1943. Before being elected works council chairman in 1963, he worked as a lathe operator in the tool shop for 16 years. At the same time, he was also involved in politics: beginning in 1956, he served as an ombudsman for the IG Metall labor union, and from 1961 on, he was a member of the local council in Ailingen – he eventually became a city councilor in Friedrichshafen. Eberhard Sauter, the long-time head of technical product planning, who joined ZF as an engineer in 1968, recalls the situation:

"At staff meetings, Reizner and Ziebart were constantly butting heads. The latter was a polite, cautious sort of person who rarely spoke frankly and directly with anyone. Reizner was the exact opposite – he was defiant, and vehement in representing wage laborers' interests."[7]

Despite this friction, the Board of Management and works council came together to try to make ZF more efficient.[8] Reizner repeatedly called on his colleagues to submit their suggestions for improvement, while Ziebart implemented a more customer-oriented approach from the top down. The fact that the company was now operating with an eye to the market potential of possible new products and aligning itself with long-term societal trends was something new – up until this point, designers like Alfred von Soden and Albert Maier had determined ZF's trajectory, so the primary focus had been the technological possibilities of new products.

The automatic transmission: a new opportunity

In light of the dramatic economic slump in 1966/67, no one could have predicted that layoffs would soon cease to be an issue. German industry

experienced a massive boom, and ZF rode that wave – sales increased by approximately 22 percent. Gains in some areas, such as combine harvester transmissions, commercial vehicle steering systems, and passenger car transmissions, were even higher. Thanks to the economic boom, the company was able to set its automatic transmission business unit on a solid foundation. The technological challenges in this area primarily involved transmission control, as engineer Hansjörg Dach explains:

"The hydraulic-mechanical control unit was inflexible, because the shifting points were determined entirely by the position of the gas pedal and the current speed. If a customer wanted to change the shifting points to suit a specific application, the entire transmission control unit would have to be reworked. The only way for us to avoid being forced to constantly reinvent our design was to replace mechanical parts with electronics."[9]

Integrating electronics into transmissions was not one of ZF's core areas of expertise, so the

Native of Tettnang Frithjof Reizner (1929–1998) left his mark on the ZF works council with his strident voice and steadfast support of workers' interests. Despite their frequent disputes, ZF's Board of Management also recognized his contribution to the company. Shown here: CEO Friedrich Baur congratulates Reizner as he receives the Federal Cross of Merit, 1983.

ZF presents at the Frankfurt International Motor Show (IAA), 1969.

company began looking for a partner who had previous experience with the volume production of electronic components – and found the ideal candidate in Stuttgart-based Robert Bosch GmbH. In June 1969, both parties agreed to cooperate on developing automatic transmissions. ZF was to contribute its expertise in transmission manufacturing, while Bosch would be responsible for electronic transmission control. The partners were able to present the fruits of their labor – a gear shift assembly that they had developed together – that same year at International Motor Show (IAA) in Frankfurt am Main.

In the meantime, Plant II in Friedrichshafen had reached the limits of its production capacity. Shortly before Christmas in 1970, ZF shipped out its 100,000th 3HP automatic passenger car transmission. It is interesting to note just how many of these units were exported: of the 3,000 of these transmissions that left the plant every month, 47 percent were delivered abroad, to customers such as Peugeot or Alfa Romeo.[10] This was well above the company's average export rate, which was a mere 29.7 percent in 1970. ZF planned to expand its involvement in this area, and was already in talks with its US competitor BorgWarner by 1969. This long-standing manufacturing company had been constructing automatic transmissions for passenger cars since the early 1950s, and after making significant investments in Japan and Great

Britain, BorgWarner now wanted to expand to the European continent. The company was interested in purchasing shares in ZF Friedrichshafen AG, but ZF countered that proposal by suggesting that the two companies establish a joint venture – ZF-Borg-Warner GmbH was subsequently founded in March 1970. The location ZF selected – the German city of Saarbrücken – was quite controversial, as the company had no historical ties to the region. But unlike Lake Constance, Saarbrücken offered a large pool of workers, most of whom came from the mining industry, which had been in decline for years. BorgWarner and ZF invested a total of 48 million deutschmarks in the new company. Siegfried Goll, Chairman of the Board of Management at ZF from 2001 to 2006 and an employee of the company since 1963, gives an account of the events that occurred:

"The decision to produce automatic transmissions in Saarbrücken wasn't made by ZF alone. But then – at the eleventh hour, so to speak – our partner BorgWarner decided that there was no future for the project. In the long term, this allowed us to strike out on our own in the automatic passenger car transmission segment, but at that moment, it put us in a very difficult position."[11]

In March 1972, ZF acquired all shares of the subsidiary, which was dubbed ZF Getriebe GmbH from that point on. BorgWarner's announcement that it would exit the joint venture came at a very

In 1972, West German President Gustav Heinemann visited ZF in Friedrichshafen. The visit was decidedly informal. Shown here: Heinemann (second from right) in conversation with managers and employee representatives.

inopportune time for ZF; employees at the company had repeatedly been forced to work reduced hours since October 1971 as a result of another decline in orders. The works council and Board of Management were quick to emphasize that the company was expected to begin operating at full capacity again soon. Nevertheless, it was impossible to overlook the fundamental change in the overall economic situation: the stable boom that had begun in the early 1950s was over, and German industry was now riding an economic roller coaster.

The German President visits ZF

When German President Gustav Heinemann paid a surprise visit to ZF in Friedrichshafen on a Sunday in spring 1972, Board of Management spokesman Erwin Ziebart brought up the issue of economic instability.[12] Automotive suppliers like ZF were particularly vulnerable to fluctuations in the market. As Ziebart's colleague from the Board of Management, Ernst Braun, added, the gradual appreciation of the deutschmark since October 1969 was also making it more difficult for ZF to remain competitive. German exports were now more expensive, while the German domestic market was simultaneously more attractive for foreign companies. President Heinemann barely responded to these concerns, instead sticking to his political program as a "president of the people." He did ask detailed questions about the relationship between the workers and ZF as an employer – and received positive feedback. Both chairman of the works council Frithjof Reizner and the interpreter for the Turkish guest workers, Ismet Aksan, reported that team spirit within the company was extremely strong. Still, everyone in attendance was aware that the company would need to respond to the negative economic trends with new technologies and strategies. ZF needed a product range that was broad enough to compensate for the repeated slumps in the various individual business units. ZF was no longer quite as secure in its position as Europe's largest manufacturer of transmissions and steering systems as it had been just a few years before.

The oil crisis of 1973 resulted in some unusual scenes on Germany's roads. Shown here: people taking a stroll on the autobahn and panic-buying gasoline at a filling station in Berlin.

THE ROAD TO A FUEL-SAVING TRANSMISSION:

INSPIRED BY THE OIL CRISIS

The economy is 50 percent psychology." This statement is attributed to Ludwig Erhard, former German Chancellor and "father of the German economic miracle." While Erhard's actual comment was somewhat more nuanced[1], the seed of truth in this statement became undeniable in October 1973, when Egypt and Syria executed a surprise military strike against Israel. Their objective was to retake territory that Israel had controlled since 1967. Soon after the conflict known as the Yom Kippur War (or Ramadan War) broke out, the West declared its solidarity with the Jewish state, causing the Organization of the Petroleum Exporting Countries (OPEC) – composed primarily of Arab countries – to throttle the supply of oil to Israel's supporters.

In the West German capital of Bonn, the price for a barrel of light heating oil subsequently leapt from about 4 deutschmarks to nearly 32 deutschmarks[2]. Speculators bought up every single barrel in the Rotterdam Oil Terminal, and some motorists began converting their homes into their own private fuel depots. Politicians reacted in November 1973 with the Energiesicherungsgesetz (Energy Security Act), which, among other things, made it possible for the government to ration fuel. The law was first applied just a few days after its passage. On four Sundays in November and December 1973, the West German government prohibited the private or commercial use of any type of motor vehicle. These "car-free" Sundays produced hardly any noticeable savings – no doubt largely due to the fact that West Germany still had sufficient oil reserves. The psychological impact of the driving ban, on the other hand, was enormous. In the short term, the price bubble in the petroleum market actually grew, and demand for automobiles collapsed. What's more, customers who did buy new cars during this period often opted for smaller models – much to the dismay of auto manufacturers. In retrospect, however, there are signs that the 1973 oil crisis also had positive effects on the economy. Increasingly, the develop-ment departments of automotive companies began to consider fuel-saving and alternative drives as a viable product; in other industries, too, the issue of reducing dependency on oil became a greater priority.

Inspiration and new ideas

The developments at ZF during this period illustrate how the crisis ultimately resulted in innovative, internationally successful products. The conditions at ZF were particularly favorable: for example, in August 1971, the company had already broken ground on a new development and testing center in Friedrichshafen, which would bring an end to its previously fragmented network of testing and inspection facilities in rented premises scattered throughout the city. In late summer 1973, the development department moved more than 1,000 employees into the new 110,000-square-foot complex. The building was officially inaugurated in November 1973.

This new infrastructure provided ZF with the solid foundation it needed to develop the Ecosplit transmission, which was intended to replace the company's existing commercial vehicle transmissions for heavy trucks. The time had come for a new series of transmissions – and not just because of the barely tapped potential for optimizing fuel consumption. The full-size version of the 5S 110-series transmission that preceded the Ecosplit had 17 gears, and as a result, it was often not compact enough to be installed in the latest tractor units. There were also issues with reliability, as Karlheinz Erbacher, head of the primary quality assurance department at the time, recalls:

"The 5S110 had failure rates of up to 25 percent. Word got around among the truck drivers at rest stops; the transmission had become synonymous with unreliability. It was a highly unsatisfactory situation. And when our customer MAN decided to end its supplier relationship with ZF in favor of a partnership with our competitor Fuller because of the problems with the unit, well – that was an absolute catastrophe for us. We knew that

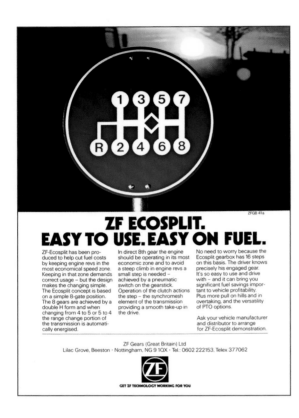

we had to make some fundamental changes. When we began working on the Ecosplit, we decided to implement a team-based development approach for the first time. From that point on, we had regular weekly meetings where all of the division heads involved in the project – from development, customer service, and quality assurance – came together to prepare the next steps in the process. In that sense, we didn't just look at things from a technological standpoint; we developed our products based directly on the needs of the market."[3]

From conglomerate to corporation

The new mindset at ZF in the mid-1970s wasn't limited to development. The company also took a different approach to quality management from that point onward, treating it as a preventative measure rather than damage control. However, one prerequisite here was restructuring. In 1974, under the keyword "corporate standardization," manufacturing documents were harmonized in an effort to reduce the number of errors caused by misunderstandings. Hermann Stahl was responsible for the process:

"We were increasingly working with computers, which made standardized formats for bills of materials and draft designs all the more necessary. In the early 1970s, there were more than 30 different versions of the same forms, in some cases. Since the individual plants – in Schwäbisch Gmünd and Saarbrücken, for example – operated like little kingdoms, our request for centralization and standardization didn't exactly meet with an overwhelmingly positive response. It took a lot of work to convince people that this was a good idea; in the end, I had each division head sign a written statement confirming that they had agreed to the corporate standardization process."[4]

The reforms to the company's occupational training program faced less resistance, however. After the program moved its training workshop to a new facility on Aistegstrasse in Friedrichshafen in 1971/72, ZF participated in a federal government research project on the "Year of Vocational

Training in Metal" in 1975/76. In this study, ZF represented a training program that combined classroom learning with practical experience – unlike alternative approaches at other industrial companies, which drew a clear distinction between training and production. Around the same time as this pilot project, ZF also started a "practice company," which the trainees managed independently in accordance with standard business practices. It was intended to give them first-hand experience with how companies operate. This project, which would have been unimaginable just a few years earlier, was the manifestation of a paradigm shift. The trainees now did more than just take orders from their supervisors; they were partners with their own ideas. The new approach was also a reflection of the changes taking place in West German society as a whole, triggered by the student movement of 1968.

Even outside of the training center, the trend toward greater levels of personal responsibility was palpable. In 1973, ZF was one of the first industrial companies in West Germany to introduce flexible working hours across the board.[5] Chairman of the General Works Council Frithjof Reizner was tenacious in his support for the new approach[6] – and helped more than his own employees in the process. With this new work structure, ZF became a more attractive employer and gained the flexibility to navigate economic downturns more successfully.

"2 by 8:" the formula for success

In the meantime, development had progressed on a new generation of commercial vehicle transmissions. While all participants agreed on the goal of reducing average fuel consumption, they were of different opinions regarding how that goal should be achieved. One thing was certain: Only a transmission with the finest possible gear ratio spread would be an option. Based on computer-aided calculations, the ZF engineers determined that 16 gears constituted the theoretical ideal. However, most drivers would consider a manual 16-gear transmission an absolute nightmare – particularly given the fact that

With the opening of its new training center, ZF was able to offer a higher standard of vocational education for young skilled workers. Shown here: technical drafting lessons, 1974.

The Ecosplit series was a lasting commercial success. Shown here: an Ecosplit transmission being assembled in Friedrichshafen (Hall 9), 1981.

the version being planned did not include synchronization, meaning that drivers would have to double-clutch with each shift of the gears. The solution was to combine an eight-gear transmission with something known as a split group. In practical terms, this meant that the driver only had to operate eight gears, which, unlike in earlier ZF transmissions, were arranged in a logical double-H shape. A toggle switch on the gear shift allowed each gear to be partitioned into a "slow" and a "fast" speed.

AFTER ITS NEGATIVE EXPERIENCE with the previous transmission model, the 5S110, ZF was dead set on developing and marketing an extremely durable transmission. During test operations, the new unit had to withstand countless gear shifts[7] – up to:

700,000

However, the design team was still unsure whether the technology would hold up under the rigors of everyday use. In order to make the transmission as maintenance-friendly as possible, ZF took some unconventional steps, as Heinz Hässle – an engineer involved in the project – explained in an article for Automobiltechnische Zeitschrift, an automotive trade publication, in 1980:

"We wanted to create a simple, straightforward transmission, to eliminate anything that wasn't absolutely necessary. Another goal during the development process [...] was to make the new series as maintenance- and repair-friendly as possible. In practice, this meant that the design engineers gathered in the workshop and called in a service technician who had no experience working on this transmission. He was then tasked with disassembling it, using only conventional tools. Every problem he had during the dismantling process was noted down and reported back to the design team to be resolved. The result was that, compared to similar transmissions, [...] the number of special tools needed had been reduced to a third, and the assembly and dis-assembly time shrunk to 80 percent [...]."[8]

The effort paid off. The Ecosplit transmission became one of the most durable products in ZF's commercial vehicle range. And the unit has remained a part of the product catalog in essentially the same form since its introduction at the International Motor Show (IAA) in Frankfurt am Main in 1979. In 2008, ZF celebrated the handover of its two millionth unit. The most significant factor in the success of the Ecosplit was its incredible reliability. "The Ecosplit," said Julius Maier, who took over technical customer service in 1981, "turned out to be so reliable that we hardly ever sold replacement parts for it."[9]

SQUARING THE CIRCLE: UPDATING THE ZF TRADEMARK

On January 8, 1976, ZF registered a new logo with the German Patent and Trade Mark Office. In this new logo, the traditional circle with the letters "ZF" that had been in use since March 1917 was supplemented to include a square in the background.[1] Not much fuss was made about the change, either within the company or externally. Customers and even employees probably only noticed the new logo in passing. And yet, there was more to it than just a simple administrative act. According to the trademark register, the old logo primarily represented

"Gears and other [...] wheels and wheel components." When the new logo was registered, on the other hand, the focus was on transmissions. With a little imagination, you can even see this interpretation in the logo. The gear – once ZF's main product – is now integrated into a diagrammed, square housing. ZF had traveled a long path from manufacturing gears to designing and producing complex transmissions in the intervening years; with this new trademark, the company's growth was now illustrated for the outside world. At the same time, the first modernization of the ZF logo lettering – which had been tested for the first time at the 1961 International Motor Show (IAA) in Frankfurt – officially became part of the corporate design.[2] The clear lines and sans-serif font were in perfect harmony with the spirit of the times.

The new ZF logo proved just as durable as the company's products: it is still in use today. In January 1992, the abbreviation "ZF" – which was originally reserved for the trademark and only ever used internally – came to represent the company as a whole.[3] Finally, Germany's largest transmission manufacturer had a name that no longer reduced it to its roots as a "gear factory." Additionally, the name "ZF" was much easier to explain to partners in other countries – an important aspect as the company continued to expand internationally.

BEYOND THE DOMESTIC MARKET:

ZF GOES GLOBAL

Italian company saim S.p.A. represented ZF at the 1980 Turin Motor Show. Lemförder and Sachs, two companies that ZF would later acquire, were also represented by saim, as this photo shows.

ZF's journey onto the global stage consisted of many small steps – both forward and backward. The company's exports had increased slightly every year since the end of the war. In 1972, exports totaled 35 percent of overall sales. In fact, that percentage is actually higher if the transmissions and steering systems ZF sold to domestic customers to be shipped abroad in finished vehicles are taken into ac-

count. In the meantime, ZF do Brasil – the only foreign production facility – had developed very well. Between 1971 and 1972, sales at the Brazilian plant increased by 35 percent, to 45.8 million deutschmarks – just under five percent of ZF's total business. In Germany, however, the company was facing more intense pressure. The costs of raw materials, energy, logistics, and personnel had risen significantly in recent years, but economic growth had not kept pace. In order to limit inflation, the German Central Bank raised the prime interest rate – not a good prerequisite for investment. The labor market had nearly dried up, and the saturation of domestic sectors – particularly the automotive segment – did not improve the situation for ZF. An internal dossier that the managers at ZF and the municipal council of Friedrichshafen received in July 1973 shows that ZF's management had recognized what needed to be done:

"With the exception of Brazil, our production facilities are located exclusively in West Germany. This means a [...] one-sided dependence on [the] development of costs and currency [in West Germany]. Multi-national corporations have multiple locations for reasons [such as] better distribution of economic fluctuations, improved market access, [and] general distribution of risk for [their] property and business. For ZF, Brazil is a positive example. We must face this problem, even if we don't want to."[1]

The company made good on its word: In December 1973, ZF acquired 50 percent of Spanish company Industrias Subsidiarias de Aviación S.A. (ISA) headquartered in Seville – the second foreign production facility after Brazil (which had been operating since 1958). The company planned to manufacture commercial vehicle transmissions and marine reverse gears, among other things. ZF had great hopes for this production facility on the Iberian Peninsula, because Spain – still under the control of the authoritarian Franco regime – had been experiencing above-average economic growth for years. ZF attempted to make use of this momentum and invested in modernizing production and expanding its product range. In two phases in 1979 and 1983, ZF also increased its shares in its Spanish subsidiary to 100 percent. However, the subsidiary did not meet profit targets, and between 1978 and 1982, ISA fell permanently into the red.[2] Causes included the economic instability in the Spanish automobile industry and personnel costs, which ZF felt were always higher than pro-

ductivity allowed for. In October 1985, the Board of Management announced that the subsidiary in Seville had been liquidated.[3] ZF gave up the production facility in Spain, and the ISA sales and customer service departments were transferred to ZF España S.A. (headquartered in Madrid) in 1982.

Groundbreaking work in South America

The acquisition of Fabrica Argentina de Engranajes S.A.I. y C. (FAE), headquartered in Buenos Aires, proved to be longer lasting; ZF initially acquired 49 percent of the company's shares in 1979. Ford, John Deere, Chrysler, and Fiat were among the company's first customers.[4] The concrete reason for the acquisition was Daimler-Benz's desire to cooperate with ZF in Argentina – and ZF's supervisory board had also agreed that it was a good time to set up a production facility in that country. One other objective was to beat American automotive suppliers to the punch and prevent European automakers from possibly selecting other partners for manufacturing in South America. Additionally, the Board of management and supervisory board wanted to protect their investments in Brazil. After all, if a competitor had established a successful business in the Argentinean market, it would have limited ZF do Brasil's opportunities for generating sales. Entering the Argentinean market wasn't without its risks, however. The country had been under the control of a right-leaning military junta since 1976; extreme neoliberal economic policies were the order of the day – and the Argentinean authorities gave themselves great credit for the "resounding" success of these policies when the inflation rate dropped from 700 percent to 160 percent. In the process, however, the standard of living for the lower and middle classes declined so sharply that a revolution seemed likely to break out at any moment. The regime reacted by terrorizing its own citizens. Naturally, a West German company was completely unprepared for this type of situation and the unpredictability associated with it. Max Mugler, who originally helped establish ZF's South American presence, recalled the situation:

Exhibition (left) and production (right) at Fabrica Argentina de Engranajes (FAE), in which ZF had held a participating interest since 1979.

"Back then, I was the financial director at ZF do Brasil. We had been successfully cooperating with Daimler-Benz in Brazil for years at that point, and they had asked us to commit to acquiring a company called FAE in Argentina. The company was in dire straits, the political situation was extremely difficult, and we suddenly had a hundred new employees that we had to put to good use. Shortly thereafter, Daimler-Benz withdrew from Argentina; we knew we wouldn't be receiving any more orders from them in that country. So we needed a new strategy. It was difficult to come to an agreement with FAE's management, because our negotiating partners were Peronists – followers of the authoritarian regime that had been in place since 1976 – who were under threat of persecution in the political climate of the time. In the end, however, we were able to communicate on a personal level – we set the company on a solid footing, and none of us wound up in prison."[5]

FAE remained something of a problem child[6] initially, as it continued to struggle with the economic conditions in the country – but its founding was an important milestone in the globalization process at ZF. South America was the first region in the world where local ZF plants – in Brazil and Argentina – were able to produce products independently from the company's parent plants in Germany.

New management structure

In June 1982, Friedrich Baur – who was born in Schrozberg, Germany in 1927 – became Chairman of the Board of Management at ZF. Under his leadership, ZF also began to turn its focus toward North America and Asia. First, however, internal restructuring had become essential – by that point, the company had grown to employ more than 22,000 people, so it was no easy task. Baur might have wished for an easier start to his new job. Less than six months after Baur – who had previously

ZF was always good. But the company also recognizes that it has to change.

FRIEDRICH BAUR AT HIS FIRST MEETING OF WORKERS
AND STAFF AS CEO OF ZF, 1982

spent three years on the supervisory board – took the reins at ZF, the media began reporting that the company had "shifted into the wrong gear" with its new management, and that the change had slowed Europe's largest manufacturer of transmissions and steering systems "to a crawl."[7] In ZF's core areas of business, which included truck transmissions, passenger car transmissions, and steering systems in Friedrichshafen and Schwäbisch Gmünd, the press stated that the company was barely scraping by financially. The development of the automatic passenger car transmission for the European market, the reports continued, was an example of the company's failed product policies, and ZF had been too late in adding fuel-saving mechanical five-gear transmissions for passenger cars to its product range – "drastic cuts and new ideas" were desperately needed. These accusations were only partially correct, however. The company could not deny that reduced working hours and minimal layoffs had been instituted at several of its German locations, but on the whole, ZF was in a relatively good position. While German automobile manufacturing had grown by about four percent in 1982, ZF's sales had risen by approximately 10 percent

compared to the previous year. The automatic passenger car transmissions produced at the Saarbrücken plant, so harshly criticized by the media, actually sold 16 percent better that year. And dividend payouts of 11.3 million deutschmarks to shareholders were also an indicator that the company's situation was far from disastrous.

In that sense, Baur was wise not to try to change everything that had made ZF what it was up to that point. "I [...] will do my best to prove to you as quickly as possible that I am a true member of the ZF family," emphasized the former Siemens manager and renowned electronics specialist at a meeting of workers and staff in spring 1983. ZF, he added, was a strong company that was supported in large measure by the loyalty of its employees – still, changes would have to be made. With this statement, Baur was referring to more than just the incremental reforms to the company's management structures that began in mid-1982; one very obvious change actually affected Baur's own position.

For the first time in ZF's history, the company had a CEO – not a spokesman for the Board of Management, as had previously been the case. The stated goal behind this change was to expedite decision-making processes at the executive level. ZF's

FRIEDRICH BAUR
(1927–2006)
Baur, who held a doctorate in electrical
engineering, started his career at Siemens.
He became CEO of
ZF Friedrichshafen AG in 1982.

operational business was divided into two regional units, the first of which included the sites in Friedrichshafen and Saarbrücken and the factories in Brazil and Argentina. The second unit comprised Schwäbisch Gmünd, Passau, and Seville (Spain). Previously, these locations had been managed separately; now, sites in different geographic locations were under the same roof. The move was intended to counteract the pervasive regionalist attitude that had dominated ZF up to that point. Additionally, as part of this reform process, Group-wide management sectors (Technology, Markets, Corporate Finance and Administration, Human Resources, and Production) were created; each sector was headed by a member of the Board of Management.

New prospects across the Atlantic

Despite the fact that ZF's overseas investments in recent years had rarely paid off, the company's management was still adamant that manufacturing should be carried out on a broader international basis. Consequently, the company opted to stick with its policy of global expansion. Results of this policy included the founding of ZF Steering Gear (India) Pvt. Ltd. (Poona, 1981) and AAE-ZF Steerings SDN BHD (Penang, Malaysia, 1985). In the 1980s, the Asian market did not play quite as important a role to (West) German companies as it does today – rather, the USA was the leading global economic power at that time. For this reason, excitement was running high in Friedrichshafen when the Ford Motor Company (headquartered near Detroit) commissioned ZF with manufacturing 500,000 fully synchronized five-gear manual transmissions for pick-up trucks within five years, beginning in 1986. This major contract was all the more important for ZF because Daimler-Benz – one of the company's most important domestic and international customers – had increasingly begun producing its own transmissions during that period. ZF partnered with Maumee, Ohio-based supplier DANA to secure the job from Ford. Initially, both parties planned to combine their delivery quotas and manufacture

the necessary products via a joint venture in Brazil, the USA, and Germany. At one point, the idea of DANA purchasing shares in ZF do Brasil was under serious consideration.[8] However, negotiations with DANA stalled when ZF began to have doubts about its potential partner's financial viability.[9] It soon became clear that the joint venture was never going to materialize.

ZF's management rejected the idea of setting up its own factory in North America for the time being. Instead, the company planned to manufacture the transmissions in Brazil, but scheduling difficulties made this impossible – in the end, Friedrichshafen was chosen for the job. ZF built a brand new, 175,000-square-foot production facility with room for approximately 300 employees in record time (6 months). When the plant was inaugurated in February 1986, chairman of the ZF works council Frithjof Reizner called it a "miracle" – he was referring to the fact that it was completed on time, as well as to the profits the company expected to make from exporting the transmissions.[10] However, things turned out differently than anyone expected, as Willi Schacher – head of international customer service at the time, and head of Markets in Business Unit I beginning in 1980 – explains:

"We had some fantastic contracts already in the bag. But we couldn't profit from them, because on the very day that we shipped the transmissions to the USA, the dollar lost more than 30 percent of its value against the deutschmark compared to February 1985 – and there was no end to the decline in sight. For every transmission we delivered, we had to pay extra. There was no way we could keep doing that for long."[11]

The collapse of the dollar exchange rate also had its benefits for ZF. Above all, investments in the USA now seemed much more lucrative than they had just a few years before. ZF seized the opportunity and founded three companies in the USA in 1986: ZF Industries Inc. in Dover, Delaware; ZF Steering Gear (US) Inc. in Brewer, Maine; and ZF Transmissions Inc. in Gainesville, Georgia. In order to make use of the favorable exchange rate, ZF be-

The construction of Hall 10 at Plant 2 in Friedrichshafen was intended to expand production space so that the company could meet demand from the USA. Photos from 1985 (construction) and 1986 (ongoing production).

gan shifting the manufacturing of the transmissions intended for Ford to its Gainesville site – the subsidiary's share of production increased every year. But despite ZF Transmissions' rapid growth, it initially remained in the red. In addition to the more than 32 million deutschmarks ZF had invested between 1987 and 1989, another cause for this deficit was the gradual reduction in orders coming from Ford, which was the plant's main customer. The original plan was for the plant to produce 133,000 units per year, but this had dropped to 86,000 by 1990. The reasons for this decline were primarily tied to Ford's sales – Ford was extremely satisfied with the partnership itself and even pre-

sented ZF with the "Q1 Quality Award" for outstanding supplier quality in December 1989.[12]

New international customer service

In hindsight, it seems as though setting up a cost-effective production facility overseas was a sluggish process that did not result in commercial success until the 1990s. When ZF set out to establish an international customer service network, however, the globalization process went much more quickly and had an immediate effect. The idea of providing decentralized technical service for customers in their own countries arose in the early 1970s. Willi Schacher comments again:

Manufacturing the ZF transmission S5-42 for Ford
at the Gainesville plant, early 1990s.

"In the foreign markets where we operated in Europe back then, independent companies served as ZF's representatives in each country. Our new Chairman of the Board of Management Dr. Ernst Braun, who joined ZF from Schweinfurt-based SKF in 1971, wanted to change this structure – either by acquiring distribution companies in other countries or establishing new companies. In this way, the ZF network began to grow in Europe; it then expanded to South Africa and the USA. This expansion of our customer service portfolio was aimed at more than just the obvious goal of generating profits. We also wanted to keep a closer eye on our markets and develop a sort of warning system for quality issues. We occasionally upset the development department at ZF because we pointed out problems; the designers naturally stood behind their products. But this internal competition was beneficial to the company."[13]

Roland Schäffler, who had worked for the customer service department since 1960, agreed:

"ZF ultimately learned to view us as more than a cost factor. By offering more extensive repair services in foreign countries, we also improved our potential for sales. For instance, ZF was competing with Fuller in South Africa and Voith in the USA, and our expanded service network was a decisive factor in allowing us to gain additional market share. Incidentally, the customer service department's range of responsibilities had begun to expand in the 1980s. Departments such as inspection or the technical editors responsible for writing operating instructions were incorporated into the new structure. I used to be responsible for 16 employees; after the new structure was implemented, I was managing more than 60."

The establishment of an international network of customer service centers and sales companies began in September 1972 with ZF GmbH in Vienna –

ZF'S INTERNATIONAL
LOCATIONS IN 1988

■ Plants

● Customer service
centers and sales
companies, investments

which, in addition to the Austrian market, was responsible for the countries in Eastern and South-Eastern Europe. In the years that followed, ZF founded a veritable wave of new subsidiaries:

- ZF France S.a.r.l. (Rungis, near Paris, 1973),
- ZF Gears Ltd. (Nottingham, 1974),
- ZF Danmark ApS (Copenhagen, 1977),
- ZF Italia S.r.L. (Milan, 1978),
- ZF of North America, Inc. (Northbrook, near Chicago, 1979),
- ZF Norge A/S (Oslo, 1979),
- ZF of South Africa Pty. Ltd. (Johannesburg, 1979),
- ZF Japan Co. Ltd. (Tokyo, 1980),
- ZF España (Madrid, 1982),
- ZF International Pte. Ltd. (Singapore, 1983),
- ZF Steering Gear (US) Inc. (Brewer, Maine, 1986),
- ZF Industries Inc. (Dover, Delaware, 1986),
- ZF Australia Pty. Ltd. (Sydney, 1987),
- ZF Antriebstechnik (Schweiz) AG (Zurich, 1987)
- ZF Transtek Synayi ve Ticaret A.S. (Istanbul, 1988).

The customer service centers made a significant contribution to increasing sales at ZF. The primary focus of all these companies was to export ZF's existing expertise and expand their own market presence. However, there was one acquisition that stood out in particular: the Lemförder Group in 1984. It went beyond merely extending the company's existing business – it changed the face of ZF in the 1980s like no other acquisition.

Lemförder between 1947 and 1984:
An industrial beacon
in the German farmlands

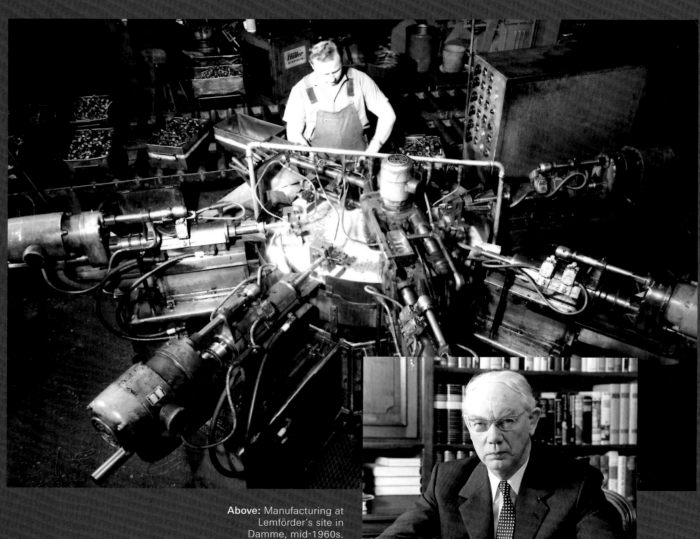

Above: Manufacturing at
Lemförder's site in
Damme, mid-1960s.
Right: Jürgen Ulderup
(1910–1991).

Even today, the LEMFÖRDER brand is still inextricably linked to one name: Jürgen Ulderup (1910–1991). Born in Cuxhaven as the son of ship captain and future general manager of Berliner Hafen- und Lagerhaus AG (BEHALA) Wilhelm Ulderup, Jürgen Ulderup attended the Technical University of Berlin (then known as Technische Hochschule Charlottenburg), where he studied economics. He also earned his doctorate at the same institution in 1934, with a thesis on global air traffic.

It was typical of Jürgen Ulderup[1] to openly criticize the powers that be while making sweeping concessions to them at the same time, as long as doing so served his company's interests. As a management assistant at Auto Union AG, Ulderup made derogatory comments about the Nazis – and Hitler's deputy Rudolf Hess in particular – in 1934; he was consequently arrested and sent to the Sachsenburg concentration camp.[2] His supervisors at Auto Union interceded on his behalf, and he was released again after two weeks. Shortly thereafter, he applied to join the military. By 1939, he had been promoted to the rank of staff sergeant in the reserves. He also joined the Nazi party in 1937; he had been a member of the SS since 1935, holding the rank of Anwärter ("candidate"). So Ulderup successfully offered his services to the regime that had treated him as an enemy of the state just a few years earlier. However, this conversion – whether purely superficial or not – was certainly conducive to his career in industry.

After serving as head of sales and, later, head of purchasing at Mitteldeutsche Motorenwerke Leipzig (1936-1941), Ulderup was ultimately selected to become head of the "technical head office for engine manufacturing" at Junkers Motoren- und Flugzeugwerke in Zittau. Between 1943 and 1945, the former concentration camp prisoner was responsible for one of the best-kept secrets in the Nazis' military arsenal: the Jumo 004 jet engine. Under Ulderup's leadership, the company manufactured several thousand turbines by the end of the war; they were used in the Me 262 interceptor jet, which was described as a "superweapon." However, the majority of people who worked on the project were forced laborers and concentration camp prisoners. According to statements made later by former employees, Ulderup did not approve of the criminal mistreatment of the workers assigned to him; on the contrary, he repeatedly advocated for better conditions for foreign workers and Germans.[3] At the same time, he did his "duty" by supporting the military supply industry, even when defeat was inevitable – behavior that was at odds with his support for workers' rights. Ulderup believed that the war had been lost even before the Germans surrendered, as a letter from Nazi party district leader Cortes to the Nazi leader of the state of Saxony Gauleiter Mutschmann dated May 3, 1945 indicates:

"According to reports by the Gestapo, Ulderup said something to the effect of: Germany had run out of weapons, further resistance and further sacrifice would be pointless, and when a department head objected [...] he responded that it was all a pack of lies, that he once held the same ideals as department head Thöle, but that he was done with that now, completely finished."[4]

These blunt statements resulted in Ulderup, now 35, being arrested and imprisoned once again. During the denazification process after the end of the war, Ulderup stated that he had been sentenced to death by firing

One of the first photos of Lemförder's factory, ca. 1950.

squad for subversion of the war effort, but was then unexpectedly returned to his post as plant manager – under SS supervision – to continue the manufacturing process.

After the war, a new company

When the war ended, Ulderup began eking out a living in his hometown in northern Germany. He also got in touch with his father, whom the British had appointed Minister of Transportation in the German state of Schleswig-Holstein in early 1946 as a result of his unobjectionable political beliefs. Jürgen Ulderup additionally revived his relationship with Bremen-based industrialist Theodor Klatte, who had served as a supplier to Junkers during Ulderup's tenure at that company. Klatte was looking for an experienced manager for materials procurement and sales – and this is where the story of Jürgen Ulderup as an ideal West German entrepreneur begins.

In spring 1946, Ulderup and his family moved to an area near the city of Lemförde, in the German state of Lower Saxony. In the years and decades that followed, he expanded the metal parts manufacturing company he and Klatte had founded in that city, eventually growing it into a global automotive supplier. Ulderup was as important to this region of Lower Saxony as Count Ferdinand von Zeppelin was to Friedrichshafen. Even today, the company he founded still sticks out from its agricultural surroundings like an industrial beacon. It is not easy to properly do justice to the 37 years of history between the founding of Lemförder Metallwaren GmbH in May 1947 and ZF's acquisition of a controlling interest in the company in January 1984 – partly because Ulderup was such a luminary that his presence still dominates the region's collective memory.

The commemorative publication marking the 25th anniversary of Lemförder Metallwaren AG in 1972 de-

scribed Jürgen Ulderup as the company's founder[5], and in the run-up to ZF's planned acquisition of the company in December 1983, the supervisory board was told the same.[6] In fact, however, Lemförder Metallwaren GmbH was founded by Jürgen Ulderup's father Wilhelm.[7] Although Jürgen was unofficially at the helm from the very beginning, one of his former employees at Junkers in Zittau, engineer Bernhard Faupel, served as the manager and external face of the company. The financier and driving force behind the company was Ulderup's aforementioned partner Theodor Klatte. Until 1948, Lemförder Metallwaren GmbH used the ballroom of the former "Hannoversches Berghaus" hotel as its manufacturing facility. In addition to signal lights for the German Reichsbahn train system and spare parts for the British Army, Lemförder produced a range of different metal goods for the local population. The company traded these products for food, which it then sometimes used to purchase materials from the Ruhr region. Production was later moved to an 8,600-square-foot, camouflaged facility that had been built before the end of the war on a 600-foot-high mountain called Stemweder Berg; it had originally been constructed to house a relocated production facility. Both Jürgen Ulderup and Theodor Klatte took a backseat during the entire process; they were politically tainted by their former membership in the Nazi party and the management positions they held at military supply companies during the war, so their hands were tied for the time being.[8]

Lemförder Metallwaren AG's trade fair stand at the Frankfurt International Motor Show (IAA) in 1967.

The testing lab in Dielingen, 1965. The type of tie rods that Lemförder typically manufactured can be seen in the foreground.

Party tent on the Stemweder Berg mountain for the celebration of Lemförder's 25th anniversary, 1972.

Tie rods: a lucrative niche product

Once he had officially taken the reins at the company in 1950, Jürgen Ulderup began searching for a market niche that would secure the long-term survival of his industrial company – and support him and his employees – in these rural surroundings. The company began manufacturing mother-of-pearl buttons in 1951, but abandoned that idea again soon afterward.[9] However, Ulderup did achieve a degree of success with a product that the company supplied to the automobile industry: tie rods, an important component in steering systems for nearly all modern vehicles. Lemförder began manufacturing these parts in 1950. In 1953, production was relocated to Dielingen, where ZF Chassis Technology operates today. Tie rods literally became Lemförder's trademark – Ulderup integrated them into the company logo that his brother-in-law Heinz-Joachim Hesse designed in 1949. The owl that had always represented the company (and was possibly a reference the founder's name, which had similarities to the Low German word for owl, "Ule") was

now framed by three tie rods. In a letter to Josef Sommer at Magirus in Ulm dated November 1952, Jürgen Ulderup wrote the following: "[...] that we have now been supplying tie rods to eight different automobile factories for years, including Daimler-Benz, Volkswagen, Klöckner-Humboldt-Deutz Köln, and Auto Union, without receiving any substantive complaints – thank God. After all, we are the only company in Germany, save Ehrenreich, that is involved in the volume-manufacturing programs at the largest automobile factories."[10]

The zero-maintenance steering system

In late 1951 / early 1952, Lemförder took the next logical step and added the manufacturing of ball joints to its portfolio. These components were used in every steering system that included tie rods. In terms of technology and quality, however, this new product segment was more demanding. A ball joint, like a human hip joint, is a ball-and-socket construction that has to work for years with as little friction or play as possible. In the early years of automobile mass-production, these

joints had to be lubricated regularly; there was no other option. It wasn't until the beginning of the 1950s that ball-joint manufacturing began to evolve, eventually producing the zero-maintenance steering systems that are standard today. Lemförder started to play a decisive role in this process when chemist Gottfried Reuter joined the company from Hamburg-based Phoenix Gummiwerke in 1954. Reuter – who had previously worked on developing Vulkollan (an early version of polyurethane) at Bayer – was tasked with setting up a center of excellence for rubber and plastic, and coming up with applications of these materials for the automobile segment. His relationship with Lemförder lasted approximately ten years before he left as a result of personal and professional differences with Ulderup. But his work was extremely beneficial to the company, as a patent application for a ball joint that Lemförder submitted in 1954 shows:

"The new aspect of this product is that both halves of the bearing are lined with wear-resistant plastic, such as polyurethane [...]. A joint of this type has shock-absorption properties that can normally only be achieved with rubber pads, but it has a much longer service life than joints with rubber pads. Additionally, unlike metal joints, it does not require any lubrication at all."[11]

Automobile manufacturers recognized Lemförder's newfound expertise as a parts supplier, and the company began to grow. In 1960, Lemförder constructed its third factory in the region: in addition to Lemförde and Dielingen, it now had a facility in Wagenfeld. Yet another plant was inaugurated in

Damme in 1963. With more than 900 employees, Lemförder had practically exhausted the local labor market, so the company began recruiting Italian guest workers in 1962; in the early 1970s, increasing numbers of Portuguese immigrants also began working in the region. One of them, future chairman of the works council Carlos Beja, recalled the situation at the time:

"My wife and I landed at Cologne Airport on June 7, 1973. Just one day later, we started working at Lemförder: my wife was a metalworker in production, and I was a lathe operator in prototype manufacturing. To be honest, we didn't really feel at home in northern Germany at first, but Dr. Ulderup helped us a great deal in that area. We were looking for a suitable space for the Portuguese community at Lemförder to hold occasional meetings – there were about 200 of us, after all. When the boss heard about that, he offered to let us use a basement in one of the company buildings for free. We set the room up as a little Portuguese club, and it's still there today. In the years that followed, Dr. Ulderup visited us there regularly; on special occasions like Christmas, for instance, he would come to the parties and even bring along gifts for the children. If he didn't have time to attend, he would send his wife Irmgard. Today, I could never imagine leaving this place."[12]

Lemförder began setting up a production facility overseas much earlier than other automotive suppliers. The company was already operating on the Argentinean market by 1966, and in 1968, Lemförder acquired shares in Spanish company Ansa. Lemförder Métal France S.A. was founded in 1973.

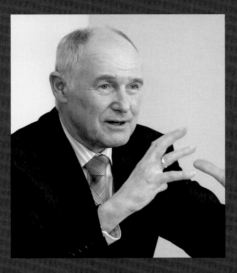

Paul Ballmeier (born 1943) joined Lemförder in 1971. He was ZF's financial director from 1996 to 2005.

The search for a successor

At 63, Jürgen Ulderup was still the undisputed leader and patriarch of his international company. But the time had come for him to consider who would succeed him. His son, businessman Christian Peter, had become a partner at Lemförder Metallwaren AG and some of its subsidiaries by that point; he also managed Lemförder Metallwaren Export GmbH (Lemex) in Bremen. However, the elder Ulderup felt that the company should be run by an engineer in the future – and in 1976, he decided that he had found just the man for the job in Karl-Heinz Thomas. Thomas had previously managed automotive supplier Ehrenreich, which was part of the TRW Group. The partnership between Lemförder's founder and his intended successor eventually dissolved as a result of their differing strategic visions for the company, however. The split occurred in November 1981; it wasn't until that point that Jürgen Ul-

derup began looking for alternatives. His son Christian Peter recollects:

"In the early 1980s, the trend in the automobile industry was consolidation. It seemed sensible to integrate Lemförder into a larger company, so that we could make the transition from providing individual components to supplying whole systems. Initially, my father considered selling the company to another supplier. I was the one who suggested ZF after I had gotten to know the company indirectly through a job for BorgWarner in the USA. An acquisition by ZF seemed like a logical step to me, because Lemförder's main products – steering columns and tie rods – could potentially be combined with the steering gears that ZF manufactured to form modules. Several of Lemförder's managers also supported this idea, so I was ultimately able to convince my father."[13] Before negotiations with ZF could begin, however, two important changes took place at Lemförder. First, management expert Paul Ballmeier – who had joined the company in 1971 – was appointed Vice Chairman of Lemförder Metallwaren KG. He would later play a central role in the negotiations with ZF. And second, the Dr. Jürgen Ulderup Foundation was established in March 1983; its original purpose was to promote vocational training and education in the region. The foundation later adopted the preservation of nature and the countryside as additional objectives. Because the foundation could potentially serve as a shareholder of Lemförder after the Ulderup family withdrew from the company, its founding was an indirect factor behind the future merger of Lemförder and ZF.

Lemförder was and continues to be an important industrial employer in its region of Lower Saxony. Jürgen Ulderup also made large investments in employee training at an early stage. Shown here: the vocational training center in Lemförde, 1978.

THE ACQUISITION OF LEMFÖRDER:

SHIFTING INTO HIGH GEAR

The ZF Board of Management under the leadership of Friedrich Baur had agreed that ZF would need to expand its portfolio in order to better compensate for downturns in certain segments, as well as to profit from synergies. The key word was "diversification:" the

Board of Management was looking for successful companies in related market segments for a possible acquisition. A lucky coincidence brought ZF into contact with businessman Jürgen Ulderup, who was thinking about selling Lemförder Metallwaren AG, the company he had founded in 1947.

In December 1983, the ZF Board of Management suggested to the supervisory board that ZF acquire a majority share in the company:

"Lemförder Metallwaren AG's products have a very good reputation among our most important customers in the automobile industry. [...] The company is primarily focused on manufacturing and distributing accessories for the automobile industry; these components are installed in the chassis and driveline. All shares of the company are owned by the Ulderup family. Dr. Ulderup has managed the company himself since he founded it, but he has decided to step down on account of his age. He will not be handing over the reins of the company to a family member, so he decided to get in touch with ZF."[1]

From Friedrichshafen's perspective, the benefits of the deal were clear. Lemförder's core competencies covered certain aspects of chassis technology – including tie rods, torque rods, and suspension joints – that were an excellent complement to ZF's steering systems portfolio. In the aforementioned segments, Lemförder had market shares of around fifty percent with countless German and European customers, including Audi, BMW, Citroën, Daimler-Benz, Magirus, MAN, Opel, Renault, Volvo, and VW.[2] Lemförder primarily produced components that required mandatory documentation – meaning

that they were vital to the safety of a vehicle. Because of the complex quality requirements for these products, the company had few competitors. Max Mugler, assistant financial director at ZF at the time, reflects on how the negotiations proceeded:

"Member of the Board of Management Gerhard Kühn brokered the contact with Lemförder. As an engineer and former plant manager at Büssing in Lower Saxony, Mr. Kühn had a good relationship with Dr. Ulderup. I was brought into the discussion to manage the contractual aspects. The atmosphere during the process with Dr. and Mrs. Ulderup was immediately positive and friendly, which was important, because other companies (such as Thyssen) were also interested in acquiring Lemförder. The decisive conversation took place in Switzerland. Jürgen Ulderup was ready to sell, but his wife Irmgard – who was intensely involved in the negotiations – made her approval conditional on the Lemförder name remaining in place for the time being, and she wanted the company to be allowed to continue developing its strategies independently. We were happy to agree to this smooth transition; after all, the Lemförder name was worth as much as ZF, and the company's manager in Dielingen, Mr. Ballmeier, was doing an excellent job."[3]

The contracts are signed

On December 7, 1983, the supervisory board at ZF agreed to acquire a 51 percent share of Lemförder Metallwaren AG, which was acting as a holding company, as well as the operational limited partnership Lemförder Metallwaren Jürgen Ulderup AG & Co. The contract was signed on December 28, 1938 and went into effect on January 2, 1984. After the acquisition, the Dr. Jürgen Ulderup Foundation remained a minority shareholder in the company.[4] In that sense, the acquisition was complete from a legal standpoint, and ZF's sales and workforce immediately grew by approximately 22 percent.[5] Now, the actual challenge for both sides was to merge the two companies into a single entity internally as well. ZF took its agreement to respect the independence of the compa-

Max Mugler (1931–2013) was ZF's financial director from 1983 to 1991.

After Lemförder was acquired by ZF, it continued to operate mostly independently for many years – as evidenced by the fact that the LEMFÖRDER and ZF brands were still represented separately at trade fairs, like here at the 1985 Frankfurt International Motor Show (IAA).

nies Jürgen Ulderup had built very seriously, as the head of Lemförder's in-house print shop at the time, Horst Meyer, explained:

"ZF's acquisition of Lemförder was barely even made public. Hardly anything changed for us, in a positive or a negative sense. We still saw ourselves as Lemförder, wholly and completely. Even after

ALTHOUGH COMPETITORS HAD SUBMITTED MUCH HIGHER BIDS, ZF and the Ulderup family – who owned Lemförder Metallwaren AG – agreed to set a moderate price for Lemförder:

200 million deutschmarks

Dr. Jürgen Ulderup passed away in 1991, there was an internal campaign targeting all employees. It was called MEILE, which stood for "Mein Erfolg ist Lemförder Erfolg" ("My Success is Lemförder's Success") – ZF wasn't even mentioned."[6]

The Lemförder Group was initially managed independently within ZF, as Business Unit III – counter to the management structure that had been introduced in 1982, which was actually intended to eliminate the individual locations' focus on themselves. The ZF and Lemförder brands, which had very disparate regional roots, were only merged gradually. Ingrid Griepenstroh, who represented Lemförder at the most important trade fairs for many years, gives a detailed example that is representative of how things changed:

"At first, we continued to have our own trade fair booth for several years; the design was markedly different from ZF's. There was always a friendly, familiar atmosphere at our booth; that

Lemförder Metallwaren AG's products have a very good reputation among our most important customers in the automobile industry.

FROM A FILE SENT TO THE SUPERVISORY BOARD BY THE BOARD
OF MANAGEMENT AT ZF, 1983

was due to Irmgard Ulderup, who was in charge of every aspect of our exhibit. ZF, on the other hand, presented itself to the outside world as a corporation. Initially, the ZF and Lemförder booths were separated from one another by maybe four booths; the next year, it was two, and then we were suddenly next-door neighbors, so to speak. In the end, we got our own stand within the ZF booth, although we did have a number of discussions about the positioning of our traditional logo, the owl. Things continued like this until the Frankfurt International Motor Show (IAA) in 1992, when the CEO of ZF at the time, Dr. Bleyer, decided that ZF's logo had to take priority from then on. But despite the occasional friction, we knew that we had a good partner in ZF. It was important to us that we were working for a company that was owned by a foundation, a company that planned for the long term – and we knew that this kind of federalism wouldn't have been possible if another company had acquired Lemförder."[7]

The acquisition pays off

From ZF's perspective, the acquisition of Lemförder turned out to be everything the company had hoped. The business unit grew steadily, and ZF was able to significantly expand its chassis technology portfolio. Additionally, Lemförder's areas of expertise opened a number of new doors for ZF with its customers. As the 1989 annual report indicated, Lemförder's know-how in chassis technology meant that the company was "involved in all major development projects for Ger-

man and European vehicle manufacturers."[8] In terms of capital, there were two important milestones after ZF's acquisition of Lemförder that resulted in the ownership structure we know today. First, in 1989, Christian Peter Ulderup sold his shares of Lemförder Metallwaren AG to ZF, which increased ZF's share of that company to 76 percent. Then, in 2003, there was a stock swap: ZF acquired 100 percent of Lemförder's shares, and in exchange, the Dr. Jürgen Ulderup Foundation received 6.2 percent of the shares in ZF.

Friedrich Baur, who was set to resign his post a CEO at ZF in late 1989 / early 1990 and hand the job off to Klaus Bleyer, considered the acquisition of Lemförder – the largest in ZF's history – as a success. The critical media reports from the early days of Baur's tenure on the Board of Management were already long forgotten when Baur invited journalists to one last press conference summarizing his time at ZF in July 1989. Local daily newspaper Schwäbische Zeitung reported that the company presented "an annual report [...] that was practically flawless [...] with a dramatic improvement in profits."[9] ZF had indeed undergone an impressive recovery in the 1980s – in particular, the company's productivity had increased significantly. Between 1980 and 1989, ZF's workforce increased by 44 percent, to 34,559 employees, while the Group's sales rose by 157 percent, to 5.47 billion deutschmarks, during the same period. Even taking inflation into account[10], sales more than doubled – an impressive boost in productivity.

1990
—
2005

New markets around the world

German reunification is a political triumph, but its economic impact is mixed. While ZF's foundation in Germany is strong, most of the opportunities for growth available to the company lie outside of the country's borders.

ZF AND GERMAN REUNIFICATION:

A NEW ECONOMIC HORIZON

Scrapping East German "Trabant" cars in Berlin, July 1990: after the fall of the Berlin Wall, many people in the former East were excited to purchase a western car. In technological terms, the East German automobile industry lagged far behind the West; its products simply were no longer marketable.

The fall of the Berlin Wall was followed by the "German Gold Rush."[1] Millions of East German citizens made use of their newly acquired freedom and dove head-first into a capitalist world of consumption – with 100 deutschmarks of "welcome money" in their pockets. And for West Germany, new prospects opened up in the disintegrating Eastern Bloc. At that point, it was already clear that the majority of East German companies would be privatized as part of the transition to a market economy. Potential investors saw an opportunity to purchase property and production machinery at a low price, if they showed up in the right place at the right time. On June 17, 1990, the right place was in East Berlin, the headquarters of the Treuhandanstalt (privatization agency), which managed the fate of more than 8,000 formerly state-run companies in East Germany from July 1, 1990 onwards. The agency was tasked with either privatizing these companies or shutting them down in the most socially responsible way possible. It was a mammoth project; nearly every day, production facilities with thousands of employees changed hands, attracting numerous investors from the West – including honest brokers and idealists as well as shady profiteers. The situation was chaotic, but ZF also had to decide whether it was sensible to invest in the East, and if so, where. Arriving too late and missing out on a "piece of the pie" from these new markets, so to speak, seemed like a significant risk.

ZF reacted with relative restraint to the overwhelming change in the political situation in 1989/90. When the ZF employee newspaper "ZF-Ring" interviewed CEO Klaus Bleyer about the situation in East Germany in March 1990, he only promised that the company would "soberly take stock."[2] Bleyer gave two reasons for why ZF would not immediately press ahead with the penetration of the Eastern Bloc market: first, the company needed to wait and see how the major automobile manufacturers would act. And second, ZF had already established ties to Eastern Europe many years before[3] and, consequently, had extensive expertise in a number of market segments. In fact, ZF had had contacts in the Soviet Union since 1980, where steering systems and commercial vehicle transmissions were being produced under license from ZF.[4] The company had also been cooperating with licensing partners in Hungary since 1974, and its ties to companies in Yugoslavia extended back to 1967.[5] Additionally, ZF had invested a great deal of money and personnel in setting up a factory in North America, and the process of integrating Lemförder into ZF was not yet completed either. So it was no wonder that ZF's management was not particularly open to the idea of taking on another major project in Germany's East.

Closer ties with East German companies

However, even before East and West Germany were officially reunified, ZF explored the possibility of establishing ties with various companies in East Germany, including manufacturers of transmissions and steering systems in Buchenau, Chemnitz, Leipzig, Ronneburg, Schwerin, and Triptis.[6] Negotiations never produced any real results, however, because ZF was averse to the risk of making large investments, and the East German companies had practically no customers of their own as a result of the collapse of the markets in the East. After a period of searching, ZF considered Hydraulik Nord in Parchim (Mecklenburg-Western Pomerania) and Getriebewerk Brandenburg as possible candidates for investment. Parchim seemed like a good place to produce the hydrostatic steering systems that were being manufactured

BY 1990, computer-aided product development was already well established at ZF. During that year, the number of computer workstations with CAD systems rose to:

450

*ZF has agreed to work with Getriebewerk
Brandenburg to quickly determine whether we can offer
any work, and if so, what kind.*

MEETING MINUTES, AUGUST 1, 1990

by Business Unit IV (Schwäbisch Gmünd) at the time, as Hydraulik Nord had constructed similar systems for the Eastern Bloc before the fall of the Berlin Wall. When ZF began to scrutinize the plant more closely, however, it discovered that the potential for synergy was actually very limited – there were fundamental differences in the way the technology was constructed in the East and the West. Consequently, the interest that management at ZF Schwäbisch Gmünd had initially shown in partnering with Hydraulik Nord quickly abated.[7]

ZF and Getriebewerk Brandenburg, on the other hand, were slowly approaching an agreement. In April 1990, ZF had rejected the idea of licensing production at the company in Brandenburg an der Havel because it was "too expensive, too big, [and there was] no need."[8] However, after a planned acquisition of Getriebewerk Brandenburg by Daimler-Benz failed, management in Brandenburg – in partnership with the Berlin privatization agency – decided to try its luck with ZF again in August 1990. Time was of the essence, as Getriebewerk Brandenburg – now a limited liability company – was on the brink of losing its two main customers, Traktorenwerk Schönebeck and IFA-Automobilewerke in Ludwigsfelde. Employees at the company were already forced to work reduced hours two days a week. The state of Brandenburg was suffering the after-effects of decades of scarcity under the socialist economy. Additionally, for political reasons, East Germany was integrated into the West German economic and currency area extremely rapidly, which deprived the plant of its economic foundations. The deutschmark had been in circulation in Brandenburg an der Havel since July 1, 1990, which meant that the

region's last remaining competitive advantage – low prices and wages due to the weak Ostmark – had been eliminated as well.

Investment in Brandenburg

As a first step toward establishing a lasting business partnership, the privatization agency – acting as the owner of Getriebewerk Brandenburg – offered ZF Friedrichshafen AG a seat on the company's supervisory board. In September 1990, the ZF Board of Management decided to accept the offer.[9] By that point, ZF was convinced that investing in Brandenburg would bring with it a number of important advantages, including the potential for new markets in Eastern Europe, access to skilled labor and production facilities, and, last but not least, the fact that ZF might have the chance to tap the East German market before its competitors did. A file intended for the supervisory board and dated November 1990 also attests to the fact that by acquiring Getriebewerk Brandenburg, ZF hoped to be able to partner with West German automakers as they expanded their production facilities into East Germany as well.[10]

The purchase of Getriebewerk Brandenburg was essentially a done deal by late 1990, but the negotiations continued to drag on. The contract wasn't signed until March 1991, and the privatization agency officially handed ZF the keys to Getriebewerk Brandenburg at a meeting of workers and staff on July 22, 1991. At that point, the Brandenburg plant still employed around 600 people – compared to 2,900 in early 1990.[11] The privatization agency guaranteed 40 million deutschmarks in equity for the limited liability company; the purchase price was 5 million deutschmarks.[12] These figures give some indication of the momentous task facing the management and employees of the newly established company, ZF Brandenburg GmbH. This was about more than "just" integrating a thriving company into ZF, as had been the case with Lemförder. The company formerly known as Getriebewerk Brandenburg had to be restructured from the ground up – and above all, it needed prospects for future growth and development. ZF could only meet these needs if its employees in the West were also willing to make a few concessions, as Klaus Beyer, CEO of ZF at the time, explained:

"At first, we planned to use the Brandenburg plant to supply transmissions to IFA-Lastwagenwerke, a former East German company that had been acquired by Daimler-Benz. After reunification, however, the customer base for the technologically obsolete IFA trucks dried up, even in the former Eastern Bloc. So we decided to relocate production of the S5-24 commercial vehicle transmission from Schwäbisch Gmünd to Brandenburg, and to develop the plant in the East into a modern production facility for manual transmissions. Despite the fact that at the same time, in 1991 and 1992, we had to cut more than 3,000 jobs – most of them from the West German ZF plants – the majority of our employees demonstrated a great deal of support and solidarity for this process. In financial terms, the restructuring was as sensible as it was necessary, because our manufacturing costs in the early 1990s were too high for the new competitive environment we were facing. A positive side effect of the relocation was that it freed up capacity for expanding steering systems manufacturing in Schwäbisch Gmünd. Demand was increasing in this area, so in 1992, sales in Schwäbisch Gmünd rose by approximately two percent, despite of the relocation of some production to Brandenburg."[13]

The company formerly known as IFA-Getriebewerk Brandenburg became a part of ZF in July 1990. Initially, the company manufactured the manual transmissions for passenger cars that had previously been produced in Schwäbisch Gmünd.

A pace-setting motorcycle from Brennabor, shown here with racing cyclist Franz Krupkat, 1920s.

THE ORIGINS OF ZF BRANDENBURG:

PIONEERS ON THE ASSEMBLY LINE

The history of the company on the banks of the Havel River dates back to 1871, long before ZF was founded.[1] Originally, the factory manufactured baby carriages and bicycles under the brand name Brennabor; in 1902, the company owned by the Reichstein family began mass-producing motorcycles. The three-wheeled, 3.5-horsepower vehicle "Brennaborette" included

a two-gear transmission and was introduced in 1907 – it marked the company's entry into automobile manufacturing. Its first four-wheeled compact car was launched in 1908. During World War I, Brennabor manufactured grenades and containers for transporting munitions, among other things. After Germany's defeat, the company resumed the production of automobiles and grew increasingly successful. In 1925, Brennabor became one of the first manufacturers in Germany to successfully transition to assembly-line production. Co-owner Eduard Reichstein had studied the underlying process in great detail between 1908 and 1920, while he was in the USA. Despite a string of successes in the 1920s, Brennabor was suffering under the pressure of competing with international companies and the dominant automobile manufacturers like Opel or Daimler-Benz. When the Great Depression began in fall 1929, the fate of Germany's largest family-owned automobile manufacturing company was sealed. Brennabor AG, a publicly traded company, was founded in April 1932 using bankruptcy assets, but this company was unable to keep up with the rapid pace of technological development in the automobile industry. In late 1933, automobile manufacturing was discontinued; however, as a producer of various metal products, Brennabor rebounded during the Nazi era. During World War II (1939-1945), the company employed large numbers of forced laborers and female workers to produce gun mounts and bicycles, for example. The plant in Brandenburg was largely unaffected by air raids, but the fighting on the ground during the final days of the war caused severe damage to the facilities.

After the war, the Soviet occupying powers took control of the company formerly known as Brennabor AG and partially dismantled it. Then, in late summer 1948, construction of a tractor factory began among the ruins of the former plant; the first tractor produced by this new facility was presented at the Leipzig Spring Trade Fair in 1949. In 1961, the company – now known as Brandenburger Traktorenwerke, and owned by the state – began producing its first transmissions. The following year, the East German Council of Ministers decided that transmissions should be its only product; all other products in development were to be discontinued. The plant began to expand, and eventually needed to find a new home – the neighboring premises of now-defunct Arado-Flugzeugwerke were the perfect spot. The company now known as Getriebewerk Brandenburg relocated all of its production facilities to the new location in 1967, which is still the site of ZF Brandenburg today. In 1978, Getriebewerk Brandenburg became part of East German state holding company IFA; it was assigned to the branch in Ludwigsfelde, which produced commercial vehicles. Until the fall of the Berlin Wall, Getriebewerk Brandenburg remained the only producer of truck transmissions in the whole of East Germany. During its early years as part of the state holding company, the plant was highly profitable; however, as the entire economy of East Germany began to collapse, so too did the plant in Brandenburg. In 1989, as party leaders and heads of government celebrated 40 years of socialism in East Berlin 30 miles from the plant, Getriebewerk Brandenburg was generating sales that were well below the company's own costs. Even by the standards of the communist planned economy, it was clear that the company was in trouble. However, little did anyone know at the time that the whole world was about to change – and that Getriebewerk Brandenburg would soon become part of the ZF family.

German ad for the Brennabor Model 1928, a luxury car produced just before the Great Depression began.

A EUROPEAN MANUFACTURING ASSOCIATION:

ACQUISITIONS IN THE 1990S

Expansion in Germany and Europe: ZF Luftfahrttechnik GmbH in Kassel (left), ZF Marine in Arco (top right), and assembling axle drives in Gotha (bottom right).

After surviving the automobile industry crisis in the early 1990s, ZF entered into a phase of expansion – and it went beyond the budding market economies of the former Eastern Bloc and the emerging markets in Asia. The company also found opportunities for growth in Germany and Western Europe.

ZF had owned half of the shares in Henschel Flugzeug-Werke GmbH since September 1982, but in 1994, the company finally acquired the remaining 50 percent of the Kassel-based Henschel. Now, the wholly owned subsidiary became part of a newly founded company in the same city: ZF Luftfahrttechnik GmbH. At the beginning of 1995, aircraft transmission manufacturing – which used to be part of the Special Driveline Technology business unit, alongside mechanical engineering and military technology – became its own independent business unit.

Marine transmissions manufacturing underwent the same process – beginning in 1995, it was converted into an independent business unit called Marine. After the production sites in Friedrichshafen, Vernon Hills, São Paulo, and Padua were merged under the same management, ZF also acquired HURTH Marine Gear S.p.A. based in Arco, northern Italy in January 1995.

During that same year, ZF also purchased parts of Munich-based HURTH Group, albeit in other sectors. At the beginning of 1995, ZF acquired the HURTH Group's railroad technology and industrial truck divisions, and during the period that followed, a center of excellence for material handling systems and axle drive assembly was constructed on the premises of the company formerly known as HURTH-Getriebewerk Gotha, now ZF Gotha GmbH.

In its core area of business as an automotive supplier, ZF faced intensifying price pressure beginning in the mid-1990s. As a result, the company was forced to outsource some of its manufacturing to countries with lower wages. In Hungary, where ZF had entered into licensing partnerships as early as the mid-1970s, the company purchased a transmission factory from commercial vehicle manufacturer Csepel in the city of Eger in 1995. Under the name ZF Hungaria Kft., the plant began producing transmissions for light and medium-weight trucks the following year.

The fierce competition in the automotive sector affected more than just suppliers, however. In 1997, Renault V.I. – the commercial vehicle segment of the long-standing French vehicle manufacturer – was forced to stop producing its own transmissions. This cleared the way for the Renault transmission factory in Bouthéon (Departement Loire) to enter into a joint venture with ZF – and with a share of 60 percent in the new venture, ZF was put in charge of management. In 1998, the partners began manufacturing Ecomid transmissions for medium-weight commercial vehicles in Bouthéon. These compact, affordable manual transmissions held a central position in ZF's portfolio, between the heavy commercial vehicle transmissions from Friedrichshafen and the light to medium-weight units from Eger, Hungary. This broad range of acquisitions eventually created a European manufacturing network – ZF gained technological expertise and became more profitable while simultaneously making a contribution to the process of European integration.

The Renault V.I. transmission plant in Bouthéon became part of a joint venture under ZF's management in 1998.

179

CRISIS IN THE AUTOMOBILE INDUSTRY AND
TRANSITION TO GROUP TECHNOLOGY:

MANUFACTURING GOES CELLULAR

The cellular manufacturing process introduced in 1992 required employees, in particular, to be more proactive.
At the same time, it also made their work days more varied and gave them the chance to shape the company with
their own ideas. Shown here: employees in Friedrichshafen, 1997.

Fiercer global competition, fewer customers buying new cars, a lack of business from the former Eastern Bloc countries, high manufacturing costs at home: the German automobile industry was entering a difficult phase. In the 1991 fiscal year, ZF nominally generated an annual surplus of 282 million deutschmarks, but this was primarily a result of tax credits and a new accounting system.[1] In operational terms, nearly every business unit recorded losses. Klaus Bleyer, Chairman of the Board of Management since 1990, emphasized that ZF needed to implement structural changes in order to counteract this upheaval in the markets.[2] Once again, the primary focus was on decreasing production costs – which were too high when compared with other companies internationally – while maintaining high levels of product quality and innovation. This was not a new problem, but it required new solutions. For the first time since its founding, ZF's corporate culture was being put to the test – a corporate culture that seemed to have stayed the same since the early days of motorized vehicles and assembly-line production. In December 1991, employee newspaper "ZF-Ring" declared that this era had come to an end:

"This time, the man – and not the machine – is the focus of an industrial restructuring process, and [...] here's why: The majority of production methods you'll find in Europe [...] can no longer keep up with customers' growing demand for quality, individuality, and speed. They are also much too expensive. The greatest obstacle has proven to be [...] the constantly increasing division of labor. [...] Very few people are able to see their own work in the finished product. [...] At the risk of exaggerating, most people are left with nothing to do but turn the machines on and off or load them. [...] Employees' motivation and initiative has declined to the same degree to which the division of labor has increased."[3]

Since 1950 or so, Japanese engineer and production manager Taiichi Ohno had been systematically researching these developments for his employer, Toyota. Through his research, he came up with a series of principles that were reflected in the Toyota Production System (TPS). Essentially, Ohno's approach – rather than treating people in a company like gears in a transmission, always repeating the same motion – required critical thinking and individual responsibility at all hierarchical levels. By empowering industrial workers to make use of their previously untapped intellectual potential, this system was intended to create a type of manufacturing that would consistently optimize itself and reduce material and labor waste to a minimum. Many of today's prevalent methods, such as just-in-time production or the continuous improvement process, have their roots in Taiichi Ohno's original ideas. A book detailing the production system based on Ohno's insights, which had already been implemented at Toyota, was published in Japan in 1978, but did not become available in English until 1988 and German until 1993. At that point, the managers of American and European companies could read in black and white why their Japanese competitors had been outstripping them for years – and they learned quickly.

Toyota as a role model

Many large companies began to adapt the Toyota Production System to suit their own needs. ZF did the same, as evidenced by the numerous Japanese terms still used to describe elements of the ZF

Ideas, not hierarchies, are what counts: TQM event, 1994.

production system today. For example, the cards used to label material containers at ZF's factories are internally referred to as "kanban" (Japanese for "signboard"). Head of production at the time, Karlheinz Erbacher, recalls the early days of this system:

"In January 1992, we set up three pilot 'cells' at Plant I in Friedrichshafen in order to test a method called cellular manufacturing, which was based on the theory of group technology. All of the machines required for manufacturing a certain product were lined up next to one another in the order that they were needed. Just rearranging things wouldn't really have improved anything though; we needed our employees to start thinking differently as well. Unlike before, each individual worker now had to master every step of the process, and all members of the team responsible for a given product shared the responsibility for it; the product was 'theirs,' so to speak. The employees themselves were now even responsible for modifying the machines to produce one product instead of another. In the beginning, every changeover required four to five hours, but by the end, our colleagues were able to get production up and running again within 20 minutes. Once they had adjusted to the new routine, they were able to get a single product through every step of a manufacturing cell in just two to three hours. Before we introduced these new manufacturing structures, that kind of speed would have been unthinkable. The noticeably higher levels of efficiency and the increased importance of each individual employee also made the workforce much happier. No one longed for a return to the days of the assembly line."[4]

The promising results of the internal test run and the success that manufacturers from Japan and the USA had achieved with similar methods paved the way for ZF's manufacturing to continue to evolve in the years that followed. The pilot manufacturing cell concept was gradually expanded; by late 1995, cellular manufacturing had been implemented throughout most of the company. At the same time, ZF began to reduce waste and inefficiency in the production process – the key phrase was Total Quality Management (TQM), and it followed the Japanese example to the letter. In a 1992 article for the magazine "Automobil-Produktion," member of the ZF Board of Management Hubertus Christ described the differences between the new policy and the company's previous practices:

"Company quality at ZF [...] is today considered an overarching term; it doesn't just involve the quality of the parts produced [...] rather, it affects all aspects of the company's operations – our interactions with one another, our response times in correspondence, our friendliness on the telephone, our cooperation to ensure the quality of our final products, and much more. [...] As an example: at our Passau site in early 1991, we introduced [...] an implementation plan that was [...] intended to change all employees' conduct. The results so far have been encouraging: employees are concentrating on finding the source of errors and preventing them in the future, rather than assigning blame and scrambling to fix mistakes."[5]

In the process of implementing TQM, ZF also managed to dust the cobwebs off its employee suggestion program and improve it to a level that was at least on par with its Japanese competitors. In Passau, the number of suggestions for improvement submitted increased from approximately 500 per year to 2,800 in 1992.[6] One out of every five employees participated in the program. How-

3 pilot manufacturing cells

were set up at Plant I in Friedrichshafen in 1992 in order to pave the way for the implementation of cellular manufacturing. Today, this Toyota-inspired method is an integral component of the ZF Production System.

Under the heading of Total Quality Management, ZF began to raise employees' awareness of quality issues in the early 1990s. Prizes were awarded to the best teams once a year.

Where do I reduce costs? With suppliers!

JOSÉ IGNACIO LÓPEZ, MEMBER OF THE BOARD OF MANAGEMENT AT VOLKSWAGEN AG,
1993 TO 1996

Founding of ZF Italia S.r.l. in summer 1990: member of the ZF Board of Management Ernst Braun congratulates new CEO Giorgio E. Donà.

ever, the overwhelming response presented a challenge – the company now had to actually implement as many suggestions for improvement as possible. Up to that point, dedicated employees had been frustrated to discover that their ideas often got lost in the maze of internal bureaucracy. ZF counteracted this problem by decentralizing the employee suggestion program and setting up mentoring programs that paired supervisors with their employees who had submitted suggestions.

The "López era"

Improvements such as these were urgently needed, as price pressure on the automotive supply industry had risen significantly. A major factor here was a change in the relationships between OEMs and suppliers in the automobile industry

– a change that was triggered by one man in particular. Native of Spain José Ignacio López, the son of an impoverished laborer from Basque country, first appeared on the radar of German suppliers when he was appointed head of production at Opel in 1987. When he was later selected to head up procurement at General Motors – the world's largest automobile company – his approach determined the course of the entire industry. In 1993, he was poached by Volkswagen and continued his policies there, until he was forced to step down as the result of a legal dispute between VW and his former employer, GM. The effects of the "López era" were more lasting than his relatively short tenure would indicate, however. In particular, his policy of cutting costs by any means necessary was a popular tool adopted by many large automakers. López himself had never left any doubt as to where he felt the greatest savings could be generated:

"So the question is: how can I satisfy the customer? My goal: give him what he wants! The customer only wants three things: a quality product, service, and a low price. [...] In order to achieve that goal, I only have to do three things: improve quality – together with workers; improve service – by dealing with the retailers and workshops; and reduce costs. Where do I reduce costs? With suppliers! [...] 80 percent of all components for a car are supplied – meaning they are produced externally. Suppliers are responsible for 80 percent of the costs of producing a car."[7]

When López appeared on the scene, the tone between ZF and its customers changed, as Giorgio Doná – CEO and partner at ZF Italia S.r.l. at the time – recalls:

"In the past, good customer relationships were mainly based on personal relationships; engineering expertise, combined with precise technical knowledge of the products, was also important. But under López's dogma, the only thing that mattered was which supplier could provide a consistently high level of quality while offering maximum discounts. That was how we wound up in a showdown with our long-time customer Iveco in the mid-1990s; at the time, ZF's prices were approximately 15 percent higher than those offered by our competitors Eaton and TRW. The new procurement manager at Iveco demanded that we immediately slash our prices by 15 percent – completely ignoring our existing business relationship – or ZF would lose Iveco as a customer. After a series of turbulent negotiations, we came to a compromise – one that was beneficial to both sides, incidentally, as it cleared the way for a very successful partnership centered on the development and testing of the fully automatic truck transmission AS Tronic, which was manufactured from 1997 onward."[8]

1993: a rough year

Before ZF could reach this point, however, it had to survive the worst crisis in the German automobile industry since the end of World War II. In 1993, passenger car production in Western Europe – still ZF's most important market – declined by 15 percent. In the heavy commercial vehicle segment, that figure was as high as 29 percent.[10] At this point, ZF finally began to benefit from the fact that it had made radical internal changes before the

market bottomed out. Still, the company's management felt that further layoffs were unavoidable. This put the managers at odds with employee representatives, who would have preferred more employees to work reduced hours instead. Johann Kirchgässner, vice chairman of the works council in Friedrichshafen at the time, looks back:

"Until summer 1993, the employees at our site regularly worked overtime. Our customers continued to award contracts – but mostly because they didn't want the media to suspect that they were facing a crisis. When the first of our customers started having their employees work reduced hours, though, the others followed hard on their heels. But we firmly believed that this was just a temporary slump and that the economy would pick up again soon. Management, on the other hand, was preparing for a more long-term decline in sales. So we supported reduced working hours, while management in Friedrichshafen wanted to lay off workers. We subsequently filed a number of individual appeals and were ultimately able to prevent the majority of firings, or at least legally delay them. And when the economic recovery we had hoped for finally came in 1994, ZF rehired most of the employees that had been laid off. The crisis of 1993 was a difficult time, there's no doubt about that, but it also had its upsides. I would say that both the works council and the company's management learned some important lessons from the experience, which would later help us handle the economic crisis of 2009."[11]

JOHANN KIRCHGÄSSNER
(born in 1952)
The automotive technician joined ZF in 1973.
In 2002, he became Chairman of the Group
Works Council. Additionally, he was the
vice chairman of the ZF hilft e.V. foundation.

DR. KLAUS P. BLEYER

"A company with staying power and a soft spot for innovation"

Interview with Dr. Klaus P. Bleyer, CEO of ZF Friedrichshafen AG between 1990 and 2001

In 1989, the chairman of the supervisory board at the time, Dr. Bernd Wiedmann, offered you the opportunity to transfer from US company ITT to the top position at ZF. What motivated you to move all the way from the East Coast of the USA to the shores of Lake Constance?

Precisely because of what my old company couldn't offer me. At that time, ITT was the largest conglomerate in the world. They were proud of the fact that they were always able to pay out increasingly higher dividends, but since the company's telecommunication business had been sold off in 1986, ITT had lost its technological heart. ZF was completely different: focused on the long term, driven more by innovation than by profits, a company owned by a foundation that was largely independent from the capital market. Policies focused on quarterly results, like those at ITT, might appeal to other managers, but I was more interested in ZF's pragmatic strategy, particularly since it offered a wide range of opportunities for me to play a role in shaping policy. And of course, as a native of Bavaria and an avid skier, I was excited to move to Lindau.

Would you say that joining ZF provided very good prospects for you?

When you join a new company in a managerial role, you obviously won't understand how everything works right away. But even for outsiders, it was clear that ZF was facing serious challenges. The simple fact that that ZF was willing to bring me on board – an American-style manager with particular experience in automotive electronics, an area that ZF had neglected for quite some time – indicated that change was necessary, and that the supervisory board wanted it. In strategic terms, two issues were especially relevant in the early 1990s: first, ZF hadn't been consistent in making the transition to the international stage. It was heavily involved in the USA – particularly regarding its cooperation with Ford – but this investment was not profitable. And second, ZF was burdened by an inefficient hierarchical structure. Operational management was left up to the managers of the individual business units; some of the management boards of these units functioned as collectives, while others were managed by a single leader. The Board of Management focused

186

almost exclusively on central coordination: a system that didn't work for me at all. I wanted to be able to make substantial changes, and it was important to me that I could manage the sales department myself as well. My reasons for this were more political than anything; in our industry, it's often beneficial if the company's top management is directly involved in initial contact with new business partners.

In the early 1990s, the business climate became increasingly difficult for German automotive suppliers. The crisis in 1992/93 also hit ZF hard...

Yes, indeed! We weren't even able to avoid layoffs in Friedrichshafen, which, as far as our company's history goes, was extremely unusual. But the crisis also gave us inspiration for the future. It became clear to all of us that we needed to become more competitive. To achieve this goal, we organized the company into about 30 business units, each of which had a certain degree of independence. We were then able to quickly tell which segments were not operating cost-effectively – such as the manufacturing of drivelines for fixed-wing aircraft. Consequently, we sold that business unit to our partner Liebherr, a long-standing avionics supplier.

Another area which unfortunately didn't live up to our expectations was the continuously variable transmission (internally referred to as CVT). Our engineers – along with much of our industry – believed that the continuously variable transmission was the future for compact passenger cars. We partnered with Ford and VW to develop CVT units. However, Volkswagen ultimately abandoned the CVT project, preferring to concentrate on alternative drivelines instead – such as the dual clutch transmission, which is prevalent today. We were left out of the development of that technology back then. Ford – a classic technological follower – took its cues from Volkswagen and also decided to discontinue its work with the CVT. In hindsight, we stuck with this technology

> *In* TECHNOLOGICAL TERMS, *Sachs was a good fit for us.*

for too long; even today, it hasn't caught on in Europe. Luckily, we were much more successful in other areas.

Where, for example?

Personally, I particularly remember how we acquired Volkswagen as our second major German customer, in addition to our long-time partner BMW. That business relationship came about in a somewhat unorthodox way, via a transmission for the Audi Quattro that Ferdinand Piëch, CEO of Audi at the time, asked us to construct. Piëch didn't want to fall back on using the drivelines made by Audi's parent company Volkswagen; he preferred to commission the development of a new unit, although he didn't have an official order to do so. We at ZF still decided to agree to the project – in the worst-case scenario, we'd be left sitting on the 30 million deutschmarks in development costs. In the end, Piëch got his way internally, and when he was promoted to the top management position at his parent company, ZF's status as supplier for Volkswagen improved significantly.

You mentioned the job of making ZF more international. Which regions were most important on the road to becoming a global company?

The USA was one country where we were able to grow at an above-average rate. However, that growth was primarily in the areas of industrial drives and engines for agricultural and construction machinery, and not in passenger car transmissions as we had originally planned. In 1993, we were even on the verge of acquiring Allison, the largest North American manufacturer of bus and commercial vehicle transmissions. Parent company GM wanted to divest itself of Allison, because the products it was manufacturing were no longer in line with the company's core business. However, the acquisition by ZF was shot down by the American Federal Trade Commission, which took a more restrictive approach after Bill Clinton replaced George H. W. Bush as US President.

We were also extremely satisfied with the business we were able to build up in Asia. In 1995, we manufactured automatic transmissions in Japan for the first time as part of a joint venture with Komatsu. In the period that followed, we also opened a new factory in China almost every year. At first, we mainly produced axles there; later, we added steering systems for passenger cars. Our expansion strategy in China was guided by our partner Volkswagen, which also achieved significant growth there.

Would it be fair to say that even in the 1990s, ZF had left its German roots behind to a certain extent in order to explore new frontiers in other countries?

That's not quite right. In fact, the real challenge in this situation was to uphold the values that make ZF what it is – a German company owned by a foundation – while still dealing with the fact that the market for our products was increasingly shifting to Asia. But this never meant pulling up stakes in Europe; on the contrary, we needed to continue to expand our portfolio at home. One example of our expansion in Germany is our founding of ZF Lenksysteme GmbH in Schwäbisch Gmünd in 1998, in partnership with Robert Bosch GmbH. This move was preceded by many years of cooperation with Bosch in the area of automotive electronics; the goal was for us to secure a leading role in the development of electric power steering systems. They were going to be installed in the new VW Golf as a fuel-saving alternative to hydraulic systems. The joint venture was a challenge for us, pushing us to the very limits of our techno-

logical and financial capabilities, but in hindsight, it was absolutely the right decision. Today, we can rightfully claim that the project produced one of the world's leading electric power steering plants.

During your tenure as CEO, ZF was also preparing for its acquisition of Mannesmann Sachs, which was completed in 2001...

In technological terms, Sachs was a good fit for us. We already had a strong presence in the chassis segment thanks to ZF Lemförder, and Sachs provided us with vital expertise in the areas of shock absorbers and clutches, which brought us one enormous step further on the road to becoming a systems supplier for driveline and chassis technology. However, we were well aware that we couldn't impose ZF's identity on a long-standing company like Sachs overnight; after all, every manager in our industry was well aware of the difficulties that Daimler and Chrysler had faced in this regard when they merged. That's why from the very beginning, our policy was to promote integration through project-based cooperation.

In a nutshell: in your experience, is there one particular aspect that makes ZF stand out from other major companies in the automobile industry?

ZF is owned by a foundation. The company isn't necessarily unique in this regard, but in my opinion, it's something that all of ZF's employees should be more aware of. After all, the major advantage of this model is that the money generated largely remains within the company. The other side of the coin, of course, is that it's more difficult for ZF to acquire additional funds than it would be for, say, a publicly traded company. ZF either finances its growth out of its own pocket, or it simply doesn't grow at all.

SUPPLYING SYSTEMS TO THE WORLD:

GREATER OPPORTUNITIES, GREATER RESPONSIBILITY

Hoisting the German flag in China: ZF Drivetech (Suzhou) Co. Ltd.

The issue of China was at the top of ZF's agenda from a very early point in time," emphasizes Siegfried Goll, who had headed the car powertrain technology business unit since 1993 and held a seat on the Board of Management since 1997. "We started to establish business relationships in China in the 1980s, initially through licensing agreements. When I retired in 2006, we had no less than 20 production facilities in there."[1] In fact, there is evidence that the Chinese also recognized that ZF was going above and beyond in their country. In October 1990, for example, Jiao-Tong University in Shanghai, one of the oldest and most respected universities in the country, bestowed the honor of an "Advisory Professor" title on ZF technical director at the time, Hubertus Christ.[2] At a time when many German companies treated China as nothing more than a place to outsource contract manufacturing work, Jiao-Tong University and ZF had shared a strong partnership in the area of "research, development, and production technology" since 1985. In addition to practical training for postgraduates under ZF's supervision, the partnership also included the joint publication of the technical magazine "Drive System Technique," which first hit the presses in 1987 in both English and Chinese.

Pioneers in the Far East

With this strong relationship as a starting point, it was relatively easy for ZF to develop a fiscally viable business in China. ZF first entered into a joint venture with a Chinese company – Beijing North Vehicle Works (NVW) – in 1993. The two companies built a shared service center in Beijing's Fengtai district; ZF held a 70 percent share in this company.[3] At this location, ZF products that had been installed in Chinese vehicles could be properly repaired and exchanged. After two years of negotiations, in 1994, ZF Shanghai Steering Co. Ltd. was founded – the first manufacturing company that resulted from this joint venture. The manufacturing of steering systems as part of a joint ven-

ZF established its first production facility in China in 1994: ZF Shanghai Steering Co. Ltd., a joint venture with Beijing North Vehicle Works.

ture between ZF (51 percent) and Shanghai Automotive Industry Corp. (49 percent) first started out by supplying Volkswagen's Chinese locations.[4] In 1995, ZF invested more money in its foreign business than ever before in the company's history – and China was a particularly important investment destination. Two new joint ventures were

IN 1998, ZF reached an important milestone in annual sales:

10 billion deutschmarks

We have to be at home in all major markets. This has nothing to do with actively outsourcing work from our German locations; it's just that we can only tap global markets if we have a global presence.

WERNER ARNOLD, MEMBER OF THE ZF BOARD OF MANAGEMENT
RESPONSIBLE FOR THE MARKET DEPARTMENT

founded during that year alone: Liuzhou ZF Machinery Co. Ltd., which was established in partnership with China's largest manufacturer of wheel loaders and hydraulic excavators, Guangxi Liugong, and Shanghai Lemförder Automotive Components Factory Ltd., a partnership with Shanghai No. 8 Auto Components Works. By 1998, ZF's position on the Chinese market was so secure that it was able to found its own wholly owned subsidiary for the first time. The establishment of ZF Drivetech Co. Ltd. with headquarters in the eastern Chinese metropolis of Suzhou also fulfilled a promise that CEO Klaus Bleyer had made in fall 1997 during an interview with Constance-

based daily newspaper Südkurier: if finding a joint venture proved difficult, he said, ZF would attempt to enter the commercial vehicle transmission business in China on its own. After all, considering the rapid pace of economic growth in Asia, this sector would play a key role.

ZF's US business comes of age

Despite the dynamic growth in China, the USA remained the most important foreign market for German automobile manufacturers in the second half of the 1990s. ZF already operated multiple locations in the country, but all things considered, they were not generating much added value. Elizabeth Umberson, who, in 1999, became the first woman in ZF's history to be promoted to plant manager, recalls the situation:

"When I arrived in Gainesville, Georgia for the first time in 1994 to interview at ZF, the company was almost completely unknown in the US. No wonder, since ZF's American sites were procuring almost everything they needed from Friedrichshafen. And ZF's products up to that point weren't exactly a perfect fit for the US automotive market. For example, vehicle electronics in the US had a different standard operating voltage than in Europe, and the preferred configuration for transmissions also differed from European vehicles. Both of these factors combined meant that we weren't taking full advantage of all of our opportunities to generate profits – not by a long shot. The managers at ZF had recognized these problems and made it their goal to further regionalize manufacturing in North America in the years that

ZF Drivetech Co. Ltd., which was founded in Suzhou in 1998, was ZF's first wholly owned subsidiary on the Chinese market. Shown here: manufacturing transmissions for commercial vehicles.

Elizabeth Umberson has been the plant manager at the Gainesville location since 1999.

followed. I felt like there was huge potential there. So I flew back to my family in Houston, and I told my husband: this is a company where I can succeed. And I wasn't disappointed: once ZF started to develop its US business independently, we generated double-digit annual savings."[5]

For ZF, "cutting the cord" on its US business, so to speak, was both a financial necessity and a commercial success. However, some employees in Germany were worried that ZF would gradually begin to curb production in Europe as a result. After all, the company already had nine production sites in North America by the mid-1990s. Werner Arnold, member of the Board of Management responsible for the market department, attempted to allay these fears in a 1995 interview with employee newspaper "ZF-Ring:"

"The NAFTA zone (USA, Canada, and Mexico) is currently an extremely cost-effective location. In order to supply those local markets, however, we have to produce locally – we can't provide supplies from our German factories, because we wouldn't be able to cover our costs that way (with the exception of a few niche markets). We've had

some painful, costly experiences in this area. This policy is also in line with the idea of what I like to call a 'multi-domestic company' [...] meaning that we have to be at home in all major markets [...]. This has nothing to do with actively outsourcing work from our German locations; it's just that we can only tap global markets if we have a global presence."[6]

Paradigm shift in the industry

In fact, sales at the entire ZF Group increased by approximately 62 percent between 1994 and 1999 as a result of the new strategy, while the company's workforce grew by 6.4 percent during the same period. These were signs of a significant increase in productivity. In 1998, ZF's sales exceeded 10 billion deutschmarks for the first time: a psychologically important milestone. However, it would be incorrect to attribute this success to ZF's policy of consistent globalization alone; the company also benefited from a change in strategy among the major automakers. Rather than producing their own components or partnering with a series of smaller parts suppliers as they had

done before, the OEMs made an effort to procure complete vehicle systems from highly productive individual partners in the late 1990s. A company like ZF – which, with well over 30,000 employees, was already one of the major players in its line of business – was able to benefit from this trend. When the Frankfurter Allgemeine Zeitung daily newspaper published an extensive report on the developments in the industry, it was no coincidence that the editors referred to the "example of ZF." Shortly before the article was published, it was announced that ZF had been awarded the contract to manufacture axles for the new Mercedes M-Class.

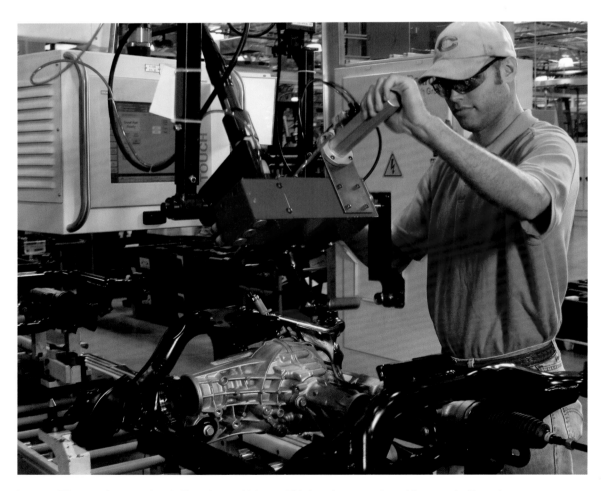

In 1997, ZF opened a new plant in Tuscaloosa, Alabama. This location was selected because it allowed the company to easily supply the nearby Mercedes-Benz M-Class production facility.

In Passau, our strategic goal was to use our core business – manufacturing components for agricultural and construction machinery – as a jumping-off point that would allow us to gain a foothold in other segments of automotive manufacturing. And we succeeded; our very successful portal axles for commuter buses and the axles we manufactured for the Mercedes M-Class were among the products that helped us get there.

HANS-GEORG HÄRTER, CHAIRMAN OF THE BOARD OF MANAGEMENT AT ZF PASSAU GMBH, 1994-2002

"As simple as the word 'axle' sounds, the products that ZF manufactures for Daimler-Benz are actually extremely complex: hubs, wheel bearings, steering knuckles, control arms, and subframes are as much a part of these systems as steering gears, tie rods, and stabilizers, brake calipers, brake discs, and parking brakes, as well as axle drives and lateral input shafts. [...] ZF was able to prove that it had the basic ability to manufacture these systems – meaning that its organization included a global network of companies – and that it also had the expertise required in the areas of driveline, chassis, and steering systems technologies. Another significant factor in ZF's favor was that from the very beginning, the company was prepared to set up a factory near its customer."[7]

In 1998, only the second year since the plant had opened, 136,000 axle systems were shipped out of Tuscaloosa.

The new location was set up under the direction of ZF Passau in Tuscaloosa, Alabama, approximately 26 miles from the Daimler-Benz plant in the small town of Vance, and launched operations in 1996. This approach, which involved assembling the products as close to the customer as possible in order to guarantee "just-in-time" delivery, wasn't entirely new for the company, of course. In mid-1994, ZF had already set up two factories in Spartanburg and Duncan, South Carolina in order to manufacture axles for the BMW Z3 Roadster; volume production started in early 1996. What was new about the manufacturing process for the Mercedes M-Class, however, was that the axle module had been designed entirely by ZF.[8] Daimler-Benz had handed off important aspects of vehicle development to ZF. The greater complexity of the tasks now facing ZF gave the company grounds to reassess its self-image: from then on, ZF officially began to refer to itself as a systems supplier (instead of merely a parts supplier).[9] The goal behind this move was for ZF to play an active role in shaping the future of the automobile industry.

Today, the Zeppelin NT is a flying landmark, representing Friedrichshafen and its industry.

The Zeppelin NT experiment: Back to the future

The Zeppelin era may have ended in 1939, but the idea of bringing airship manufacturing back to Friedrichshafen never really died out. In the late 1980s, a group of advocates that included Mayor of Friedrichshafen and chairman of the supervisory board at ZF Bernd Wiedmann and ZF financial director Max Mugler decided to make another attempt. They claimed that state-of-the-art airships could be not only profitable; they also had the advantage of being more environmentally friendly than airplanes.[1] A market analysis conducted in 1989 indicated that potential buyers for a "Zeppelin Neuer Technologie" (Zeppelin New Technology, or Zeppelin NT) mainly came from the tourism and outdoor advertising industries; however, with its minimal vibration levels and potential to remain airborne for long periods of time, the Zeppelin also seemed well suited to scientific applications. The financial risk was negligible, as development costs for the prototype would run about 30 million deutschmarks[2] – and considering the advertising impact the company expected to generate, the plan seemed reasonably viable: "After all, in the eyes of the public, Friedrichshafen is the city of Zeppelins; the Zeppelin NT could serve to underscore that message," said Max Mugler, who was heavily involved in the project at the time.[3]

New technology, familiar problems

In order to concentrate the development process for the new airship in one place, ZF founded Zeppelin Luftschifftechnik GmbH (ZLT) in September 1993. Shareholders included Luftschiffbau Zeppelin GmbH (which had existed since 1908), Zeppelin Metallwerke GmbH, and – as important financial pillars for the new company – ZF Friedrichshafen AG and its subsidiary, Lemförder Metallwaren. Unlike its historical predecessor, the Zeppelin NT was not designed as a rigid airship with a full frame; rather, it was a semi-rigid design. It was filled with helium gas – an expensive, but safe alternative to highly flammable hydrogen, which can no longer be legally used as filling gas. The propellers on the Zeppelin NT are swivel-mounted, which drastically improves the airship's maneuverability during takeoff and landing, as well as in strong wind.

All of these upgrades took their toll, however, especially considering that airship manufacturing technology had stagnated in recent decades. By late 1996, it had become clear that the Zep-

pelin NT did not have enough ascending force to convey the planned twelve passengers in addition to two pilots. The rear was hastily extended by about 23 feet so that it could hold more gas. By this point, development costs had risen to about 50 million deutschmarks. By the standards of the industry, this was still a relatively low sum to invest in the development of a brand new product – but the fact that from 1997 to the present day, the company has only managed to produce eight Zeppelin NTs (instead of the planned two airships per year) is still a painful reality to accept.

While it is now possible to cost-effectively operate the Zeppelin NT, it seems unlikely that ZF will recoup the investments it made in developing the technology and procuring the materials. In that sense, the project is following in the footsteps of the historical

Zeppelins to a certain extent – they also relied on donations and subsidies. Despite their shaky financial footing, the airships are still wildly popular today, just as they were when they were first invented. Since sightseeing flights on the Zeppelin NT first became available in 2001, nearly 200,000 passengers from around the world have taken to the skies in this innovative airship, and even more people have taken snapshots of the Zeppelin NT from the ground as it hovered above them; the image of this airship is also popular as an advertising theme among the companies in the Lake Constance region. In recent years, the Zeppelin NT has been successfully used in campaigns to promote environmental protection, as well as for many other scientific applications. In this regard, at least, the NT has far exceeded expectations.

Swivel-mounted propeller on the Zeppelin NT: one aspect that makes this new model much more maneuverable than its historical predecessors.

THE ACQUISITION OF MANNESMANN SACHS:

"LIKE A BOLT AND A NUT"

On his trip through Baden-Württemberg in 2001, German Chancellor at the time, Gerhard Schröder, also visited ZF.
He is shown here in conversation with ZF CEO Klaus Bleyer.

It was one of the most expensive handshakes in corporate history. On February 3, 2000, shortly before midnight, CEO of Mannesmann Klaus Esser and Vodafone CEO Chris Gent sealed the deal – the model German company would be acquired by its British competitor.

Even before its acquisition by Vodafone, Mannesmann – which employed more than 130,000 people at the time – abandoned the conglomerate concept and decided to focus on telecommunications. In 1999, its entire industrial division – including Sachs, which would later become a subsidiary of ZF – was spun off to form Atecs Mannesmann AG. Originally, this corporation was supposed to go public, but after Vodafone acquired the Mannesmann Group, Atecs Mannesmann AG was sold to a consortium directed by Siemens and Bosch. Siegfried Goll, a member of ZF's Board of Management since 1997, described the situation as follows:

"Bosch and Siemens began the process of demerging the conglomerate they had purchased. Bosch was primarily interested in Rexroth, a plant engineering company that had been part of Mannesmann since the 1970s. Siemens wanted to acquire automotive supplier and electronic instrument manufacturer VDO. Sachs, a company headquartered in Schweinfurt, had been partially acquired by Mannesmann in 1987, and then fully acquired in 1991; now it was up for sale. Although Sachs' portfolio was a perfect complement to ZF's, we didn't actually enter into concrete negotiations until a relatively late stage. At that point, numerous potential buyers had already registered serious interest, but each of them only wanted to acquire part of Sachs' traditional portfolio. ZF, on the other hand, announced that it was interested in fully integrating all four of the company's main divisions – driveline, chassis technology, rubber-metal components, and spare parts. This won us points with Sachs' management in Schweinfurt."[1]

Considering the size of the two companies, ZF's subsequent acquisition of Mannesmann Sachs went relatively smoothly and quickly. After more than a year of preparation under the direction of Klaus Bleyer, CEO of ZF at the time, Bleyer's successor Siegfried Goll signed the acquisition agreements in August 2001; they went into effect in October 2001. Shortly thereafter, Mannesmann Sachs was renamed ZF Sachs AG. In November, the EU Commission also retroactively approved the acquisition without any restrictions under anti-trust law. In December, employee newspaper "ZF-Ring" reported on the largest acquisition in the company's history. In several feature stories, members of the Board of Management and works council in Friedrichshafen described the acquisition of Sachs not as a disruption, but rather, a return to continuous, independent development at ZF. "Communication between the companies and with our colleagues is very good," said chairman of the Sachs works council Willy Dekant. "[...] Our contact with the Board of Management at ZF [...] also hasn't been characterized by conflict – on the contrary. We have [...] encountered an atmosphere where we are permitted and encouraged to discuss everything. With our integration [into ZF] [...], a period of uncertainty and upheaval [...] is finally coming to an end. We have really been in limbo since November 1999. First, there were Mannesmann's plans to float Sachs and other business units on the stock market, then came acquisition offers from Thyssen Krupp and Bosch Siemens, and finally, the acquisition by Siemens – the whole process was unsettling for many of our employees."[2]

Biggest acquisition since ZF's founding

At that point in time, Sachs employed around 18,000 people. By continuing to handle all of Sachs' previous business after the acquisition, ZF consequently doubled its workforce by nearly 50 percent. In percentage terms, the company had not experienced such extensive growth within a single fiscal year since 1954; in absolute numbers, it was actually the biggest increase since the

New ZF Sachs development center in 2003. Sachs' technological expertise was a major reason for ZF to acquire the company in 2001.

company was founded. ZF wanted to maintain the constructive atmosphere that had existed during negotiations even after the acquisition was complete, so it opted for a policy of federalism, just as it had after acquiring Lemförder. The renowned Sachs brand was retained in the name of the new business unit, "ZF Sachs AG." At first, related departments at ZF and Sachs were not merged, in Germany or abroad. And layoffs were not part of the acquisition process either. ZF Sachs initially continued to operate independently with its own product range; the two long-standing companies would only merge gradually. ZF's new partners in Schweinfurt also knew how important it was to everyone involved that the integration process succeeded. Hermann Sigle,

Vice Chairman of the Board at Mannesmann Sachs since 1996, explains:

"With the acquisition of Sachs, which involved a 1.5-million-euro investment, ZF Friedrichshafen AG was close to its financial limits. ZF's involvement was vital to Sachs' survival – no one can say where we would be today if ZF hadn't offered us long-term prospects for the future. On the other hand, we also contributed a huge range of assets: while we were still under the umbrella of Siemens, in 2000, we initiated a number of important investment projects, such as the expansion of our development center and increasing our business in China, Korea, Mexico, and a number of Eastern European countries. In that sense, ZF acquired a company that was already looking to the future."[3]

More than the sum of their parts

Together, the two long-standing companies were in a much better position to offer complete modules and systems – a capability that increasing numbers of major automobile manufacturers were expecting from their suppliers. So when the 2001 annual report declared that ZF and Sachs fit together "like a bolt and a nut,"[4] it was more than just a catchy marketing slogan. The clutches, torque converters, and shock absorbers produced by Sachs aligned perfectly with the drivelines, transmissions, steering systems, axle systems, and chassis components from ZF. However, the two companies did not unlock the full potential of the merger until they began to coordinate their development processes.

One example of this synergy is the Mercedes-Benz CapaCity articulated bus, which has used a range of different ZF technologies since 2009. These buses service commuter traffic in cities such as Stuttgart and Istanbul. Measuring in at 64 feet in length, the CapaCity buses include ZF Eco-Life transmissions, which are particularly efficient – thanks in large part to a Sachs torque converter that allows for rapid acceleration even at low engine speeds. The system concept is also reflected in the buses' chassis: the portal axles with independent suspension come from ZF Passau, and the corresponding twin-tube shock absorbers are Sachs products. However, back in 2001, the year that ZF acquired Sachs, true integration of the various product segments remained a long-term goal. At that point, potential synergies at the corporate level were more about finances than technology; ZF had a broader product range and a larger pool of possible orders, making it the more competitive partner.

Financially challenging transition

Despite the obvious successes the company had achieved since the acquisition, a look at its balance sheets showed that the Sachs takeover was

Manufacturing Sachs dual-mass flywheels, 2003.

No one can say where we would be today if ZF hadn't offered us long-term prospects for the future. On the other hand, we also contributed a huge range of assets.

HERMANN SIGLE, FORMER VICE CHAIRMAN OF THE BOARD AT MANNESMANN SACHS

still a financial burden, albeit a temporary one. Many of the market segments relevant to ZF had reported a drop in demand in 2002 and 2003, which exacerbated the already difficult situation. ZF Friedrichshafen AG's annual surplus, which had been 150 million euros in 2001, shrank to just 29 million euros in 2002, despite the fact that the company's sales increased by approximately 36 percent during that same period. In 2003, ZF

Sachs multi-disc clutch, manufactured in 2003.

ultimately recorded losses of 162 million euros, accompanied by a 3 percent drop in sales. However, this was only partly due to the large investments the company had made in ZF Sachs. ZF's withdrawal from a joint venture with Ford in Batavia, Ohio, where the two companies had manufactured continuously variable automatic transmissions, was a much more significant causal factor behind the losses.

ZF's management, in consultation with the Dr. Jürgen Ulderup Foundation, decided to change the company's ownership structure. On May 13, 2003, ZF acquired 100 percent of the shares in Lemförder Metallwaren AG; the Dr. Jürgen Ulderup Foundation traded the 24.4 percent share it held in the ZF Lemförder subsidiary for a share of 6.2 percent in the entire company. The remaining 93.8 percent of ZF's share capital stayed in the hands of the Zeppelin Foundation. This exchange of shares was aimed at creating clearer structures in the growing passenger car chassis technology segment, facilitating cross-sector product development and the associated investments.

At the same time, the merger with Sachs had begun to change ZF's corporate culture, as Hans-Georg Härter recalls:

"I came to Schweinfurt from Passau in 2001, to take on the role of CEO at ZF Sachs. Although ZF and Sachs shared a great deal of common ground in terms of technologies and customers, there was a different atmosphere after the merger. Sachs had been part of a publicly traded cor-

Assembling chassis components at ZF Sachs, 2003.

poration, after all, so its employees were used to a certain mindset and way of doing things – like the way they conducted meetings, for instance. I personally learned a great deal here, as I suspect many of my colleagues on the ZF management team also did. Another area where ZF drew inspiration from Sachs was the aftermarket segment: the sale of replacement parts and the provision of the associated services. As a provider of clutches and shock absorbers, Sachs had traditionally been a leader in this area, so we took the merger as an opportunity to reposition ZF in this segment – we merged several of our foreign trading companies with service and sales companies that had existed in parallel, for instance."

The ZF Group's growth in 2004 and 2005 suggests that the company's management had put ZF

on the right track for the future during this financially difficult phase. ZF managed to reduce its investments to a level that was normal for the industry (first to 6, then to 5 percent of annual sales), and profits demonstrated a clear upward trend. After the losses it suffered in 2003, ZF could boast a positive annual result the following year: 181 million euros. And profits increased even more in 2005; it is difficult to make a comparison to previous years here, however, as at this point, ZF changed its accounting practices. It had previously adhered to the regulations of the German Commercial Code (HGB), but now transitioned to International Financial Reporting Standards (IFRS), which became mandatory for all capital market-oriented European companies on January 1, 2005.

THE DEVELOPMENT OF THE SACHS BRAND FROM 1895 TO 2001:

FROM BICYCLES TO CHASSIS

The Sachs name represents both the triumph of the bicycle and the successful family of industrialists and playboys who ran the eponymous company.[1] Since the early 1930s, Sachs has been an important pillar of the German automobile industry – a fact that fans of motor sports are well aware of. Sachs clutches and shock absorbers are in wide use in race cars. The founder of this extraordinary German company – the story of which reads like something from a Hollywood film script – was toolmaker Ernst Sachs (1867–1932).

The son of a sawmill owner in Constance, Sachs first made a name for himself as a cyclist. The bicycle was considered an exotic method of transportation at the time – and, thanks to the high-wheel construction that was standard back then, it was also an exhausting and dangerous one. It first became popular among high-society young men. In 1889, Sachs became a member of the Frankfurter Velociped-Club, where he won competitions and made important connections. During his years in Frankfurt, Sachs also made a life-long friend in Rüsselsheim native Wilhelm von Opel, whose daughter Elinor would later go on to marry Sachs' son Willy.

Ernst Sachs first came to Schweinfurt, where he eventually founded the company, in 1894. At the time, he was recovering from a broken lower leg that he had suffered during cycling practice. He was forced to take a break from any athletic activity, which brought one of the young mechanic's hidden talents to light: he understood the shortcomings of the era's bicycles better than any other cycling enthusiast, and he was obsessed with the idea of developing a new method of transportation that everyone could use. The experiences Sachs had as a racer – people and materials subjected to high levels of stress, painful falls and accidents, a frequent lack of funds – shaped his approach as an inventor. He was not the kind of engineer who was only interested in the most complex designs; rather, he preferred simple, precise constructions that were extremely durable, lightweight, and compact,

and that could be manufactured at a reasonable cost. These were the principles upon which his company eventually built its success.

It all began with a ball bearing

In 1894, Sachs registered his first patent: for a ball bearing that had lower levels of play and was much more durable than comparable products from competitors. However, Sachs lacked the money to set up a factory – and this is where Schweinfurt-based businessman Karl Fichtel (1863-1911) came into the picture. He provided the 15,000 marks in start-up capital that Sachs needed, as well as rent-free premises with a workshop on his parents' garden property. On August 1, 1895, the two men founded Schweinfurter Präzisions-Kugellagerwerke Fichtel & Sachs OHG. Fichtel handled the business aspects, while Sachs

1920s German newspaper ad celebrating the Sachs Torpedo bicycle wheel hub.

Ernst Sachs was a master of product advertising. Parades like this one were regularly held in major German cities.

Manufacturing ball bearings at Fichtel & Sachs, ca. 1920.

managed the technical side of things. The company was only moderately successful at first, partly because the market couldn't keep up with the pace of Sachs' innovation. In 1898, when the young entrepreneur presented his first bicycle featuring a locking hub – the design we know as standard today – an article in the trade press mocked the product as a "silly fad"[2] that offered "absolutely no practical benefit" and would, the article continued, only increase the risk of accidents. Granted, the spoon brake mechanisms of the era did look somewhat untrustworthy on bicycles without a rigid axle, but Sachs knew just what to do. In 1903, he introduced a wheel hub that combined the ball bearings, freewheel, and coaster brake: its brand name was "Torpedo." This new invention earned Sachs his big break. By 1905, the company had already produced 367,087 units, and demand continued to rise. While the company was expanding rapidly, Karl Fichtel decided to step down from his position for health reasons. In 1911, Fichtel passed away in Schweinfurt – but Sachs' drive to create continued unabated. He began opening factories abroad at a relatively early stage: in Černýš, Bohemia and Lancaster, Pennsylvania in 1912. During World War I, production of bicycle wheel hubs, ball bearings, and munitions at the factory increased, as did the number of employees at Fichtel & Sachs – to approximately 8,000.

The end of the war resulted in a temporary slump, which, in turn, caused the company to lose its production facility in the USA. However, Sachs finally achieved his goal: the bicycle became a mass-market product, and the company's locking hubs were selling like hotcakes. In January 1923, Germany was already suffering the effects of runaway inflation when Fichtel & Sachs went public. The ownership structure remained the same despite this change; the company still belonged to the Fichtel and Sachs families. In the years that followed, Sachs began to shift the company's product portfolio in the direction of the future ZF Sachs AG. Fichtel & Sachs entered the clutch and shock absorber business in 1926 with the acquisition of Stempel-Werke in Frankfurt; the first clutch designed by Sachs was introduced in 1929. During the same year, Sachs sold his company's ball bearing manufacturing business to Swedish competitor SKF; he then used the profits to buy out the heirs of his former business partner Karl Fichtel.

When Ernst Sachs passed away in 1932, he left his 36-year-old son Willy a thriving company – and an innovative product that would help it continue to grow. With the aid of Gustav Steinlein, who would later become the company's chief designer, Ernst Sachs – tough and persistent till the end – designed a compact, affordable, powerful, and durable 2.25-horsepower two-stroke engine shortly before his death. It was known as the "98er Motor." It was as if the new engine had been tailor-made for motorized bicy-

cles, which were the hot new trend at the time. As was typical for most Sachs products, the engine was already so sophisticated when it hit the market that the company was able to continue producing it with very few alterations until 1950. While the new product met with immediate commercial success, the workers in Schweinfurt refused to rest on their founder's laurels; instead, they continued to work on a smaller and lighter engine that could be installed as a wheel-hub motor on nearly any standard bicycle. It was launched in 1937 under the name "Saxonette." The "Stamo" followed shortly thereafter – it was a stationary engine with a cooling fan that could be used for a range of different applications, including agriculture and construction.

Swedish royal consul in Nazi Germany

By that point, new managing director Willy Sachs – who had been awarded the title of Swedish royal vice consul in 1930, and consul in 1933 – was primarily making a name for himself as an associate of the Nazi regime. The Sachs family had purchased an estate in Bavaria in 1912 (Gut Rechenau), where Willy Sachs regularly organized hunting parties for the Nazi leadership, including Hermann Göring, Heinrich Himmler, and Reinhard Heydrich. Sachs had been a member of the Nazi party and the SS since 1933; he was later named a Wehrwirtschaftsführer ("defense economy leader"). He also donated generously to the Nazi organization. While he left the running of

THE TORPEDO BICYCLE WHEEL HUB was Fichtel & Sachs' first hit product. By 1955, the Schweinfurt-based company had sold

70 million units

The Saxomat automatic clutch was introduced in 1957, which eliminated most of the exhausting pedal operation for drivers.

his company to the managers he had hired, Willy tended to family matters – ineptly and recklessly. His first wife Elinor von Opel (1908–2001) divorced him in 1935, in part because she couldn't stand to see her husband currying favor with Nazi party bigwigs. When she drew the attention of the Nazi authorities by criticizing their policies, she fled to Switzerland with the couple's two sons, Ernst Wilhelm (1929–1977) and Gunter (1932–2011). Willy Sachs used his ties to Himmler and Heydrich to organize two abduction attempts, both of which failed. The public was unaware of all of this, however; Sachs remained a highly respected figure in his hometown, partly because of his generous cultural patronage – Schweinfurt dedicated a number of buildings to him, including the 15,000-seat Willy Sachs Stadium, which was inaugurated in 1936.

Fichtel & Sachs played a key role in supplying the Nazi regime with military equipment. Nearly all German tanks were equipped with Sachs clutches, and even the company's low-power mo-

tors were used for military purposes – as starter motors for tanks and airplanes, for instance. In order to keep its factories operating while many employees were conscripted into the Wehrmacht, Fichtel & Sachs began making extensive use of forced labor. Schweinfurt was the center of Germany's ball-bearing production industry, and as such, it suffered a similar fate to Friedrichshafen: with a total of 15 major air raids between 1943 and 1945, Allied bombers essentially flattened the city. On April 11, 1945, Schweinfurt was occupied by US troops. Willy Sachs was imprisoned in three different camps in the American zone of occupation between May 1945 and February 1947. His denazification proceedings were held at the Schweinfurt state Spruchkammer, a special court set up for this purpose. He was classified as a "follower," meaning that he was not considered a serious offender – a particularly striking example of the whitewashed justice system in post-war Germany.

Sachs and the "economic miracle"

Meanwhile, Fichtel & Sachs set sail for new horizons in the wake of Germany's "economic miracle." The demand for bicycle wheel hubs, low-power motors, clutches, and shock absorbers was enormous, making it possible for the company to revitalize its civilian product range, which it had been neglecting since the start of the war. The Sachs 50 driveline, which was introduced in 1953, was outstanding in both a technological and a financial sense. During that decade, it was installed as a drive system in countless motorbikes. The motor, transmission, and foot pedal were all contained in the same housing – an early example of a systems approach in vehicle manufacturing. Fichtel & Sachs set the course in other areas as well; for example, long-standing head of the clutches and shock absorbers department, Richard Binder, and his team of designers managed to develop an automatic clutch that was launched in 1957 under the name "Saxomat."

In 1959, approximately one year after Willy Sachs had taken his own life at his family's estate,

Fichtel & Sachs began setting up a factory for shock absorbers, springs, and clutches in São Paulo, Brazil. In the meantime, Ernst Wilhelm Sachs had followed in the footsteps of his father and grandfather, despite disputes with his family. However, the grandson of the company's founder was unable to duplicate the success that previous generations of his family had achieved. There were a number of reasons for this, including the general economic downturn in the mid-1960s; disagreements with Volkswagen, the company's primary customer at the time; and the investment of significant sums of money into the development of the torque converter clutch, which failed to generate the returns the company had hoped for. In 1967, Ernst Wilhelm was forced to step down from day-to-day management of the company. By that time, Ernst Wilhelm's brother Gunter, who engaged in a broad range of artistic and athletic pursuits, had become a popular topic for gossip columnists. The press framed him as the

ultimate gentleman playboy, and Gunter Sachs was happy to embrace that image. His affair with former Queen of Iran Soraya and subsequent marriage to actress Brigitte Bardot captivated West German audiences, who enjoyed living vicariously through Sachs' escapades.

In 1976, the two Sachs brothers attempted to sell Fichtel & Sachs to British automotive and aeronautics supplier GKN Plc. However, their plan was struck down by the anti-trust authorities. It wasn't until the years between 1987 and 1991 that Gunter Sachs and the three daughters of Ernst Wilhelm Sachs (who had since passed away) managed to sell their shares of the still-prosperous company and make a profit. The buyer was Mannesmann AG. The new parent company sold the bicycle parts manufacturing business in 1997 and stopped producing motors. The company was renamed around the same time: the company founded by Ernst Sachs in 1895 was now called Mannesmann Sachs.

Two very different brothers visiting a factory in Brazil: Gunter and Ernst Wilhelm Sachs in 1961.

"When a company gives you this much, you don't even think about retiring"

Interview with Dr. Siegfried Goll, CEO of ZF Friedrichshafen AG
from 2001 to 2006

It was 1961 when you first came into contact with ZF as part of your mechanical engineering degree program in Constance. What was so fascinating about this company to 21-year-old intern Siegfried Goll that he ultimately decided to work there for almost 45 years?

To put it briefly: the products! The automatic bus transmissions that I learned about during my internship sparked my interest immediately, and when I finished my degree in 1963, I applied for a job as a test engineer for mechanical components. I was hired, and when I arrived at my office – which I shared with four other engineers – I was surprised to find a stack of books on my desk, all about the technological principles of gears. This wasn't exactly how I'd pictured my transition from academia to the working world; I didn't think I'd be spending my work days reading technical literature. But ZF was a very scientifically driven company back then, and to a certain extent, it was even doing fundamental research in some areas. For example, I was assigned the task

of refining the materials and heat treatments used in the gears that ZF produced. In that sense, I actually spent my first years at the company dealing with our technological roots.

If you compare ZF back then and today, how has the culture changed?

In my opinion, ZF was a highly centralized company in the 1960s. The people at the top – first Dr. Maier and, beginning in 1967, Professor Ziebart – were the ones pulling the strings. Dr. Baur, on the other hand, favored the idea of a decentralized management culture – one that also demanded a high level of personal responsibility from its middle management. Dr. Bleyer also believed in this approach, and I followed in his footsteps as CEO. What hasn't changed is the fact that ZF has always operated with an eye to the long term. You can see that in our product range and in our globalization strategy. ZF is a company owned by a foundation, so you might say that continuity is in our DNA. This continuity offers numerous advantages, as we saw with the launch of our electric power steering system. We entered into this field – a new field for ZF – in partnership with Bosch, and we had to fight a great deal of resistance, both in the minds of some of our employees and in terms of the technology and finances involved. During that process, I was thankful every day for the fact that we are not a publicly traded company.

Up to that point, we were used to growing in
SMALL STEPS.

But would you still agree that ZF's tendency toward continuity can also pose a risk? We're specifically thinking of the year 1989, when you and the management of ZF Getriebe GmbH in Saarbrücken acquired a business unit that hadn't been profitable for years...

That's true; we sometimes ignored the economic realities for too long. We did excellent development work on the automatic passenger car transmission back then, but we suffered from the fact that European drivers still preferred manual transmissions. Manufacturers like Citroën, Opel, Peugeot, or Renault offered hardly any passenger cars with automatic transmissions. Many of our customers in countries like France felt that cars with automatic transmissions were too expensive and not sporty enough; automatic cars were thought of as an option for the elderly, the infirm, or people with disabilities. And the market penetration of automatic transmissions was correspondingly low. While 80 to 90 percent of all cars on the roads in the US and Japan had automatic transmissions, that figure was

just 10 percent in Germany, and in France and Italy, it was significantly lower. At the Frankfurt International Motor Show in 1989, however, we presented the 5HP 18 as a premium transmission for luxury automobiles. The transmission had its own highly complex electronic control unit which, for the first time, functioned completely independently from the electronic engine control unit. The development process wasn't without its share of headaches – I basically wound up commuting between Saarbrücken and Munich, where our most important OEM partner, BMW, was located. It got off to a bumpy start, but in the end, the product was a great success for us. Today, even in Europe, people no longer doubt that the automatic passenger car transmission has merit. In that sense, ZF's lasting dedication to the concept has paid off. Of course, in our industry – as in any business – there will always be ups and downs, and not every development project will pay off in the end. The CVT is a good example of that fact.

We learned elsewhere that the CVT (continuously variable transmission) didn't gain the broad acceptance the company had hoped for. The crisis surrounding this product reached its climax in 2005, when ZF withdrew from the joint venture with Ford in Batavia, Ohio which had been in place since 1999...

This was, without a doubt, the most difficult and painful decision I had to make as CEO. But it was necessary: the plant, which belonged to Ford, had 1,250 employees who produced approximately 400,000 conventional four-gear automatic transmissions per year. At the time, the conventional wisdom in our industry was that CVT technology would eventually become prevalent, at least for the lower and mid-range vehicle performance classes, partly because CVT could save up to 10 or 15 percent more fuel compared to the widely used multi-ratio transmissions of the time. We projected that we would produce about one million continuously variable automatic transmissions per year in the US, and we had plenty of space to expand production in Batavia. We invested a great deal of money, but the market developed in a different direction. The trend was toward high-torque engines that were installed lengthwise, and CVT technology simply wasn't suited to that purpose. It was lucky for ZF that Ford took over 100 percent of the shares in the Batavia plant in 2005, because it allowed us to make a controlled exit from the CVT manufacturing business.

After that, we concentrated on multi-ratio transmissions for lengthwise installation – such as the 6HP, and later, the 8HP. Development of the compact front-transverse transmission took a backseat for the time being; it wasn't until the launch of the 9HP that we added another front-transverse product to our portfolio.

Did withdrawing from the joint venture with Ford have a long-term impact on ZF's business in the USA?

The business climate in the US in the early 2000s was a serious challenge for us. We faced a decline in sales, and we also had to reduce the number of people we employed in the NAFTA zone. But we invested a great deal of money in restructuring and setting up new plants – such as the facility in Newton, North Carolina, which produces chassis components.

When you became CEO in 2001, ZF was on the verge of making the biggest acquisition in its history. Can you give us your perspective on this event?

Well, first of all, the acquisition of Mannesmann Sachs had a decisive impact on my personal plans. Originally, I had planned to retire in 2001, but when Dr. Bleyer stepped down as CEO, I decided to stay on at the company until I turned 66, in order to guarantee a certain degree of continuity in upper management. We needed this stability, because integrating a company with around 18,000 employees and annual sales of approximately 2.1 billion euros was a unique challenge for ZF. Up to that point, we were used to growing in small steps, in a rather organic way – the acquisition of Lemförder in 1984 might be the one exception to that rule. Still, taking advantage of the opportunity to acquire Sachs was a smart choice, and it was absolutely the right one. This is partly evidenced by the fact that after the acquisition, there was no predatory competition between the old and new locations, because the product range of each company logically complemented the other. For me, the opportunity to oversee the merger of Sachs and ZF as CEO was an exceptional privilege and the highlight of my career.

2005
—
2015

Setting course for the future

Sachs is successfully integrated, and the Group experiences a series of very good years. But suddenly, the global economy faces its most severe downturn since 1945. Thanks to its successful crisis management strategies, ZF is able to use the weak economy to strengthen its own market position. The acquisition of TRW in 2015, the year of the company's 100th anniversary, marks the beginning of a new era for ZF.

EFFECTS OF THE ECONOMIC CRISIS
AND NEW DRIVE TECHNOLOGY:

INNOVATING
IN AN AGE OF ECONOMIC
UNCERTAINTY

ZF production facility in Araraquara, Brazil, 2013.

In 2003, ZF was weighed down financially by its acquisition of Mannesmann Sachs and its exit from US companies ZF Batavia LLC and ZF Meritor LLC. However, the company was quickly able to find its footing again and get back on the path to growth. Group sales in 2005 exceeded 10 billion euros for the first time ever; compared to 1995, sales had more than doubled. The automobile industry remained the most important by far for ZF. The sales the company generated in this segment accounted for 87 percent of total revenue in 2005. In that sense, it was vital to ZF's survival that the company not only reacted to the changes taking place in the automobile industry, but also helped to actively shape them.

At the beginning of the new millennium, there were a number of obvious global trends in this area. For example, growth in the automobile industry shifted from North America and Europe to Asia, and to China and India in particular. In these newly industrialized countries, demand for affordable vehicles for the emerging middle class was rising sharply – and the top models from Germany's luxury car brands were considered status symbols by the growing upper class. Traditional auto markets such as the USA or Germany still maintained a high volume of sales, but because of the existing vehicle density in these countries, their markets grew only slightly. In terms of quality, western markets underwent a fundamental shift during this period. In urban centers, a generation shaped by the digital world was growing up; their transportation needs and consumption habits differed greatly from those of their parents.

For ZF – which, at this point, was ranked at least third in nearly every segment of the global market[1] – these developments resulted in contradictory challenges. In both newly industrialized countries and "traditional" markets such as the USA and Europe, large, comfortable vehicles with high-performance drive units were still in demand. But at the same time, ZF also had to fulfill the wishes of many consumers who wanted fuel-efficient vehicles, particularly since government policies were also increasingly tending in this direction. In April 2009, the European Parliament enacted a regulation regarding the reduction of CO_2 emissions from passenger cars[2], which required manufacturers to gradually reduce their vehicles' average CO_2 emissions and, consequently, their fuel consumption beginning in 2015. If the manufacturers did not comply, they could be fined. However, fuel consumption was not measured based on individual models, but rather on the emissions of an entire fleet of cars from the respective manufacturer. This gave premium manufacturers like Audi and BMW an incentive to add low-emission hybrid or electric vehicles to their product ranges in order to lower overall fuel consumption in their fleets. German OEMs, in particular, already had the necessary concepts on hand. In 1997, for example, Audi produced its first hybrid vehicle – the Audi duo – in small batches, while Daimler-Benz tested vehicles with fuel cells.

Old drive concepts, revisited

ZF, too, already had experience with alternative drive concepts. At the 1994 IAA Commercial Vehicles, ZF presented the EE Drive, an electric wheel-hub motor specially designed for low-floor buses. The technology proved its worth in the years that followed, as the company conducted large-scale field tests in places such as Oberstdorf, Leiden, and Berlin. A total of 17 EvoBus (Mercedes-Benz) diesel-electric vehicles were added to the public transportation system in Stuttgart, and a

IN 2015, the CO_2 emissions for fleets of newly certified cars in the European Union were capped at a per-kilometer limit of

130 grams

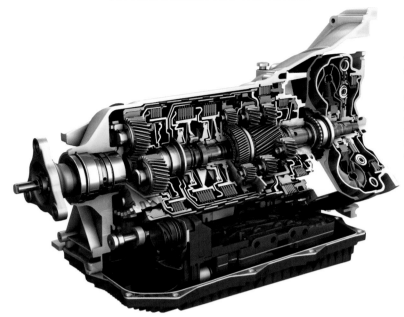

The 8HP automatic transmission for passenger cars is one of ZF's most successful products of all time. Between 2009 and 2014, the company produced approximately 7.5 million units.

fully electric bus from MAN intermittently traveled back and forth between the ZF plants in Friedrichshafen. This was likely the first time that many ZF employees had ever seen an electric vehicle in regular traffic. Scania also tested the new technology. In the meantime, ZF had successfully developed a new, more advanced version of this alternative drive concept for city buses that included the electric axle AVE 130. When Volkswagen developed its first one-liter vehicle, the "Studie 1L," in 2002, ZF Sachs provided the ultra-light shock absorbers and tie rods, as well as a combination clutch and starter generator. The ZF technology played a decisive role in the vehicle's impressive consumption data – it made it possible to automatically decouple and shut off the compact diesel engine when the accelerator was released. Similar drive concepts were also tested for commercial vehicles; DaimlerChrysler and ZF, for example, presented a prototype Mercedes Sprinter at the IAA in Hanover in fall 2014 that could potentially travel short distances (up to about 19 miles) emission-free and on pure electrical power.

Although all of these alternative drive projects demonstrated great potential, ZF and its partners did not manage to launch volume production at this point. Japanese vehicle manufacturers Toyota and Honda, on the other hand, had been selling these types of models since the late 1990s. In 2005, ZF decided to finally establish itself in the future-oriented hybrid drive segment and entered into a strategic partnership with automotive supplier Continental. Volkswagen commissioned the partners with constructing a complete hybrid drive module in 2006, and by 2007, this innovative product was ready to be presented as a prototype in a VW Golf V at the IAA. The start of volume production was planned for 2008, but it didn't actually begin until 2010, when the VW Touareg underwent a facelift. ZF, on the other hand, did roll out its own hybrid technology in 2008: the Mercedes S 400 hybrid presented that year featured an electric engine from ZF Sachs.

Conventional transmissions remain important

Despite the intensity with which ZF worked to expedite the development of alternative drive systems, no one in the company's management believed that the technology would replace conventional combustion engines anytime soon. "In the long term," said Dr. Michael Paul, Member of the Board of Management responsible for development, in a 2009 interview, "different types of drives will exist side by side. [...] Conventional drives – and consequently transmissions, as well – will dominate [...] the market in both the passenger car and commercial vehicle segments. We would be remiss if we didn't push ahead with development in this segment as intensely as possible."[3]

In keeping with this approach, ZF had already presented an eight-gear automatic transmission (8HP) in 2007; compared to the six-gear unit, this new version saved up to six percent more fuel. Considering the fact that countless vehicles with four- and five-gear transmissions were still on the roads, actual fuel savings when these drivers switched to the 8HP were often much higher, however. The transmission – which, as a modular kit, also included a hybrid version – was created as part of a partnership between several locations and departments; potential customers were also deeply involved in the development process. Volume production of the 8HP had already begun in 2009.

In the meantime, the entire automobile industry was suffering the effects of the 2008 global financial crisis; manufacturers of trucks and construction machinery were hit particularly hard. In some cases, sales in these departments at ZF dropped by more than 50 percent. The passenger car segment was not affected as severely as the commercial vehicle segment, but the worst recession since the end of World War II also took its toll in this area. In 2009, passenger car production in Europe declined by 17 percent. However, this downturn did nothing to slow the market launch of the 8HP transmission – manufacturers needed the new generation of transmissions to optimize consumption in their vehicles.

And yet, when the crisis reached its worst point in 2009, Group sales at ZF were 26 percent lower than they had been in 2007. As a result, ZF recorded losses of 421 million euros in 2009.

In February 2011, German Chancellor Angela Merkel visited innovative companies in the Lake Constance region, including ZF. The Chancellor is shown here in conversation with CEO Hans-Georg Härter.

Given these dramatic figures, the fact that ZF did not have to lay off any of its core workforce speaks to the effectiveness of the company's crisis management policies – as does the relatively low number of layoffs in North and South America, where reduced working hours were not part of the crisis management toolbox. Between 2008 and 2009, the company's workforce shrank by just over one percent overall; compared to 2007, the year before the crisis, the number of employees at ZF actually increased during this period. The company implemented a range of different measures to cut costs and ensure liquidity, which saved approximately 600 million euros. The state-run KfW Development Bank also provided ZF with a 250 million euro loan that served as an emergency fund, but the company did not use the full amount.

Emerging from the crisis stronger than ever

In retrospect, the development of the automobile industry between 2008 and 2009 is a good example of how a crisis can be an opportunity. ZF's strategic position in 2010 had improved compared to 2007, partly as a result of the consolidation process triggered by the economic crisis. The sharp decline in stock markets, the dramatic drop in demand, and the fact that credit was difficult to come by as a result of the banking crisis had put many of ZF's competitors under extreme pressure – a situation that consequently provided ZF with a number of opportunities to expand its business. For

example, the company gained significant market share in the USA as a supplier for Chrysler. In France, meanwhile, ZF went into damage control mode: when light metal specialist Honsel AG filed for bankruptcy in October 2010, it also meant that the manufacturing of housings for ZF automatic transmissions was at risk. For this reason, one month after Honsel's bankruptcy was announced, ZF acquired Honsel-owned Fonderie Lorraine near Saarbrücken. In 2011, the company also took over the Honsel plant in Nuremberg. With these acquisitions, ZF ensured it could manufacture housings under its own roof in the future.

When the crisis came to an unexpectedly early end in late 2010, oil prices also hit a new record high. This meant that greater focus had to be placed on exactly the innovative areas in which ZF had already invested years of work: efficient, fuel-saving drive technology and lightweight chassis components. The 8HP-series automatic transmissions were in such high demand that production capacities in Saarbrücken quickly reached their limits; the facility had to be expanded in 2010. Just a few months before, employees at this site had been working reduced hours. Of course, despite the tremendous success of the eiht-gear automatic transmission, the passenger car automatic transmission segment still had room for new products. After all, the 8HP was specially designed for large and mid-size vehicles with engines installed lengthwise, but the sales trend was headed in a different direction, as Head of Development Michael Paul recalled:

"It's important for us to also be able to provide high-quality, efficient technology for smaller, more affordable models at a reasonable price. Because one thing is clear: demand is shifting toward smaller vehicles. This segment will eventually account for around 50 percent of the global market, and it will grow the fastest." [4]

First of its kind: the 9HP

Since 2009, ZF engineers had been working on the world's first nine-gear automatic transmission

THE STEP up from the 6HP to the 8HP meant a measurable increase in efficiency. Depending on the car model and the way it was driven, the new transmission with a start-stop system could save much more fuel than the previous model: savings had the potential to reach

11%

Production of 9H automatic transmission at the Gray Court, South Carolina location, 2013.

Production of the 8HP automatic transmission for passenger cars in Saarbrücken, 2013.

(9HP) – the company wanted to be able to offer the right kind of product for this market segment. The 9HP was intended for lateral installation in the front of the vehicle, which meant that unlike the 8HP series, it could also be used in compact vehicles. For the first time, this state-of-the-art engine included high-performance control electronics developed by ZF Electronics. ZF Electronics originally emerged as part of the acquisition of the Cherry Corporation in 2008. In June 2011, the engine was presented to international experts and the media for the first time, and production launched in Gray Court, South Carolina in 2013. In the years prior, ZF had invested around 350 million euros in reconstructing this site to cater to the production of the 8HP and 9HP transmissions. ZF was easily able to finance the expansion, as the company's annual net profits had held steady at between 330 and 540 million euros since 2010. Four years after the global economic crisis, it was clear: ZF had passed the stress test.

Considering that it has nine gears, the 9HP is extremely compact – ideal for lateral installation in the front of modern mid-size cars.

Despite a temporary slump in 2012 and 2013, the market for wind power transmissions has strong potential for growth.

Entering the wind power transmission business: From newcomer to number 3

You might be thinking: ZF has been making transmissions since 1915. How could the company possibly surprise us now? Does it matter whether we make transmissions for compact cars, helicopters, ships, or wind turbines? The underlying technology is the same – the size is the only thing that changes, right? From my own experience, I can tell you that things aren't so simple. When we started producing wind power transmissions in 2010, it was one of the greatest challenges I've ever faced in my career."[1]

Elizabeth Umberson, plant manager in Gainesville, Georgia since 1999, had just successfully guided the automobile transmission production facility in the southeastern USA through the difficult years of the global economic crisis when she learned that ZF would be setting up a new factory for wind power transmissions at her site. The client was global market leader Vestas of Denmark. ZF initially had contact with Vestas in 2007, as head of development for the project Tino Kirschner explains: "The story behind the project is that the Danish company was dissatisfied with the transmissions it was using at the time. They weren't reliable enough. It's a typical problem that we've seen in the large turbines constructed since the early 1990s." ZF's experience with the mass production of a wide range of components and its consistently high quality in series production weren't the only reasons why it was the perfect partner for this project. With its global network of manufacturing and service locations, the ZF Group also had the necessary structures in place to keep pace with the rapid growth of the renewable energy market. The first step in this partnership – which was planned for the long term – was the redevelopment of Vestas' two-megawatt platform[2], which was scheduled to go into production in 2012. Despite the fact that, compared to today's wind turbines, this performance class would be considered average, the dimensions are still mind-boggling: the key data for this project called for rotor diameters between 295 and 360 feet and wind speeds during operation of up to 55 miles per hour. The result was the highest level of torque that ZF had ever designed a transmission for.

But this wasn't the only challenge associated with the new product. Wind power transmissions are extremely sensitive: tiny imperfections on the transmission's gear teeth or excessive play in the bearings can be amplified by the enormous rotor blades to the point where the effectiveness and durability of the entire system is severely compromised. For this reason, the calculations for wind power transmissions involve extremely narrow margins. Additionally, this new transmission required production logistics that were completely different than anything ZF had dealt with in the past. Hardly any parts could be moved by hand. The immense weight of the individual gears and housings required new machining methods that ZF had to develop in parallel with the actual product.

Acquisition of Hansen Transmissions

In November 2011, ZF acquired Belgian specialist Hansen Transmissions International NV in order to benefit from the company's existing expertise in the wind power market segment. In addition to its production facility in Belgium, Hansen also had factories in China and India.[3] In the blink of an eye, ZF had suddenly become the number 3 company on the global market for wind power transmissions. However, the acquisition process wasn't without its bumps in the road. Much of the growth in the renewable energy industry shifted to China between 2012 and 2013 – a region where ZF was not well represented in this market segment.

ZF still opted to move forward with the project, despite the fact that it lay outside of the company's traditional area of expertise, the automobile business. In February 2014, the first wind power transmission developed by ZF was presented under the name "Atlas 1." ZF also wanted to be able to provide customer service for this new product, so the company made significant investments in its infrastructure. At the Dortmund, Germany and Vernon Hills, Illinois sites, the company opened regional wind energy service centers that were equipped with cutting-edge dynamometer test rigs and cranes. These centers had the capacity to handle 200 repair orders annually. When the market for wind turbines began to show signs of another upward trend in 2014, ZF was prepared to help shape the future of energy in a decisive field.

Inspection of a wind power transmission at the ZF plant in Lommel, Belgium, 2014.

HANS-GEORG HÄRTER:

"The 'ZF family' is more than just a word"

Interview with Hans-Georg Härter,
CEO of ZF Friedrichshafen AG, 2007–2012

You were a part of ZF for nearly 39 years, but you spent the early years of your career – right after finishing your college degree in technical management – at companies such as Voith in Heidenheim, Germany. How did that particular company view ZF?

First, it's important to note that in terms of corporate culture, both companies are quite similar, and they only compete with one another in a very narrow segment of the market. Traditionally, Voith had always relied on as broad a portfolio of products as possible, while back in the 1970s, ZF was still focused almost entirely on driveline technology. Naturally, ZF held a very strong market position in this field, and Voith also recognized the company's technological expertise. I would go so far as to say that ZF was considered the gold standard in certain segments of driveline technology.

After moving over to ZF, you worked in Passau for some time. What kind of challenges did you face there?

Passau's business in agricultural and construction machinery is subject to its own market cycles. Fluctuation is relatively high; slumps and booms tend to follow one another in rapid succession. So it was essentially normal for us to have to work reduced hours every few years as a cost-cutting measure. In other departments, however, reduced working hours were considered a last resort. Management accepted our special status, not least because our business was, on the whole, very profitable. Still, one of my strategic goals was to reduce the Passau production facility's dependence on economic trends, and by manufacturing portal axles for low-floor buses and getting involved in the passenger car axle drive for brands like Porsche and Audi, for example, we managed to achieve this goal.

From agricultural machines to sports cars – aren't those two different worlds?

On the contrary! The general public might not be aware of this, but the technology employed in modern agricultural machines is often absolutely state of the art. For Porsche, we used ground bevel gearsets that were based on our steering axles for tractors, for example. The unique geometry of our high-performance axle drives is what makes them so incredibly durable, and yet so compact. There's also a great deal of discussion today about future-oriented technologies like driver assistance systems and autonomous driving; agricultural machinery has been at the vanguard of this field for years.

224

In 2001, you transferred from Passau to Schweinfurt to take over the management of ZF Sachs. What was the relationship between that subsidiary and Group headquarters in Friedrichshafen like?

ZF Sachs provided the torque converters for automatic transmission production in Saarbrücken, so ZF Friedrichshafen AG was actually our customer in this market segment. The fact that we were able to successfully navigate this situation – which was rife with potential for conflict – is due in part to the good personal relationship that I have with the general manager of ZF Getriebe GmbH, Dr. Michael Paul.

Despite any friction there may have been, both sides were well of aware of how valuable we were to one another. ZF benefited immensely from Sachs in terms of chassis technology, for instance. And from my own experience, I can say that the culture at Sachs helped ZF become a stronger international company. When I later became a Member of the Board of Management, I took a great deal of inspiration from Sachs. On the other side of the coin, the employees at ZF Sachs really appreciated working for a parent company that started out as a supplier and grew from there. From the very beginning, ZF and Sachs always shared a technological affinity.

We managed to improve our global MARKET POSITION during the crisis.

Let's take a look beyond the borders of Germany. The internationalization process at ZF, which started in 1958 with the establishment of the company's first foreign production facility in Brazil, has been gathering significant steam since the 1990s. How has this process affected ZF strategically?

After Dr. Bleyer took over as CEO in 1990, ZF began to rethink its international orientation – today, we might refer to the new strategy implemented at that point as "design to market." We became aware of the fact that our customers in China or South America had different requirements for a certain product than our German customers did. This even held true when ZF took over from another German company as a supplier, as was the case with Volkswagen in China, for example.

Today, ZF is a global company, and as such, it is more susceptible than ever to fluctuations in the various markets around the world. You had the painful experience of witnessing this first-hand when you took over the chairmanship of the Board of Management at ZF in January 2007, right before the global financial crisis hit ...

In the beginning, ZF showed no signs of being affected by the crisis. My predecessor, Siegfried Goll, created a solid foundation on which I was able to build; he wrapped up the 2006 fiscal year with positive results. It wasn't until the final quarter of 2008 that we began to feel the effects of the downturn in the global markets. In 2009, sales in the truck and construction machinery departments dropped by more than 50 percent, and in Friedrichshafen by a full two thirds. No matter how independent a company's individual locations are – in a situation like that, they all look to the Board of Management for guidance. I had a lot of sleepless nights during those months, I can tell you, but in the end, our crisis strategy proved successful. Obviously, our first priority was to prevent massive impending layoffs. Our plan consisted of several phases. The first step was to have employees start emptying their time accounts. We then had to cut back on the number of temp workers we employed; after that, we negotiated reduced working hours and short-time work in accordance with our employees' tariff agreements, and finally – when all of these tools still proved insufficient – we implemented sabbaticals and qualification measures to further reduce our production capacities. Additionally, we established a solidarity fund of approximately 20 million euros to provide additional assistance to our temp workers. Our connections within the German Association of the Automotive Industry (VDA) were extremely beneficial in helping us manage the crisis – in fact, we even improved our global market position during that period.

How did you achieve that?

With a market initiative in the USA. As a result of the crisis, many companies there had collapsed, which gave us the opportunity to supply our American customers more extensively. The most important milestone in this context was our acquisition of a plant for manufacturing axles and axle drives in Marysville, Michigan, which allowed us to supply our customer Chrysler. This step was certainly risky, but it paid off; we were rewarded with a trusting business partnership that is still in place today. Ultimately, ZF was able to get back in the black relatively early, thanks to our somewhat counter-cyclical strategy.

Your crisis management strategies weren't just directed externally, however. Internally, many of your colleagues associate your name with the keyword "Go4ZF!" ...

There's a story behind that term. We came to the realization that the structures within our company – which had developed over the course of our history as a series of largely independent regional units – were no longer in line with our customers' needs. Imagine buying a transmission from ZF and being invoiced for it four separate times! That was the reality at the time; the plants involved in producing these products all issued their own invoices independently, so sometimes, each component of the unit would be billed separately. This was a source of friction within the company, and it was beginning to alienate our customers. At the beginning of 2011, we restructured the entire Group into four centers of competence: Car Powertrain Technology, Car Chassis Technology, Commercial Vehicle Technology, and Industrial Technology. ZF Lenksysteme GmbH, which was founded as a joint venture with Bosch in 1999, was the only area of the Group that was not affected by these reforms. Four divisions, one company, and a clear focus on the market – that was "Go4ZF!"

Would you say that the new structure also helped improve overall team spirit throughout the company's various locations?

I think that's possible, yes. In 2013, when Passau was hit by the worst flood in recent memory, I was extremely pleased and gratified that our colleagues in Schweinfurt were so generous with their donations. That's just one example. At that moment, I really felt that the "ZF family" was more than just a word.

CORPORATE SOCIAL RESPONSIBILITY:

GLOBAL CITIZENS AND LOCAL HEROES

Above: Exhibition by Judith Saupper ("Das Große Rauschen," 2014). **Lower left:** Herbert Schuch, winner of the ZF Music Award in 2004. **Lower right:** Tower studio for the ZF Art Foundation "artists in residence" at the Zeppelin Museum.

A strong commitment to employees, society, and the environment has long been an integral component of ZF's corporate policy. The company's goal was to continue supporting the arts, regardless of how business developed; the ZF Art Foundation, with its three million deutschmarks in capital stock, was established in 1990 for exactly this purpose. "The idea was to collect the numerous requests we were receiving from clubs, initiatives, and private individuals and to put them in competent hands," says Dr. Klaus Bleyer, CEO of ZF at the time. "We also wanted to improve the quality of our sponsorship and declare our commitment to Friedrichshafen as the company's headquarters."[1]

After supporting a number of smaller projects in its early years, the foundation began to focus its activities on exceptional individual institutions and event formats beginning in the mid-1990s. Today, the foundation has long-term sponsoring partnerships with organizations such as the Kunstverein Friedrichshafen art society, the Kulturufer tent festival, and the Internationale Weingartener Tage für Neue Musik music festival. In 1996, the foundation financed the first major special exhibit at the newly designed Zeppelin Museum in Friedrichshafen entitled "Die Kunst des Fliegens" ("The Art of Flight"); during the same year, it began awarding fellowships to artists from the countries bordering Lake Constance. The artists were given an apartment and a studio in the tower of the museum in Friedrichshafen – with an unobstructed view of Lake Constance – for the duration of the six- to nine-month fellowship. Additionally, the artists in residence were granted space for ZF Art Foundation exhibitions at the Zeppelin Museum.

Since 1999, the ZF Art Foundation has been sponsoring the Internationales Klavierfestival junger Meister (International Piano Festival of Young Masters) in Lindau, Germany. This project was the inspiration behind an endowment for young pianists – the ZF Music Award, which was presented for the first time as part of a competition in 2001. The competition has been held every two years since 2004, alternating with the piano festival. Today, the ZF Art Foundation is a permanent fixture of the cultural landscape in the Lake Constance region – and ZF plans to keep it that way. The company has increased the foundation's capital stock multiple times; the current total is four million euros.

Fostering education and science

Like most large technology companies, ZF has a vested interest in the availability of engineers and other highly skilled professionals on the labor market. For this reason, it is only logical that the company would tailor its investments in social responsibility to this need. As early as the year 2000, financing from ZF made it possible for students at the Baden-Württemberg Cooperative State University (DHBW) in Ravensburg to major in Vehicle and System Engineering. A major in Hybrid Technology was added at the Friedrichshafen campus of this university in 2007. The private Zeppelin University in Friedrichshafen has also been receiving support from ZF since its founding in 2003; the company funded an endowed chair in Personnel Management and Leadership at the university, for example. Additionally, one million eu-

Zeppelin University has been sponsored by ZF since its founding in 2003.

ros' worth of donations went into setting up the university's IT infrastructure and library.

In partnership with other companies in the automobile industry, ZF has been financing an endowed professorship in Automotive Mechatronics at the University of Stuttgart since 2003. In 2010, the company's university sponsorship program was expanded through the creation of three additional endowed professorships: in Driveline Technology at DHBW Ravensburg-Friedrichshafen, Mechatronic Systems Design at the Ravensburg-Weingarten University of Applied Sciences, and Electronic Automotive Driveline Technology at the Hochschule Konstanz University of Applied Sciences (HTWG). Furthermore, ZF has maintained university partnerships with schools in China for many years, including the endowed chair for Car Chassis Technology at Tongji University in Shanghai established in 2012. At all of its German and foreign locations, ZF also supervises numerous student research projects. The company made its largest contribution to an educational institution in 2012: by donating a total of 20 million euros, ZF made it possible for Zeppelin University to construct a new campus on the site of the former Fallenbrunnen barracks in Friedrichshafen.

The Wissenswerkstatt ("knowledge workshop") non-profit association, which is supported by ZF, is intended to get kids excited about technical and scientific issues at an early age.

The engineers of tomorrow

Long before a child decides where to go to college, the Wissenswerkstatt ("knowledge workshop") non-profit association – which opened its doors in Friedrichshafen in early 2009 – steps in to help. Peter Köpf, former head of development at the ZF Group, explains the association's approach:

"Our idea was to get kids – especially girls – interested in technology at a young age. To that end, we set up a 4,800-square-foot learning workshop; 4,000 young people visit every year. The costs were significant, but ZF contributed two million euros, which initially secured our financing for ten years. The concept was so successful that step by step, we were able to expand to other locations throughout Germany – Passau, Schweinfurt, Schwäbisch Gmünd, Diepholz, and Saarbrücken. To me, Wissenswerkstatt is a good example of the kind of long-term thinking that is characteristic of ZF. We invest in the future, even if the kind of success we achieve can't immediately be measured in profits. That's why I always loved working here."[2]

In 2015, the year of the company's 100th anniversary, the Friedrichshafen-based association is moving into its new home: the "glass workshop" on the campus of the newly established ZF corporate headquarters. The fact that ZF engineers volunteer their time at this educational association in the same neighborhood as the ZF Board of Management's offices shows just how important the initiative is to the company.

ZF helps around the world

The non-profit association ZF hilft (ZF helps) is proof of the fact that countless employees at the company are actively involved in corporate social responsibility. The initiative was founded in April 2005, as a response to the devastating tsunami that claimed the lives of around 230,000 people along the coast of the Indian Ocean on December 26, 2004. Its initial purpose was to serve as a single point of contact for the many ZF employees around the world who wanted to donate to victims, as well as to funnel donations to suitable aid

With "100 Years – 100 Schools," ZF launched the largest humanitarian education project in its history – in 2015, the same year that marked the company's 100th anniversary.

projects. The first campaign collected approximately 447,000 euros in donations and converted working hours from employees, and ZF decided to contribute enough to raise that amount to one million euros. The idea was to help people help themselves. In the period that followed, the association brought multiple projects to fruition, including the procurement of five school buses in Indonesia and the construction of a drinking water treatment system in Thailand. Since then, the association has supported a plethora of other projects, sometimes in cooperation with other organizations, such as the German Federal Agency for Technical Relief (THW) or the Catholic aid network Misereor. In 2010, ZF hilft provided 350,000 euros in micro-loans to help women in the Indian state of Chhattisgarh establish an independent livelihood for themselves. The next year, the association donated 100,000 euros to the victims of the earth-

quake and nuclear disaster on the Japanese coast, and the year after that, it collected 415,000 euros for projects in Chad and Kenya.

2013 was marked by the association's support for the victims of the flood in Passau, Germany, where ZF has an office. Because many of the company's employees were affected, their colleagues donated at record levels: the association raised 750,000 euros, and the corporation contributed a further 250,000 euros. At that point, the overall total invested in aid projects since the association's founding already amounted to more than five million euros. In 2015, the year the company marks its 100th anniversary, ZF hilft launched the largest humanitarian project in the company's history: 100 Jahre – 100 Schulen ("100 years – 100 schools") in partnership with UNESCO. Its ambitious goal is to finance 100 educational institutions in the poorest regions of the world.

CEO Dr. Stefan Sommer, Mayor Andreas Brand, and Chairman of the Supervisory Board Prof. Giorgio Behr
at the groundbreaking for the ZF Forum on February 5, 2013.

ROOTS ON THE SHORES OF LAKE CONSTANCE AND GLOBAL EXPANSION:

ON TRACK FOR
A SECOND CENTURY

Ever since ZF set up its plant in Berlin in 1926 – its first production facility outside of the Lake Constance region – the balancing act between regional identity and global strategy has been one of the major factors shaping the company. A tendency toward a federalist attitude was always typical for ZF – under the motto "unity in diversity," the larger plants, in particular, were granted a certain degree of autonomy. The acquisition of Lemförder Metallwaren in 1984 and Mannesmann Sachs in 2001 made this fact all the more evident; both companies remained independent under ZF's roof.

However, this decentralized structure also entailed a range of problems – including the fact that customers often had to deal with several different contacts in the context of a single vehicle project. The reorganization of the company into four divisions, which ZF carried out in 2010 under the motto "Go4ZF!," was also intended to make the company's competencies clear to the outside world.

Additionally, nearly all of the German ZF companies (with the exception of ZF Services GmbH, ZF Luftfahrttechnik GmbH, and ZF Lenksysteme GmbH, which was a joint venture with Bosch) were absorbed into ZF Friedrichshafen AG on August 1, 2011, and they began operating under the same name for the first time – another sign of change.

The ZF Forum takes shape

In the course of the reorganization process, the demands facing corporate headquarters in Friedrichshafen began to increase. The research and development center that simultaneously served as ZF's headquarters had been expanded in 2007 and was already reaching the limits of its capacity – ZF had been hiring additional development staff for years. In April 2011, the Board of Management announced that ZF was planning a new, multi-functional building on the two-hectare premises of the former freight depot in Friedrichshafen. The new location was close to downtown Friedrichshafen and easy for out-of-town visitors to access by train, car, or from the airport – the six-story complex

was immediately visible. It was meant to be more than just an office building for 600 employees; the goal was to design a corporate headquarters that would function as an interface between the company and the public. Even its name, "ZF Forum," reflects this aspiration – as does the building's freely accessible foyer, which contains an exhibit and event spaces. A corporate headquarters open to interested visitors, where anyone has the chance to learn more about the company, is a very rare thing among industrial companies. Mayor Andreas Brand also addressed this fact at the groundbreaking ceremony on February 5, 2013:

"From an urban planning perspective, the ZF Forum was a complete success. Above all, it expresses that ZF is a part of Friedrichshafen – ZF has gone global, but the company and its products have their roots right here."

Apart from its political implications, the building also fulfills an important practical function by physically separating corporate headquarters from the development center, as Hans-Georg Härter, CEO until April 2012, explains:

"If we're thinking in terms of sensitive customer data and projects, research and development requires a high level of confidentiality. With corporate headquarters and its central Group functions, on the other hand, we wanted to be as transparent and people-oriented as possible."

Investments in Asia and North America

By merging several of its previous subsidiaries with ZF Friedrichshafen AG, the company helped

321

STEEL POSTS comprise the foundation of the ZF Forum, which has around 325,000 square feet of usable floor space.

The first floor of the ZF Forum will be open to visitors – unusual for the headquarters of a global company.

its German locations grow closer to one another in the years after the financial crisis in 2009 – resulting in tangible benefits for its customers. Thanks to the strong bridges ZF had built between its divisions and regions, the company was able to react to changes in the market more quick-

In 2013, production of car axles began at a new location in Beijing.

ly and in a more coordinated way. Meanwhile, at the company's locations outside of Germany, the winds of expansion were blowing. Construction on a factory for assembling car axles began in Beijing in 2012; production launched in 2013. This was the first ZF production location in the Chinese capital. ZF also strengthened its partnership with LiuGong, one of the world's largest manufacturers of construction machinery. The companies had been partners since 1995; a new joint venture involves the production of axles for wheel loaders in the city of Liuzhou in southern China. The products are specially tailored to the Chinese market. Further evidence of ZF's increased commitment to China is its establishment of an endowed chair for Car Chassis Technology at the Chinesisch-Deutsches Hochschulkolleg (Chinese-German College), part of Tongji University in Shanghai, in 2012.

There is only one other market that ZF has focused on more strongly in recent years than China: the USA. After purchasing an axle drive

We have long valued ZF as a successful company in our industry, with a shared set of values and a comparable focus on innovation.

JOHN C. PLANT, CEO OF TRW AUTOMOTIVE

production plant in Marysville, Michigan in 2009, expanding production of electric power steering systems in Florence, Kentucky in the 2010 fiscal year, and constructing a new production line for wind power transmissions in Gainesville, Georgia in 2011 and 2012, ZF launched construction on a factory for producing the new eight-gear and nine-gear automatic transmissions in Gray Court, South Carolina – the facility was ready by summer 2013. And the company wasn't finished yet: ZF announced an even larger growth spurt in July 2014. The acquisition of its American competitor TRW gave ZF the op-

portunity to achieve a whole new dimension of technological and market leadership. After all, TRW was nearly as big as ZF itself, with around 65,000 employees and approximately 17.4 billion dollars in sales in 2013. On September 15, 2014, Stefan Sommer – who had been CEO at ZF since May 2011 – confirmed that acquisition negotiations had concluded successfully:

"The transaction unites two successful companies who both demonstrate impressive levels of innovation and growth and boast a solid financial foundation. [...] This is an acquisition in the spirit of partnership."

Transmission manufacturing at ZF Transmissions (Shanghai) Co. Ltd., 2012.

TRW AND ITS PREDECESSORS BETWEEN 1900 AND 2015:

FROM THE STREETS TO SPACE AND BACK AGAIN

TRW predecessor Thompson Products started out producing engine valves. Shown here: the production process around 1910.

The company name "TRW" has only officially existed since 1964, but the company's roots can be traced back to the year 1900. Back then, a small group of lawyers and businessmen from the burgeoning industrial city of Cleveland, Ohio acquired a license to manufacture screws via a resistance welding process patented by British engineer Elihu Thomson. On December 28, 1900, the Cleveland Cap Screw manufacturing company was founded – it is the oldest of the many companies that are part of TRW today.

The idea behind Cleveland Cap Screw was to mass-produce a product that was in high demand as a result of industrialization, and to utilize a superior process to do so. Previously, screw heads and threads had to be milled out of massive metal rods – a labor-intensive process that produced a great deal of waste. The plan at the new company was to manufacture the shaft and the head separately and then weld them together: a process that would make better use of materials and dramatically speed up production. That was the theory, anyway. In reality, business was poor in the years after the company's founding. The costs of licensing and implementing the new production method meant that Cleveland Cap Screw had to set prices for its products that were well above the market average, so most customers continued to buy the cheaper screws manufactured using the standard method. By 1905, bankruptcy seemed practically inevitable – TRW's history almost came to an end before it even truly began.

From screws to valves

But before the worst could occur, bicycle manufacturer and automotive pioneer Alexander Winton (1860–1932) and two wealthy partners stepped in and took over the young company. Winton believed that the new manufacturing process had potential, and he was convinced that the factories of the future would utilize strictly standardized components like the ones Cleveland Cap Screw was offering. Above all, however, Win-

ton hoped that the resistance welding process could be used to manufacture valves for combustion engines. Winton had his sights set on remedying the Achilles heel of the early automobile – in some engines, these valves survived just a few hours before bringing the whole machine to a standstill. This lack of durability in most of the valves available on the market was a constant source of frustration for vehicle owners and manufacturers – and any company that came up with a solution to the problem was looking at millions of dollars' worth of business. Alexander Winton was not the only one who believed that Cleveland Cap Screw would be that company; Charles E. Thompson (1871–1933), head of production at Cleveland Cap Screw since 1901, shared his conviction. For this reason, it was only logical that Thompson was named executive director of Cleveland Cap Screw by the new owners in 1906. At the same time, the company began manufacturing two-part valves for combustion engines with heads made of a high-strength nickel alloy and shafts made of cheaper machine steel.

In 1907, Cleveland Cap Screw registered multiple patents for the manufacturing process – just in time to profit from the meteoric rise of the

Cleveland Cap Screw, the company from which TRW was born, had owned this factory (formerly the Grant Ball Company) in Cleveland since 1901.

American automobile industry. Until the patents expired 20 years later, the company essentially had a license to print money, as American historian Davis Dyer put it. The company's management in Cleveland was not content to rest on its laurels, however, and Cleveland Cap Screw's revenue continued to grow. The company also began producing forged valves for high-performance engines in 1913, entered into the drag link production business in 1915, and celebrated the success of its new heavy-duty, silcrome-alloy valves beginning in the early 1920s.

The "T" is born

In the meantime, the company's name was changed several times: Cleveland Cap Screw became Electric Welding Products in 1908, and by 1915, it had been renamed Steel Products – in order to make it clear that the company no longer limited itself to a certain product or technology. By this point, the company run by Charles E. Thompson was supplying 90 percent of all engine valves for American vehicles. However, Thompson's ambitions extended even further: in partnership with his Steel Products management colleagues – Head of Production William D. Bartlett and Chief Financial Officer J. Albert Krider – he staged a successful management buyout in 1916, which garnered him approximately 47 percent of the company's shares. Ten years later, it was decided at a shareholders' meeting that from then on, the company should bear the name Thompson Products (TP) – and thus, the "T" in the eventual brand name "TRW" was born. Once self-made millionaire Charles E. Thompson had enjoyed the prestige of having his own name represent an extremely successfully company, he gradually began to withdraw from day-to-day operations.

The pioneering spirit of the company's early years remained, however. TP was one of the first manufacturers to successfully volume-produce sodium-filled valves according to a concept patented by aeronautical engineer Samuel D. Heron. The mechanics of this new design were based on the excellent thermoconductivity and low melting point of the light metal sodium. When the engine was running, the sodium would liquefy and transport the heat inside the valve away from the head to the shaft. This meant that the temperature difference between the two ends of the valve was significantly lower, and the valve became much more durable, particularly under extreme conditions. The new technology passed the acid test in May 1927, with the first-ever non-stop flight from New York to Paris, piloted by none other than Charles Lindbergh. Lindbergh's single-engine experimental airplane, the Spirit of St. Louis, took 33.5 hours to travel the 3,600-mile route – a travel duration that would have been almost unthinkable without the valves that TP delivered to Lindbergh shortly before the plane took off. However, all the good publicity that this event and other campaigns generated was not enough to prevent TP from crashing along with the global economy in fall 1929. Sales in 1932 – the worst point of the Great Depression – were 70 percent lower than pre-crisis levels.

Things finally started to change in 1933, when the US economy showed the first signs of recovering from the depression. In the same year, Charles E. Thompson passed away from a heart attack, and Frederick C. Crawford (1891–1994) took the reins at TP, putting a new generation at the head of the company. The new man at the top was considered a communicative genius and was proud of managing the company largely independently of the national labor unions. Crawford, who won over the workforce with a combination of informational policies and a talent for rhetoric, never got tired of pointing out that everyone at the company – from upper management to the workers on the production line – was in the same boat. And that boat was now gradually picking up speed. In the newly revitalized US automobile market, TP enjoyed equal success with OEM components and spare parts. Its third important area of business, aviation technology, initially failed to meet expectations.

On his non-stop flight from New York to Paris in 1927, Charles Lindbergh used innovative sodium-cooled valves from Thompson Products.

Economic advancement during the war

In late 1940, however, the situation in the aviation sector fundamentally changed. Against the backdrop of World War II, the US government be-gan ordering unprecedented numbers of military airplanes. Additionally, as a supplier for the automobile industry, TP experienced further growth after the US entered the war in December 1941. On the whole, the company's sales increased by 15 times between 1939 and 1943, while its workforce grew fivefold, to nearly 20,000 employees. This growth also brought about a shift in TP's business practices. Rather than competing on the free market, TP became a contractual partner of the US Department of Defense and other government agencies for the first time – a field of business that would remain important even after the end of the war. TP's product portfolio barely changed during World War II: in addition to various chassis components, engine valves for automobiles and airplanes remained the company's most important products. In wartime, TP added products such as fuel pumps for bombers and, beginning in early 1945, its first components for jet engines. In order to meet demand from the U.S. Air Force, the Thompson Aircraft Products Company was founded in 1941, and an enormous factory was constructed in the city of Euclid, Ohio, near Cleveland.

After the war, TP acquired the factory, despite concerns that a drop-off in orders for military equipment might send the automobile and aviation industries into another recession. However, management at TP took this severe financial uncertainty into account and decided to diversify – successfully. While the aviation segment did suffer the expected losses, the automotive sector balanced things out; TP once again emerged as a supplier of specialized, heavy-duty components. Once the war was over, the company began producing products such as piston rings and ball joints. In the early 1950s, the American aviation sector recovered, and TP was able capitalize on the experience in jet engine technology it had gained during the final year of the war. In the period that followed, TP established itself as an important supplier of turbine blades and other jet engine components.

Thanks to their significant involvement in the US missile defense program, Ramo and Wooldridge − two of the men who gave TRW its name − rose to national prominence during the Cold War.

The men behind the TRW name come together

TP's economic strength put the company in the position to consider acquisitions and act as an investor in the emerging technology sector. This financial success laid the foundation for Thompson Products to ultimately become TRW. To be more precise, the second chapter in the long prolog of the American automotive supplier's story began in summer 1953, with a night-time telephone call from Harold George, one of the general managers of aviation company Hughes Aircraft, to J. David Wright, who had been assistant CEO at TP since 1949. TP had just abandoned its planned acquisition of Hughes Aircraft, but George had another suggestion: in partnership with two of the most important developers at Hughes, Simon Ramo and

Dean E. Wooldridge, he planned to set up his own company that would produce electronics for military and civilian applications. He just needed 450,000 dollars in seed capital. If TP could contribute this amount, it would own 49 percent of the shares in the new company. Wright agreed and went back to bed.

The implications of this investment only gradually became clear to TP's management. The new company was founded without much fanfare: on September 16, 1953, the Ramo-Wooldridge Corporation (RW) officially launched operations in a former hair salon in Los Angeles. The company's first project was to develop a fire-control system for the U.S. Air Force − a project that picked up where Hughes had left off. RW was also tasked with adapting military electronics for commercial purposes, in fields such as IT and communication. Shortly after the company was founded, however, Ramo and Wooldridge were invited to join the "Teapot Committee," a group of experts who evaluated strategic nuclear weapons. One year later, it became clear that RW would take over technical management of intercontinental ballistic missile (ICBM) development for U.S. Air Force. At the time, the Soviet Union was also attempting to become the first global power to acquire these supremely powerful weapons − which is why in 1955, US President Dwight D. Eisenhower declared the missile program a top national priority.

Think tank for the US missile program

RW no longer had difficulty acquiring significant financial resources, as long as development on the ICBMs progressed. The company was hiring new, highly qualified personnel at a breathtaking pace; its workforce grew from 30 employees in 1954 to more than 1,000 just three years later. After the Soviets' first successful test of an intercontinental ballistic missile in August 1957 − and their launch of first satellite to orbit Earth, Sputnik 1, on October 4 of the same year − RW faced increased pressure to succeed. On December 17, the first successful test flight of a US ICBM, the Atlas A, was conducted, and in September 1959, first Atlas D missiles armed with nuclear warheads were commissioned. The era of nuclear deterrence finally began in earnest in January 1960, when the USSR announced that its R-7 missiles were operational. In the decades that followed, both superpowers steadily expanded and improved their deadly arsenals. In the US, the Atlas was succeeded by the ICBM programs Titan and Minuteman, as well as by the Thor project, which concentrated on constructing medium-range ballistic missiles. RW was involved in all of these projects at critical junctures in development and coordination.

Despite the fact that RW boasted impressive growth and was fully booked with various governmental projects from the get-go, the young company generated no profits in the first years after its founding. In fact, it was so hungry for capital that it took advantage of a tempting offer made by its minority shareholder TP. In summer 1955, TP loaned its financial foster child a further 20 million dollars in exchange for the option to acquire more than 80 percent of RW's ordinary shares by the mid-1960s. In that sense, the acquisition was practically a fait accompli. Both sides had a vested interest in making the process as short as possible. RW was still facing liquidity issues, while TP was in desperate need of RW's contacts and expertise in the field of missile technology and electronics, as the airplane market was experiencing another downturn. On October 31, 1958, the deal was finally done – a new company, Thompson Ramo Wooldridge, Inc., was born, and it employed around 23,000 people. In order to avoid conflicts

In the mid-1960s, TRW was involved in multiple development projects that were of national importance, so the company employed a large number of specialists. Staff meetings often included complex scientific debates.

of interest, project management for the government missile programs was decoupled from production and spun off into a new company called Space Technology Laboratories (STL); STL remained an independent subsidiary with approximately 1,000 employees. For practical reasons, the company name Thompson Ramo Wooldridge, Inc. was shortened to TRW, Inc. in 1965.

One name, two cultures

However, the new name could hardly hide the fact that in actuality, two companies existed under the same roof. TRW's two separate headquarters were a visible external symbol of this fact: one in the heavily industrial city of Cleveland on the shore of Lake Erie, and the other thousands of miles away in Los Angeles, the center of the US space flight industry. The geographical distance wasn't the only thing separating the two companies, but the cultural differences between "T" and "RW" were smoothed over by numerous further acquisitions beginning in the mid-1960s, including steering sys-

tem manufacturer Ross Gear in 1964 – ZF had used this company's license in 1932 to produce its first steering systems in Friedrichshafen. In West Germany, TRW acquired Bayrisches Leichtmetallwerk, an engine valve manufacturer, in 1967, and the following year, it took over Lemförder Metallwaren's most important competitor in the steering system segment, Ehrenreich & Cie. One acquisition that had an enormous impact on the future development of TRW was Repa Feinstanzwerk GmbH of Alfdorf, northeast of Stuttgart. In 1961, this medium-sized company had introduced the world's first automatic three-point seatbelt – meaning that TRW now owned a product that would soon become the industry standard. Moreover, the acquisition of Repa also marked TRW's entry into the field of passenger safety, which, today, is one of the most important pillars of TRW Automotive.

Although TRW's involvement in this wide range of different sectors meant that the company didn't have the clearest of profiles, the TRW name is now associated with countless innovative tech-

With its experience in missile technology and space flight, TRW has traditionally had a high level of electronics expertise. Today, TRW is considered one of the pioneers in driver assistance systems.

TRW's trade fair stand at the IAA in Frankfurt, 2013. The company generated approximately 41 percent of its sales in Europe in 2013.

nologies, particularly in the field of space flight. For example, TRW was responsible for the drive unit of the lunar module during the Apollo missions. It was a module developed and constructed by TRW that allowed astronauts Neil Armstrong and Edwin "Buzz" Aldrin to safely land on the surface of the moon on July 20, 1969. During the Apollo 13 disaster, the three astronauts used the drive unit that was actually intended for a moon landing to help them get safely back to Earth after their power module failed. Astronaut James A. Lovell, played in the 1995 Hollywood movie by Tom Hanks, appeared in person at the TRW development center Space Park after the landing to thank the employees for their help "during the last 300,000 miles."

Return to the automobile business

Although TRW had divested itself of several unprofitable business units back in 1975, by the mid-1980s, the company had still grown into a multi-industry corporation with 85 different divisions – it more closely resembled a corporate conglomerate than a rationally structured whole. For this reason, in 1985, TRW launched a comprehensive restructuring process that ultimately resulted in the incremental downsizing of its industry and energy, consumer electronics, and airplane components units. While its armaments business began to decline in the mid-1980s – first gradually, and then much more rapidly after the fall of the Iron Curtain in 1989/90 – TRW's oldest business unit, automobile component manufacturing, returned to the forefront in the early 1990s. This was also tied to the fact that beginning in 1990, federal law in the United States required that all new vehicles include passive restraint systems (airbags) on the driver's side. From 1995 on, the law also applied to the passenger's side. At that point in time, TRW did not yet have the capacity to manufacture airbags, but the company did have experience with crash tests, as well as a general understanding of passenger safety, thanks to its many years of producing seatbelt systems. The sensors, gas inflators, and electronic components required for airbags also bore a certain degree of similarity to the technologies that TRW utilized in its aerospace division. Correspondingly, it was no coincidence that TRW became one of the world's largest producers of airbags not long thereafter. In 1997, the company continued to expand its market position in this segment by acquiring the airbag and steering wheel division of automotive supplier Magna International, among other acquisitions. The company also took over British automotive supplier LucasVarity in 1999.

It was in 2002 that TRW Automotive first took shape as we know it today; that was when US company Northrop Grumman acquired TRW. Northrop Grumman integrated TRW's armaments and space flight units into its own portfolio, and the automotive division was sold to the investment company Blackstone Group, which initiated TRW Automotive's stock market launch in February 2004.

"A tradition of breaking the mold"

Interview with Dr. Stefan Sommer, CEO of ZF Friedrichshafen AG since May 2012

In mid-2012, shortly after you took on the role of CEO, you gave an interview to our company magazine "drive" about the challenges of managing ZF's growth. Back then, 20 billion euros in sales seemed like a realistic target for 2015. With the acquisition of TRW, the company is now looking at 30 billion euros this year – the year that ZF marks its 100th anniversary. How long does ZF plan to continue operating in the economic fast lane?

I think if ZF is to continue to hold its own in the marketplace for a second century in a row, we have to operate on an equal footing with our most important competitors. And these competitors – like Bosch and Continental – have largely already reached the point where we are currently headed in partnership with TRW.

So size will be the most decisive factor on the supplier market?

It's more complex than that. It's also about our ability to shape the future of the automobile industry. At the moment, there are three major trends that we are observing here: first, fuel efficiency and reduced emissions are playing an increasingly important role. Second, modern vehicles are now subject to much more stringent safety requirements – the EU has made it obligatory for cars to include emergency braking assistance systems, for instance. And third, the entire industry is making significant progress in assistance systems. Today, autonomous driving is more than just a dream – in the near future, it will be part of our everyday lives.

Against this backdrop, our portfolio is headed in the right direction, thanks to TRW: ZF is a leading innovator in driveline and chassis technology, which also includes the lightweight construction segment. As a specialist for active and passive safety technology, TRW has a broad product range that requires a high degree of expertise in electronics. Additionally, TRW has many years of experience in sensor and radar technology, information processing in vehicles, and actuator engineering. By combining these sectors with ZF's traditional strengths, we will be able to offer partial or fully automated vehicles from a single source. Our merger with TRW will also help us strengthen our market position in safety equipment segments where we already have an established presence, such as airbags and seat-belt tighteners. What's more, we've gained access to intelligent control technologies, which – in combination with our transmissions and chassis components – help reduce fuel consumption. In that sense, we are well prepared for the technological challenges we will face in the coming decades –

which is much more important than all the quantitative growth we've experienced.

Apart from the technological expertise you described, what do you think will be a decisive factor in ZF's future success?

Independent of the TRW acquisition, we've concentrated on major global trends and the resulting challenges for ZF as part of our "ZF 2025" strategy. We need to be a leader in terms of both technology and costs – that will be decisive for our success in the future. It's in our customers' best interest, but it also benefits our bottom line, which will help us secure our financial independence. In this way, ZF will be able to finance necessary investments and future growth using its own profits. Profitable diversification includes establishing and expanding new market segments and areas of expertise, such as industrial technology, electronics, or service. The advancement of globalization is drastically changing our sales and procurement markets, requiring our structures and competencies to become more globally oriented. In the face of the volatility and insecurity of today's markets, we need to make our business more balanced. And we also need qualified employees around the world; ZF has to position itself as an attractive employer in every market region.

We need to be a leader in terms
of both technology and costs –
that will be decisive for our
SUCCESS *in the future.*

What sort of prospects will be open to employees of both companies in the future? Where do you see the opportunities?

I see a broad range of opportunities for all of our employees, because new prospects are opening up, and because the company will have an extremely strong global market position in the future – one that ZF and TRW could never have achieved separately. And there is practically no overlap between the two companies. At ZF and TRW, the focus is less on cost-cutting – by merging plants, for example – and more on the synergies in product development and market access. TRW has demonstrated particular strength in volume business, while ZF has centered its attention on the premium segment. This strategy has resulted in different management approaches: as a technological fast follower, TRW is streamlined and efficient. ZF, on the other hand, contributes its strengths in innovation and sustainability. We will learn a great deal from each other. And when we talk about synergies and increased efficiency, we're talking about growth.

Whether or not integration between two companies is successful always depends on whether the companies manage to harmonize their disparate cultures. How do you plan to approach this challenge?

I should clarify one important aspect first: Both ZF and TRW thrive on the enormous diversity of their employees' mindsets and biographies. TRW already generates 41 percent of its business in Europe, and the share of sales that ZF earned in America and Asia was about the same in 2014. TRW's management is very international, and some of the top positions at ZF have been held by Brazilians, Chinese, or Americans for years. In that sense, I don't think that two completely foreign worlds are colliding in this merger.

We are not trying to achieve complete integration as quickly as possible. TRW will act as an independent division within the ZF Group and will continue to exist as a legal entity. TRW headquarters in Livonia, Michigan (near Detroit) will also maintain its full capacity. As a first step, we'll begin working together on a number of development projects. In the medium term, we are planning to standardize certain Group-wide

functions. And once that phase is complete, we'll decide how to proceed with more extensive integration.

Let's take a look at the latest events at the company from a wider perspective. Would you say that in the year of its 100th anniversary, ZF is on the verge of a new era, or will continuity be the order of the day?

I would say that embracing change doesn't contradict our roots – rather, the fact that we've embraced changed has been a huge part of the reason that we're now able to celebrate a century of ZF history at all. To paraphrase Benjamin Franklin, you could also say that tradition is about passing on the flame, not preserving the ashes. There are numerous examples of this in ZF's history. Even the founding of our company in 1915 was directly linked to a pioneering technological feat: for the first time in Germany, gears were manufactured according to a superior process developed by Swiss engineer Max Maag. Since the mid-1920s, ZF has supported standardization in automobile manufacturing with innovations such as the standard transmission – at a time when our industry was still a highly fragmented collection of small companies.

In the 1960s, ZF was one of the first European manufacturers to adapt automatic transmissions for passenger cars; this technology was already in wide use in the USA, but it was relatively new to the German market. It was a risky move, but it ultimately laid the foundation for the success of our current generation of innovative transmissions. In other areas, too, our company had the courage to abandon the beaten track and enter new market segments. The acquisition of Lemförder in 1984 was our gateway to the chassis technology industry, and in 2001, we became a systems supplier when we acquired Sachs. Incidentally, there were critics even back then who felt that the path we'd chosen, with all its associated risks, was the wrong one. Today, the companies we acquired are an integral part of the ZF family.

What exactly is the nature of the DNA in this family? What connects the companies that are part of ZF?

My answer might have something to do with the fact that I'm a mechanical engineer by profession: I would say that technological progress is in our blood. We're not satisfied unless we're enriching the world with our innovations – small ones, or sometimes even big ones.

Appendix

- Chronology: Members of the Board of Management and Chairmen of the Supervisory Board
- Footnotes
- Acknowledgements
- About the author
- Index of names
- Picture credits

Zahnradfabrik GmbH, Friedrichshafen
MANAGERS

1915–1921
/////////// Alfred Graf von Soden-Fraunhofen

1915–1918
/////////// Theodor Winz

ZF Friedrichshafen AG
CHAIRMEN OF THE SUPERVISORY BOARD

1921–1928
/////////// Dr. Konrad Freiherr von Bassus

1928–1950
/////////// Dr. Hugo Eckener

1950–1978
/////////// Dr. Max Grünbeck

1978–1985
/////////// Martin Herzog

1985–2003
/////////// Dr. Bernd Wiedmann

2003–2004
/////////// Dr. Wolf Hartmut Prellwitz

2004–2008
/////////// Rainer Thieme

2008–PRESENT
/////////// Dr. Giorgio Behr

ZF Friedrichshafen AG
MEMBERS OF THE BOARD OF MANAGEMENT

1921–1944
/////////// Alfred Graf von Soden-Fraunhofen

1921–1922
/////////// Gustav Habermaas

1923–1945
/////////// Hans Cappus

1938–1945
/////////// Hermann Dolt

1939–1945
/////////// Herbert von Westerman

1950–1967
/////////// Dr. Albert Maier

1950–1973
/////////// Robert Pirker

1950–1964
/////////// Konstantin Schmäh

1951–1973
/////////// Ekart Graf von Soden-Fraunhofen

1963–1983
/////////// Gerd Wolf

1966–1981
/////////// Friedrich Pohl

1967–1983
/////////// Dr. Erwin Ziebart

1971–1993
/////////// Dr. Ernst Braun

1972–1978
/////////// Otto Tiefenbacher

1973–1983
/////////// Dr. Werner Henneberg

1978–1984
/////////// Gerhard Kühn

1981–1988
/////////// Dr. Diether Walz

1982–1989
/////////// Dr. Friedrich Baur

1983–1991
/////////// Max Mugler

1983–1985
/////////// Dr. Karlheinz Radermacher

1987–1996
/////////// Dr. Hubertus Christ

1987–1994
/////////// Karl-Heinz Gorgas

1989–2001
/////////// Dr. Klaus Bleyer

1989–2009
/////////// Uwe Berner

1990–1994
/////////// Rudolf Arnreich

1990–1993
/////////// Martin Grübl

1993–1996
/////////// Werner K. Arnold

1993–1995
/////////// Dr. Wulf Warlitz

1994–2009
/////////// Wolfgang Vogel

1996–2005
/////////// Paul Ballmeier

1997–2006
/////////// Dr. Siegfried Goll

2002–2011
/////////// Dr. Michael Paul

2005–2010
/////////// Willi Berchtold

2007–2012
/////////// Hans-Georg Härter

2009–2010
/////////// Thomas Sigi

2011–2013
/////////// Reinhard Buhl

2011–2013
/////////// Dr. Peter Ottenbruch

2011–2013
/////////// Dr. Gerhard Wagner

2010–PRESENT
/////////// Dr. Stefan Sommer

2010–PRESENT
/////////// Dr. Konstantin Sauer

2011–PRESENT
/////////// Jürgen Holeksa

2011–PRESENT
/////////// Rolf Lutz

2012–PRESENT
/////////// Wilhelm Rehm

2013–PRESENT
/////////// Michael Hankel

2015–PRESENT
/////////// Dr. Franz Kleiner

10 Prologue

1 Arnold Brügmann: *Chronik der Zahnradfabrik Friedrichshafen AG. 1915–1965.* Wiesbaden, Germany 1965, p. 22. – The treatise in question served as an important source for this book; however, the circumstances surrounding its writing are problematic. The author, Arnold Brügmann, managed the main archive of the Nazi party (NSDAP) from 1942 to 1945; he was also a *Hauptsturmführer* (captain) in the SS and became a member of the Nazi party in 1931. It seems as though he was commissioned with researching ZF's history in the early 1960s, despite the fact that his history should have branded him a political offender. It is unclear whether this was done intentionally – perhaps to provide Brügmann with a source of income, as he could no longer work for a university. In my opinion, however, the publication he produced for ZF does not appear to have an obvious political undertone; it is strongly based on sources. As it is the only extensive treatise available on ZF's early history, however, it has been consulted as a source here – but under careful, critical scrutiny.

2 cf. 52 *Stadtgeschichten*, Eds.: Jürgen Oellers, Hartmut Semmler. Friedrichshafen, Germany 2012, p. 19.

3 Numerous biographical studies of Ferdinand von Zeppelin and his airship projects have been published. We will list the following here as a representative sample: Karl Clausberg: *Zeppelin. Die Geschichte eines unwahrscheinlichen Erfolges.* Munich, Germany, 1990. – Alfred Colsman: *Luftschiff voraus! Arbeit und Erleben am Werke Zeppelins.* Stuttgart, Germany, 1933. – *Zeppelin. 1908 bis 2008. Stiftung und Unternehmen*, Publisher: the city of Friedrichshafen. Munich, Germany, 2008.

4 cf. Theodor Fontane: "Der Erkundungsritt des Grafen Zeppelin am 24. und 25. Juli 1870," in: *Unser Eisernes Kreuz. Ein deutsches Heldenbuch*, Ed.: Ernst Boerschel. Heidelberg, Germany, 1915, pp. 39–46.

5 cf. Heinrich von Stephan: *Weltpost und Luftschifffahrt.* Berlin, Germany, 1874, p. 50. – Stephan refers to 91 passengers; other sources mention much higher numbers.

6 This refers to *Reichspatent* (German Imperial Patent) 98580.

7 Arnold Brügmann: *Chronik der Zahnradfabrik Friedrichshafen AG. 1915–1965.* Wiesbaden, Germany, 1965, pp. 16–20.

16 Footnotes, chapter: 1915–1933

18 Visionary technology and real war

1 Alfred Colsman: *Luftschiff voraus! Arbeit und Erleben am Werke Zeppelins.* Stuttgart, Germany 1933 (reprint: Munich, Germany, 1983], p. 205.

2 cf. "DATEN die über die historische Entwicklung der MAAG-ZAHNRAEDER AG Auskunft geben," internal documentation from the ZF Archive (Identifier: 30. Aug. 1961 DrK/Fa), p. 7. Source: ZF Archive.

3 This and subsequent anecdotes are included in a typewritten draft by Max Maag's son – unfortunately undated – that is available in the ZF Archive.

4 German patent number DE000000276936A. A facsimile of the original document is available on the website of the German Patent and Trade Mark Office (http://dpma.de).

5 British patent GB190821225, available at http://worldwide.espacenet.com/.

6 Report: "Vorgeschichte und Gründung der ZF," p. 7; cited in "DATEN die über die historische Entwicklung der MAAG-ZAHNRAEDER AG Auskunft geben," internal documentation from the ZF Archive (Identifier: 30. Aug. 1961 DrK/Fa), p. 5. Source: ZF Archive.

7 Ibid., pp. 5–6.

8 German patent number DE000000296139A.

9 Report on the founding and development of Zahnradfabrik G.m.b.H., Friedrichshafen am Bodensee, August 1920. [typewritten original], pp. 2–3. This report was apparently written at the request of MAN in Nuremberg, Germany, as MAN was planning to purchase shares in Zahnradfabrik. cf. Minutes of a meeting held on July 5 and 6 in Friedrichshafen, Germany regarding the expansion of Zahnradfabrik G.m.b.H. Friedrichshafen am Bodensee, p. 4. Source: ZF Archive.

10 Report on the founding and development of Zahnradfabrik G.m.b.H., Friedrichshafen am Bodensee, August 1920, p. 8.

11 cf. Annual report and balance sheet for the year 1920. [typewritten original from April 26, 1921], p. 4. Source: ZF Archive

12 Minutes of the extraordinary shareholders' meeting held on October 16 of this year [1920] in Romanshorn, p. 2. Source: ZF Archive.

13 Ibid.

26 Portrait: Alfred von Soden-Fraunhofen

1 cf. The following biographical studies on Alfred von Soden-Fraunhofen: Wolfgang Meighörner-Schardt: *Alfred Graf von Soden-Fraunhofen. Bilder eines Lebens.* Friedrichshafen, Germany, 1994. – Heinz Steude: "Graf Alfred von Soden-Fraunhofen," in: TRADITION 3 (1965), pp. 97–111.

2 cf. Arnold Brügmann: *Chronik der Zahnradfabrik Friedrichshafen AG. 1915–1965.* Wiesbaden, Germany, 1965, pp. 65-66.

3 Bayerisches Hauptstaatsarchiv (Bavarian State Archive) Munich, Dep. III *(Geheimes Hausarchiv)*, p. 29/01.

4 cf. The comprehensive work of: Werner Beisel: *Das Sodengetriebe.* [unpublished manuscript owned by the ZF Archive], Friedrichshafen, Germany, 2013.

5 cf. Draft by Heinrich von Soden-Fraunhofen, former auxiliary bishop in Munich, regarding his father, Karl Alfred Graf von Soden-Fraunhofen, completed in 1994 [typewritten], pp. 48–51. Source: ZF Archive.

6 cf. Fünfundzwanzig Jahre Zahnradfabrik Friedrichshafen Aktiengesellschaft. Friedrichshafen, Germany, 1940, p. 5.

7 This was how Alfred von Soden's son Heinrich told the story in the above-mentioned treatise, p. 42. On the other hand, however, there is a letter of condolence from the Inspector General of the Tank Forces (no name provided, apparently Colonel-General Heinz Wilhelm Guderian) dated July 15, 1944; it expresses personal and professional appreciation for Alfred von Soden. cf. Bayerisches Hauptstaatsarchiv (Bavarian State Archive), Dep. IV, Soden-Fraunhofen Family Archive, 412/0001.

30 Technological visions, economic constraints

1 Minutes of the Zahnradfabrik G.m.b.H. Friedrichshafen extraordinary shareholders' meeting held on March 11, 1921 in Romanshorn, March 12, 1921. [typewritten original] Source: ZF Archive.

2 The relevant documents related to the company's founding (records of the company's founding, licensing agreement with Maag, founders' report) are available in the ZF Archive. All documents are dated May 27, 1921.

3 Report to the supervisory board of Zahnradfabrik A.-G. regarding the 1921 fiscal year and the current situation of Zahnradfabrik. [typewritten original], April 1, 1922, pp. 1-2. Source: ZF Archive.

4 *Interne Nachrichten für die Betriebsangehörigen der ZF-Werke*, (3/1960), p. 8.

5 1923 annual report, Zahnradfabrik Aktiengesellschaft Friedrichshafen am Bodensee, June 30, 1924. [typewritten original], Source: ZF Archive.

6 *Die Zufriedenheit unserer Kunden zeigt sich in den Urteilen über ZF-Erzeugnisse.* [ZF advertising brochure, ca. 1924] Source: ZF Archive.

7 Werner Beisel: *Das Sodengetriebe.* [unpublished manuscript owned by the ZF Archive] Friedrichshafen, Germany, 2013, p. 11.

8 *Die Zufriedenheit unserer Kunden zeigt sich in den Urteilen über ZF-Erzeugnisse.* [ZF advertising brochure, ca. 1924] Source: ZF Archive.

9 cf. Werner Beisel: *Das Sodengetriebe.* [unpublished manuscript owned by the ZF Archive] Friedrichshafen, Germany, 2013, p. 219–222.

36 Portrait: Alfred Colsman

1 Julius Oesterle: *Die Bedeutung Colsmans für den Zeppelin-Konzern.* February 28, 1963, p. 5. [typewritten original] Source: ZF Archive.

2 Alfred Colsman: *Luftschiff voraus! Arbeit und Erleben am Werke Zeppelins.* Stuttgart, Germany, 1933 (reprint: Munich, 1983], pp. 205–207.

3 Ibid., p. 11.

4 Ibid., p. 12.

5 Horst-Oskar Swientek: "Alfred Colsman (1873–1955). Ein Leben für die deutsche Luftfahrt," in: TRADITION 3 (1965), p. 120.

6 cf. on Colsman's beliefs, e.g.: Heinz Steude: Alfred Colsman. *Generaldirektor und Mensch.* Friedrichshafen, Germany, 1993, pp. 26–28.

40 The LZ 126 airship as a payment of war reparations

1 The LZ 126 was referred to as ZR-3 by the Americans. Later, the airship was dubbed "Los Angeles."

2 Telegram from US President Calvin Coolidge to Dr. Hugo Eckener, Washington, DC, USA, October 15, 1924. English-language original in: The New York Times, October 16, 1924.

3 cf. The New York Times, October 17, 1924, p. 1, 3.

4 Julius Oesterle: *Die Bedeutung Colsmans für den Zeppelin-Konzern.* February 28, 1963, p. 3. [typewritten original] Source: ZF Archive.

42 The "Roaring Twenties"

1 Albert Maier: *22 Jahre Getriebekonstruktion. 1922 bis 1944.* Friedrichshafen, Germany [Self-published, likely ca. 1964], p. 1.

2 Ibid. p. 5.

3 Walter Ehrlenspiel: *Vom Anfang des ZF-Getriebebaues.* Friedrichshafen, Germany, July 21, 1964, p. 6. [typewritten original] Source: ZF Archive.

4 cf. Arnold Brügmann: *Chronik der Zahnradfabrik Friedrichshafen AG. 1915–1965.* Wiesbaden, Germany, 1965, pp. 193–199.

5 cf. ibid. p. 194.

6 cf. ibid. p. 191.

7 Walter Ehrlenspiel: *Vom Anfang des ZF-Getriebe-baues*. Friedrichshafen, Germany, July 21, 1964, pp. 7–8. [typewritten original] Source: ZF Archive.

8 Albert Maier: *22 Jahre Getriebekonstruktion. 1922 bis 1944*. Friedrichshafen, Germany [Self-published: likely ca. 1964], p. 10.

48 Innovation on the brink of the economic abyss

1 1931 annual report, Zahnradfabrik Friedrichshafen Aktiengesellschaft in Friedrichshafen am Bodensee, Board of Management's report [no page number given].

2 cf. Arnold Brügmann: *Chronik der Zahnradfabrik Friedrichshafen AG. 1915–1965*. Wiesbaden, Germany, 1965, pp. 210–211.

3 1929 annual report, Zahnradfabrik Friedrichshafen Aktiengesellschaft in Friedrichshafen am Bodensee, Board of Management's report [no page number given].

4 cf. Albert Maier: *22 Jahre Getriebekonstruktion. 1922 bis 1944*. Friedrichshafen, Germany [Self-published: likely ca. 1964], pp. 60–62.

5 cf. Arnold Brügmann: *Chronik der Zahnradfabrik Friedrichshafen AG. 1915–1965*. Wiesbaden, Germany, 1965, pp. 217–218.

6 cf. Heinz Rettenmaier, Werner Schnitzlein: *EDV-Geschichte der ZF – von Hollerith zum IuK-System*. [typewritten manuscript] Friedrichshafen, Germany, 1992, p. 1. Source: ZF Archive.

7 1929 annual report, Zahnradfabrik Friedrichshafen Aktiengesellschaft in Friedrichshafen am Bodensee, Board of Management's report [no page number given].

8 cf. *Chronik der Zahnradfabrik Friedrichshafen AG*. [typewritten original] Friedrichshafen, Germany, 1965, p. 215.

9 Albert Maier: *22 Jahre Getriebekonstruktion. 1922 bis 1944*. Friedrichshafen, Germany [Self-published: likely ca. 1964], p. 12.

10 cf. Hansjörg Dach: *ZF-Lenkungsbau*. Friedrichshafen, Germany, 2012, p. 3.

11 1932 annual report, Zahnradfabrik Friedrichshafen Aktiengesellschaft in Friedrichshafen am Bodensee, Board of Management's report [no page number given].

12 cf. ZF Friedrichshafen AG's report on the issue of ROSS. January 7, 1952 Staatsarchiv Sigmaringen (Sigmaringen State Archive) Wü 2 T f Nr. 764/057, p. 2.

13 cf. Report by Franz Xaver Boll, former head of production planning at ZF Schwäbisch Gmünd: "Wie kam der Lenkungsbau nach Schwäb. Gmünd," February 1986, p. 1. [typewritten report] Source: ZF Archive.

14 Hugo Eckener: "Zu meiner 'Rundfunkansprache' vom 19. August 1934," Staatsarchiv Sigmaringen (Sigmaringen State Archive) Wü 13 T2 No. 2025/003, p. 3.

54 Footnotes, chapter: 1933–1945

56 A military buildup yields growth

1 cf. *Friedrichshafen in Diktatur, Krieg und Besatzungs-zeit 1933–1950*, Publisher: "Arbeitskreis für Heimatgeschichte an den Friedrichshafener Schulen." Friedrichshafen, Germany, 1994, pp. 9–16.

2 cf. *52 Stadtgeschichten aus der Serie der*

Schwäbischen Zeitung zum Friedrichshafener Stadtjubiläum 2011, Eds. Jürgen Oellers, Hartmut Semmler, pp. 105–106.

3 cf. Excerpt of minutes: Board of Management's report [1933, typewritten original with handwritten comments]. Source: ZF Archive.

4 Excerpt of the transcript of the Zahnradfabrik Friedrichshafen AG supervisory board meeting, June 4, 1934, p. 2. Source: ZF Archive.

5 cf. Christa Tholander: "Der Zeppelin-Konzern in der Kriegswirtschaft 1938 bis 1945," in: *Zeppelin. 1908 bis 2008. Stiftung und Unternehmen*. Munich, Germany, 2008, p. 192.

6 Interview with Hansjörg Dach, April 23, 2013.

7 cf. 1945 annual report, Zahnradfabrik Friedrichshafen Aktiengesellschaft, "Heutigen Erfolge unserer innovationen Getriebegenerationen."

8 cf. Hansjörg Dach: *Panzergetriebe aus Friedrichs-hafen seit der Weimarer Republik bis in die Nachkriegszeit*, Publisher: ZF Friedrichshafen AG. Friedrichshafen, Germany, 2011, p. 37 ff.

9 cf. A. Brügmann: *Chronik der Zahnradfabrik Fried-richshafen AG. 1915–1965*. Wiesbaden, Germany, 1965, p. 248.

10 cf. Albert Maier: *22 Jahre Getriebekonstruktion. 1922 bis 1944*. Friedrichshafen, Germany, 1964, p. 20.

11 cf. Ibid. pp. 26–28.

12 "Gang der Planung III L." – Chronological record of the events surrounding the founding of the Schwäbisch Gmünd branch, dated July 22, 1938, Friedrichshafen, Germany, p. 1. Source: ZF Archive.

13 Note on the meeting at Zahnradfabrik Friedrichshafen AG., Friedrichshafen am Bodensee regarding setting up a new factory on Oct. 17, 1936, p. 1. Source: ZF Archive.

14 cf. Letter from Luftfahrtkontor G.m.b.H. to Schwäbische Zahnradwerke G.m.b.H. dated November 13, 1938. Source: ZF Archive.

15 Report by the Board of Management of Zahnradfabrik Friedrichshafen Aktiengesellschaft regarding the 1938 fiscal year.

16 cf. A. Brügmann: *Chronik der Zahnradfabrik Fried-richshafen AG. 1915–1965*. Wiesbaden, Germany, 1965, p. 292.

17 Report by the Board of Management of Zahnradfabrik Friedrichshafen Aktiengesellschaft regarding the 1938 fiscal year.

64 "In grave times"

1 *Fünfundzwanzig Jahre Zahnradfabrik Friedrichshafen Aktiengesellschaft*. Friedrichshafen, Germany, 1940, p. 5.

2 cf. Social report on the 1940 annual report, Zahnradfabrik Friedrichshafen A.-G., [p. 1].

3 Transcript of the speech by Colonel Philipps of the Army High Command, p. 1. Source: ZF Archive.

4 Interview with Klara Schultheiß, July 17, 2013.

5 Transcript of Count von Soden's speech, p. 4. Source: ZF Archive.

6 Ibid.

66 Supporting victory at home

1 Zeppelin Company plant newspaper 7, issue 5 (1942), p. 52.

2 cf. Report on the year 1942, in: Hansjörg Dach, Gisela Mattes: *Beschäftigung ausländischer Arbeitskräfte in der ZF im 2. Weltkrieg*. [typewritten manuscript, Friedrichshafen, Germany 1998], Appendix, Document 1. Source: ZF Archive. According to this report, as of December 31, 1942, 689 out of the com-

pany's 6,207 wage laborers and salaried employees were serving in the Wehrmacht.

3 cf. Hansjörg Dach: *Panzergetriebe aus Friedrichs-hafen seit der Weimarer Republik bis in die Nachkriegszeit*, Publisher: ZF Friedrichshafen AG. Friedrichshafen, Germany, 2011, p. 1; p. 24.

4 Ibid. p. 73.

5 cf. Ibid. p. 84.

6 Albert Maier: *22 Jahre Getriebekonstruktion. 1922 bis 1944*. [Friedrichshafen 1944], p. 37.

7 cf. Albert Maier: "Getriebe für Panzerkampfwagen." [typewritten manuscript] 1944, p. 22. Source: ZF Archive.

8 cf. Albert Maier: *22 Jahre Getriebekonstruktion. 1922 bis 1944*. [Friedrichshafen 1944], p. 41.

9 The 1944 design program, dated October 31, 1944, signed by Albert Maier, p. 1. Source: ZF Archive.

10 cf. Albert Maier: *22 Jahre Getriebekonstruktion. 1922 bis 1944*. [Friedrichshafen 1944], p. 34.

11 Ibid. p. 86.

12 Franz Boll: "Der Weg des Lenkungsbaus von Friedrichshafen nach Schwäb. Gmünd" [typewritten manuscript] 1986, p. 1. Source: ZF Archive.

13 cf. Transcript of the 14th supervisory board meeting at Zahnradfabrik Aktiengesellschaft, Friedrichshafen, on June 4, 1928, p. 2. – Arnold Brügmann: *Chronik der Zahnradfabrik Friedrichshafen AG. 1915–1965*. Wiesbaden 1965, Germany, p. 225.

14 cf. Hansjörg Dach: *Ein Ingenieursleben in Friedrichshafen. Oberingenieur Eugen Hartmann zum 90. Geburtstag*, Publisher: ZF Friedrichshafen AG. Friedrichshafen, Germany, 1996, p. 19.

15 cf. Contract no. M Z 5, dated September 11, 1944/ September 5, 1944. [typewritten original] Source: ZF Archive.

16 Interview with Klara Schultheiß, July 17, 2013.

74 The darkest chapter

1 We would like to thank Dr. Christa Tholander for her many helpful contributions to this chapter, as well as her careful scrutiny of its contents.

2 cf. Ulrich Herbert: *Fremdarbeiter. Politik und Praxis der "Ausländer-Einsatzes" in der Kriegswirtschaft des Dritten Reiches*. 2nd Edition, West Berlin/Bonn, Germany, 1986, p. 354.

3 An overview of this issue for the years between 1939 and 1942 (apparently drawn up in 1943) can be found in the ZF Archive. According to this document, the number of foreign workers at ZF Friedrichshafen in 1939 was still largely inconsequential: it amounted to two Italians, one Yugoslav, and four Swiss.

4 The 1940 social report makes mention of the fact that the company first began expanding separation and compensatory allowances to women conscripted to work at the factory during that year. In that sense, it is likely that 1940 was the first year that a large number of women began working at the company. Source: ZF Archive.

5 cf. Hansjörg Dach, Gisela Mattes: *Beschäftigung ausländischer Arbeitskräfte in der ZF im 2. Weltkrieg*. [typewritten manuscript, Friedrichshafen 1998], Appendix, Document 3. According to this publication, in 1943, of the company's 6,162 employees, 2,115 were foreigners; in 1944, the report lists 1,721 foreigners out of 5,088 employees. – see also: Ulrich Herbert, Fremdarbeiter, p. 270.

6 cf. Dach/Mattes, *Beschäftigung ausländischer Arbeitskräfte*, Appendix, Document 3.

7 cf. The table: "Gefolgschaft der ZF 1943–1944

(31.12.)," in: Hansjörg Dach, Gisela Mattes: *Beschäftigung ausländischer Arbeitskräfte in der ZF im 2. Weltkrieg.* [typewritten manuscript, Friedrichshafen 1998], Appendix, Document 3

8 cf. Christa Tholander: *Fremdarbeiter 1939 bis 1945. Ausländische Arbeitskräfte in der Zeppelin-Stadt Friedrichshafen.* Essen, Germany, 2001, p. 107. This statement is based on the voluntary disclosures made by the Friedrichshafen-based companies themselves to the French occupying authorities in 1946. According to this information, the following numbers of foreign workers and prisoners of war were employed at these companies between 1939 and 1945: Luftschiffbau Zeppelin: 1,612, Maybach Motorenbau: 4,819, Dornier Werke: 881, Deutsche Reichsbahn: 456, Rostan: 1,404, and ZF: 2,124.

9 For more information, cf. ibid. pp. 240–244; pp. 514–515.

10 The graphic refers to ZF Friedrichshafen AG including its subsidiaries. As a result of the sources available, the diagram includes Poles, Czechs, and Slovaks under *"Ostarbeiter;"* the category *"Westarbeiter"* also includes Yugoslavs and stateless individuals. "Prisoners of war" came from the Soviet Union, France, and Italy. The concentration camp prisoners who had worked in Passau in 1944 are not recorded here, as they had already left the plant by the date this data was collected (December 31, 1944).

11 cf. For information on wages: Christa Tholander: *Fremdarbeiter 1939 bis 1945. Ausländische Arbeitskräfte in der Zeppelin-Stadt Friedrichshafen.* Essen, Germany, 2001, p. 193. – For information on converting the wages of the time to today's currency, see also: the table "Kaufkraftäquivalente historischer Beträge in deutschen Währungen" published by the German Bundesbank, retrieved: 16.01.2014. According to this table, 1 reichsmark in 1942 would be equivalent to approximately 3.70 euros today. Source: http://www.bundesbank.de.

12 cf. Herbert, *Fremdarbeiter*, 279–280.

13 cf. Elmar W. Eggerer: "'Waldwerke' und 'Oberilzmühle.' Die Passauer KZ-Außenlager und ihr Umfeld 1942–1945," in: *Passau in der Zeit des National-sozialismus*, Ed. Winfried Becker. Passau, Germany, 1999, pp. 538–540.

14 cf. Dach/Mattes, *Ausländische Arbeitskräfte in der ZF*, p. 12.

15 Written information from Christa Tholander, April 21, 2014/August 27, 2014.

80 Stories of survival

1 Jacques Desbois. *Von 1943 bis 1945 als Zwangsarbeiter in Deutschland. Briefe und Dokumente.* Translated and compiled by Hansjörg Dach, published by ZF Friedrichshafen AG. Friedrichshafen, Germany, 1996, pp. 24–25.

2 Christa Tholander: *Fremdarbeiter 1939 bis 1945. Ausländische Arbeitskräfte in der Zeppelin-Stadt Friedrichshafen.* Essen, Germany, 2001, p. 327.

3 cf. Ibid. p.188.

4 Ulrich Herbert: *Fremdarbeiter. Politik und Praxis des "Ausländer-Einsatzes" in der Kriegswirtschaft des Dritten Reiches.* 2nd Edition, West Berlin/Bonn, Germany, 1986, p. 358.

5 Jacques Desbois. *Von 1943 bis 1945 als Zwangsarbeiterin Deutschland. Briefe und Dokumente.* Translated and compiled by Hansjörg Dach, published by ZF Friedrichshafen AG. Friedrichshafen, Germany, 1996, p.48.

6 Christa Tholander: *Fremdarbeiter 1939 bis 1945.*

Ausländische Arbeitskräfte in der Zeppelin-Stadt Friedrichshafen. Essen, Germany, 2001, p.288.

7 Oswald Burger: *Der Stollen.* 10th Edition, Eggingen, Germany, 2012, p. 48–49.

84 The war hits home

1 Letter from Antonie Fröschl to the ZF Archive, July 1994. Source: ZF Archive.

2 Letter from Hans Cappus to Alfred von Soden, March 22, 1944, pp.1–3. Source: BayHStA 953/420.

3 cf. Raimund Hug-Biegelmann et al.: *Friedrichshafen im Luftkrieg. 1939–1945.* Friedrichshafen, Germany, 2003, pp. 211–212.

4 cf. Jürgen Oellers, Harmut Semmler: *52 Stadtgeschichten aus der Serie der Schwäbischen Zeitung zum Friedrichshafener Stadtjubiläum 2011* (Series of papers in the Friedrichshafen city archive, Volume 8), Friedrichshafen, Germany, 2012, p. 119.

5 Oswald Burger: "Zeppelin und die Rüstungsindustrie am Bodensee. Teil 2," in: *1999. Zeitschrift für Sozialgeschichte des 20. Jahrhunderts* (1987), p. 74.

6 cf. Georg Wieland: *Die Zahnradfabrik Friedrichshafen im Überlebenskampf 1945–1950.* [manuscript, 2002], pp. 46–47. Source: ZF Archive. – Letter from ZF to the *Gauwirtschaftskammer Tirol-Vorarlberg* dated April 16, 1945. Source: ZF Archive.

7 Letter from Hans Cappus to Alfred von Soden, May 24, 1944. Source: ZF Archive.

8 Letter from Hans Cappus to Hugo Eckener, September 21, 1944, pp. 1–2. Source: ZF Archive.

9 Franz Boll: "Der Weg des Lenkungsbaus von Friedrichshafen nach Schwäb. Gmünd" [typewritten manuscript] 1986, pp. 1–3. Source: ZF Archive.

10 For more detailed information: Oswald Burger: Der Stollen. 10th Edition, Eggingen, Germany, 2012.

11 This is according to future head of vocational education at ZF Passau Franz Fuchs (among others), who observed the Allied attempts to bomb the site as a child from his parents' house on the banks of the Danube River. Interview on January 24, 2013.

92 Footnotes, chapter: 1945–1965

94 On a razor's edge

1 Arnold Brügmann: *Chronik der Zahnradfabrik Friedrichshafen AG. 1915–1965.* Wiesbaden, Germany, 1965, p. 328.

2 The following numbers are estimates that also include the victims in the Asia-Pacific region (particularly China and Japan). As a result of the chaos caused by the war, it is impossible to determine exact numbers regarding the total number of victims, even with modern research methods. However, there is no doubt that World War II caused the greatest loss of life of any military conflict in recorded history.

3 cf. Statement from Albert Maier, quoted in: *Panzergetriebe aus Friedrichshafen*, Ed. Hansjörg Dach. Friedrichshafen, Germany, 2011, p. 97.

4 The experience the company had gained from manufacturing tank transmissions was put to good use in the manufacturing of the 6-gear transmission with electromagnetic multi-disc clutches for buses and railbuses, however (6 E-75/ 6 E-75S); they went into production in 1946. cf. *Antriebstechnik Maschinenbau. 1935 bis 1992.* ed. Hansjörg Dach. Friedrichshafen, Germany, 2005, p. 21.

5 An overview of the situation at the end of the war

can be found in the 1945 annual report, which ZF published retroactively in 1948.

6 Hermann Ferchl: "Wie war das eigentlich damals vor 50 Jahren?," typewritten manuscript dated May 30, 1988. Source: ZF Archive.

7 cf. Georg Wieland: *Die Zahnradfabrik Friedrichshafen im Überlebenskampf 1945-1950.* [manuscript, 2002], p. 12. Source: ZF Archive.

8 cf. 1945 annual report; included therein: Board of Management report, p. 2.

9 It should be noted here that some work performed was not directly compensated (e.g., in the case of reparations) or was paid by means of bartering. Additionally, it was extremely difficult to maintain proper accounting practices in the chaotic months after the end of the war. In that sense, it is likely that this figure was actually somewhat higher.

10 cf. Georg Wieland: *Die Zahnradfabrik Friedrichshafen im Überlebenskampf 1945–1950.* [manuscript, 2002], p. 15. Source: ZF Archive.

11 Georg Wieland offers evidence from another source that the number of machines taken from ZF between May 1945 and June 1945 was 423 (plus 120 for Daimler-Benz in Gaggenau). cf. ibid. p. 19.

12 Source: List of the known party members ("Pg." or "Parteigenosse") still working as salaried employees at ZF, dated December 14, 1945. Source: ZF Archive. – Regarding the total number of salaried employees in 1945, cf. 1955 annual report, Zahnradfabrik Friedrichshafen A.-G. (Statistical Appendix), ZF Archive. A Germany-wide comparison estimates that there were 7.5 million Nazi party members in 1945, out of a population of at least 70 million (based on the territory held by the Reich at the time) (Source: German Federal Statistical Office).

13 Historian Lutz Niethammer termed this process "Mitläuferfabrik" ("follower factory").

102 The subcompact car "Champion"

1 Comprehensive information on and historical images of the only subcompact car designed entirely by ZF can be found in documentation drawn up by Hansjörg Dach: *Champion – eine Legende. Eine Idee vor 50 Jahren. (Zur Geschichte der ZF Friedrichshafen AG,* Volume 5) Friedrichshafen, Germany, 1997.

2 The name Champion had already been trademarked before the war by Julius Maier, brother of Albert Maier, as the name for a motorcycle constructed in Radolfzell, Germany. When the motorcycle manufacturing business ceased to exist, ZF bought the rights to the name. Source: telephone interview with Julius Maier, Jr. (nephew of Albert Maier, son of Julius Maier, Sr.) on October 16, 2013.

106 The long road to stability

1 This and the following depiction are based on an unpublished study by Georg Wieland: *Die Zahnradfabrik Friedrichshafen im Überlebenskampf 1945-1950.* [manuscript, 2002] Source: ZF Archive. However, the interpretation provided here deviates from Wieland's account in a number of points, such as the critical assessment of Hans Cappus.

2 cf. Georg Wieland: *Die Zahnradfabrik Friedrichshafen im Überlebenskampf 1945-1950.* [manuscript, 2002], p. 25. Source: ZF Archive.

3 Letter from employees of Zahnradfabrik Friedrichshafen to state councilor Prof. Schmid, dated July 19, 1946. Source: ZF Archive.

4 The name "Buchhorner Stiftung" (Buchhorner

Foundation) referred to the German imperial city of Buchhorn (first mentioned in official documents in the year 838); it was absorbed into the city of Friedrichshafen in 1811.

5   The ZF supervisory board was rendered incapable of making official decisions when Hugo Eckener and LZ director Karl Schmid stepped down in July 1946.

6   cf. Thiemann, *Der ZF-Betriebsrat in den entscheidenden Nachkriegsjahren 1945–1950*, p. 7. Source: ZF Archive.

7   The forerunner of Zahnradfabrik Passau GmbH was Waldwerke GmbH, which was founded in 1942. This company was established to manufacture the ZF tank transmission, funded by the Third Reich. In that sense, in the beginning, ZF Passau was actually leasing its own machinery from the Third Reich/the German Federal Government until it finally purchased the machinery in 1953 for approximately 6 million deutschmarks.

8   SOFEN = Societé Française d'Engrenages ("French Transmission Company").

9   cf. Copies of the corresponding letters from Dolt and Cappus and from Eckener to Robin, both dated March 1, 1948. Source: ZF Archive.

10 Letter from ZF's management to Monsieur Robin, March 3, 1948. This letter also contained a general outline of the planned partnership, laid out again for Robin. Source: ZF Archive. See also: Report on Mr. Leo Robin's visit, April 6, 1948. Source: ZF Archive.

11 Arnold Brügmann: *Chronik der Zahnradfabrik Friedrichshafen AG. 1915–1965*. Wiesbaden, Germany, 1965, p. 340.

12 The number of machines (304) comes from an untitled internal ZF report dated October 8, 1948. This report also mentions that 296 machines from Friedrichshafen and Gaggenau (the latter of which were among those on loan from Daimler-Benz) were taken. The lease price of 150,000 deutschmarks per year is included in the text of the contract (source: ZF Archive). Georg Wieland cites a register from October 1949 that includes a detailed list of 272 machines (cf. Wieland, *Zahnradfabrik im Überlebenskampf*, p. 59). Accordingly, it is safe to assume that in the end, fewer machines were sent than originally planned.

13 cf. Speech by Dr. Albert Maier (transcript of an audio recording) marking the 50th anniversary of Zahnradfabrik Friedrichshafen AG, October 27, 1965, p. 3. Source: ZF Archive.

114 Social programs work in ZF's favor

1   cf. inter alia: Letter from the Board of Management to the works council dated January 21, 1946: "The Board of Management agrees that female members of the Nazi party should, over time, be replaced by non-party-members, disabled war veterans, or the like." Source: ZF Archive.

2   1953 annual report, Zahnradfabrik Friedrichshafen A.-G., including subsidiary Zahnradfabrik Passau GmbH. Source: ZF Archive.

3   cf. Internal breakdown of "voluntary social benefits" dated December 31, 1963, which compares the benefits provided in 1950, 1952, and 1960. Source: ZF Archive.

4   Willy Elsholz: "Frohe Ferientage im Erholungsheim der ZF," in: *Der ZF-Ring*, No. 11/1952, p. 193.

5   cf. for ZF: 1960 annual report, Zahnradfabrik Friedrichshafen A.-G., including subsidiary Zahnradfabrik Passau GmbH, p. 17. Source: ZF Archive. – cf. for all of West Germany, with reference to male skilled

workers in industry: Boss, Alfred: "Zur Entwicklung der Arbeitseinkommen und der Transfereinkommen in der Bundesrepublik Deutschland," *Die Weltwirtschaft 3* (1993), p. 312.

118 Outpaced by success

1   Annual report and balance sheet for the year 1920, p. 8. Source: ZF Archive.

2   cf. inter alia: The documentation on the exhibition by the Stadtarchiv Friedrichshafen (Friedrichshafen City Archive) "Zwangsarbeit in Friedrichshafen" from April 29 to June 17, 2005 at VHS-FN, table: "Einsatz von Zwangsarbeitern beim Wohnungsbau." Source: ZF Archive.

3   "Erstellte ZF-Mietwohnungen im Zeitraum 1948–1975," internal document with the shorthand code "PS-Wolf" dated August 7, 1981. In another internal list titled "Bereich Soziales" [no date or department code], the purchase is dated 1948. Source: ZF Archive.

4   Robert Pirker: "Rechenschaftsbericht in der Betriebsversammlung [1956]," in: *Ansprachen von Direktor Pirker, seit 1946*, p. 26. [typewritten original, likely from 1962] Source: ZF Archive.

5   "Vergabe von zinsverbilligten Darlehen an Baugenossenschaften/Gesellschaften einschließlich Zeppelin-Stiftung zur Erstellung von Mietwohnungen" [internal document, dated August 7, 1981, PS-Wolf]. Source: ZF Archive.

6   A report on the development of Friedrichshafen during the post-war period sent to the state government in Stuttgart lists an amount of 36 million deutschmarks for local government housing subsidy programs in the years between 1949 and 1953. Baden-Württemberg State Archive (Stuttgart): EA2/015 Bü 108.

7   Max Ekart Graf von Soden-Fraunhofen, born in 1906, was the eldest son of the company's first manager, Carl Alfred Graf von Soden-Fraunhofen.

8   1955 annual report, Zahnradfabrik Friedrichshafen A.-G., dated February 25, 1956. Source: ZF Archive.

9   Transcript of the 19th supervisory board meeting at Zahnradfabrik Friedrichshafen A. G., held on July 23, 1959 in the company's administrative building in Friedrichshafen, Germany. Source: ZF Archive.

10 Interview with Georg Federle, June 28, 2013.

11 Interview with Adam Beisert, June 25, 2013.

12 cf.: Kurt Müller: *Chronik der Lehrwerkstatt der Zahnradfabrik Friedrichshafen*. [typewritten manuscript] 1981. Source: ZF Archive.

13 The ancient buildings had actually been unearthed in 1938, but as a result of new construction projects and destruction during the war, they were buried again at that point.

14 cf. For background information: Veit Becher: "Die römische Besiedlung Friedrichshafens im Spiegel der archäologischen Quellen," in: *Friedrichshafener Jahrbuch für Geschichte und Kultur* [Volume 1] 2007, pp. 9–29.

126 Beyond the shores of Lake Constance

1   cf. Julius Maier: "Aufbruch nach Brasilien" in: ZF-Ring 2/1959, pp. 24–26.

2   Interview with Max Mugler, June 25, 2013.

3   Travel report (dated: São Paulo, November 6, 1957). Source: ZF Archive.

4   Interview with Max Mugler, June 25, 2013.

5   cf. 1953 annual report, Zahnradfabrik Friedrichshafen AG, p. 5.

6   Interview with Herta and Otto Gillhausen, June 27, 2013.

130 The limits of growth

1   1960 annual report, Zahnradfabrik Friedrichshafen AG, including subsidiary Zahnradfabrik Passau GmbH, p. 8.

2   "Aufstand der Arrivierten," in: Der Spiegel 47 (1959), p. 32.

3   "Vorgänge in der VA in Zusammenhang mit dem Streik am 20.10.59" [typewritten, signed "gez. Schwab," dated October 21, 1959]. Source: ZF Archive.

4   cf. The previously cited Spiegel article (No. 47, 1959), p. 33.

5   Interview with Max Mugler, June 25, 2013.

6   The development of IT at ZF is described in detail in two previously unpublished papers: Heinz Rettenmaier (with the cooperation of Werner Schnitzlein): *Von Hollerith zum IuK-System. 1929–1991*. Friedrichshafen, Germany, 1992 [typewritten manuscript]; Erwin Piepka: *EDV in der Technik (1958–1974)*. 1993 [collection of material]. Source: ZF Archive.

7   Interview with Hansjörg Dach, April 23, 2013.

8   Hansjörg Dach: *Otto Schwab. Erinnerungen an einen großen Ingenieur. (Geschichte der ZF Friedrichshafen AG*, Vol. 8), p. 17.

9   Transcript of a supervisory board meeting at Zahnradfabrik Friedrichshafen A. G. on July 25, 1966, p.8. Source: ZF Archive.

10 ZF-Ring 15 (Issue 6, 1965), p. 8.

11 Kiesinger and Grünbeck had known each other since they had both worked in the Foreign Ministry during the Third Reich under Joachim von Ribbentrop. cf. *52 Stadtgeschichten aus der Serie der Schwäbischen Zeitung zum Friedrichshafener Stadtjubiläum 2011*, Eds. Jürgen Oellers, Hartmut Semmler. Friedrichshafen, Germany, 2012, pp. 136–138.

12 50 Jahre Zahnradfabrik Friedrichshafen AG. Ceremonial address by Minister-President by Dr. Kurt Georg Kiesinger on October 29, 1965. [typewritten] Hauptstaatsarchiv Stuttgart (Stuttgart State Archive): P12/Bü 334.

13 ZF-Ring 15 (Issue 6, 1965), p. 4.

14 Transcript of a supervisory board meeting at Zahnradfabrik Friedrichshafen A. G. on July 25, 1966, p. 6. Source: ZF Archive.

15 cf. ZF-Ring 13 (Issue 6, 1963), pp. 4–5.

16 ZF-Ring 11 (Issue 5, 1961), p. 12.

136 Racing fever

1   ZF-Ring 13 (Issue 1, 1963), p. 6.

2   German translation of a telegram from Lotus dated June 1, 1965 (translated back into English). [Internal memo, typewritten, dated June 3, 1965] Source: ZF Archive (Kempter collection).

140 A boom-and-bust cycle

1   1966 annual report, Zahnradfabrik Friedrichshafen AG, including subsidiary Zahnradfabrik Passau GmbH, p. 2.

2   Ibid. p. 3. Source: ZF Archive.

3   In 1965, the share of exports was 20.9 percent; in 1966, it rose to 22.1 percent. cf. ibid. p. 10.

4   Concept for a speech at the works council meeting on November 16, 1967 by Dr. Ziebart, p. 4. Source: ZF Archive.

5   cf. Report on the campaign to improve cost-effectiveness, audit department, Friedrichshafen, April 2, 1968. Source: ZF Archive.

6   Interview with Rudolf Spannbauer, Ottmar Dichtl, and Franz Fuchs in Passau, January 24, 2013.

[7] Interview with Eberhard Sauter, June 28, 2013.

[8] cf. e.g.: *Interne Nachrichten. Mitteilungsblatt für die Betriebsangehörigen der ZF-Werke* No. 1/1967, p. 4.

[9] Interview with Hansjörg Dach, June 26, 2013.

[10] cf. Press release from ZF Friedrichshafen AG: "100.000 ZF-Automat-Getriebe," December 21, 1970. Source: ZF Archive.

[11] Interview with Siegfried Goll, June 25, 2014.

[12] cf. "Der Bundespräsident zu Besuch bei uns," in: *ZF-Ring* (1/1972).

146 Inspired by the oil crisis

[1] cf. e.g. The chapter "Psychologie um Mark und Pfennig," in: Ludwig Erhard: *Wohlstand für Alle.* 8th Edition, 1964, pp. 235–244.

[2] cf. *Der Spiegel* 42/1973, pp. 25–27.

[3] Interview with Karlheinz Erbacher, June 28, 2013.

[4] Interview with Hermann Stahl, June 24, 2013.

[5] cf. *Soziale Leistungen der ZF* (historical overview, compiled by Gisela Mattes, June 26, 1990), p. 2. Source: ZF Archive.

[6] cf. Biographical notes on H. Reizner, p. 2. [typewritten original] Source: ZF Archive.

[7] cf. Heinz Hässle: "ZF-ECOSPLIT," reprint from: ATZ July/August 1980, p. 8

[8] Heinz Hässle: "ZF-ECOSPLIT," reprint from: ATZ Juli/August 1980, p. 8.

[9] Interview with Julius Maier, June 25, 2013.

151 Updating the ZF trademark

[1] cf. Entries in the trademark registry: DPMA registry numbers 216069 (old logo) and 939624 (new logo).

[2] cf. On updating ZF's trade fair exhibit: *ZF-Ring* 11 (1961, Issue 6), pp. 16–17.

[3] cf. Gisela Mattes: "Die Entwicklung des ZF-Zeichens," in: *ZF-Ring* 2/1994, p. 19.

152 ZF goes global

[1] *Situation und Zukunftserwartung der ZF betreffend Markt,* July 25, 1973. Source: ZF Archive.

[2] cf. Internal dossier on the subject of "ISA," ca. 1985. Source: ZF Archive.

[3] "ZF löst ihre Produktionsgesellschaft in Spanien auf," in: *akzente* (information for ZF employees), October 14, 1985. Source: ZF Archive.

[4] cf. FAE [internal dossier from January 21, 1980, drawn up by VK-ZB Wörter], pp. 10–11. Source: ZF Archive.

[5] Interview with Max Mugler, June 25, 2013.

[6] *ZF-Ring* 1/1982, p. 5.

[7] cf. "Schaltfehler mit Folgen," in: *manager magazin* 1/1983, pp. 44–47.

[8] cf. inter alia: Transcript of a supervisory board meeting at Zahnradfabrik Friedrichshafen AG on July 7, 1983 in Friedrichshafen, p. 9. Source: ZF Archive.

[9] cf. Transcript of a supervisory board meeting at Zahnradfabrik Friedrichshafen Aktiengesellschaft on July 9, 1986 in Friedrichshafen, p. 9. Source: ZF-Archive.

[10] "Große Worte des Lobes und der Anerkennung zur Fertigstellung der neuen Halle 10 der Zahnradfabrik," in: ZF press kit, February 17, 1986 [newspaper unknown]. Source: ZF Archive.

[11] Interview with Willi Schacher, June 27, 2013.

[12] cf. "Auszeichnung für hervorragende Qualität," internal notice from December 15, 1989. Source: ZF Archive.

[13] Interview with Willi Schacher, June 27, 2013.

[14] cf. 1988 annual report, Zahnradfabrik Friedrichshafen Aktiengesellschaft, p. 7.

160 LEMFÖRDER: An industrial beacon in the German farmlands

[1] To commemorate the company's anniversary, ZF Lemförder commissioned a biography of Jürgen Ulderup in three stand-alone (but related) publications. These publications served as an important source for this text: Franz Schnitgerhans: *Präzisionsschmiede in der Provinz. Unternehmensbilder aus fünfzig Jahren.* Bramsche, Germany, 1997. – Hansjürgen Reuß: *Fünfzig Jahre Lemförder Metallwaren. Daten und Fakten zur Unternehmensgeschichte.* Bramsche, Germany, 1997. – Werner Schwipps: *Annäherungen an Jürgen Ulderup. Der Lebensweg eines deutschen Unternehmers.* Bramsche, Germany, 1997.

[2] cf.: Werner Schwipps: *Annäherungen an Jürgen Ulderup. Der Lebensweg eines deutschen Unternehmers.* Bramsche, Germany, 1997, pp. 30–43.

[3] cf. ibid. p. 41.

[4] Quote from: ibid. p. 43.

[5] cf. *25 Jahre Lemförder Metallwaren AG* [no year or page numbers]. Source: Lemförder Archive.

[6] cf. "Erwerb einer Beteiligung an der LEMFÖRDER METALLWAREN AG," Appendix to point 4.1 of the agenda of the supervisory board meeting on December 7, 1983, p. 1. Source: ZF Archive.

[7] The commercial register entry dated May 20, 1947 lists Wilhelm Ulderup and Flensburg-based ship captain's wife Adolfine Kruse (apparently a friend of the family) as the owners. Kruse sold her 5,000 reichsmarks' worth of shares to Wilhelm Ulderup shortly thereafter; she was only involved as a straw man (or more appropriately, a "straw woman"). cf. Werner Schwipps: *Annäherungen an Jürgen Ulderup. Der Lebensweg eines deutschen Unternehmers.* Bramsche, Germany, 1997, p. 49.

[8] cf. ibid. p. 45.

[9] Ulderup founded this company, Optima-Knopffabrik GmbH, in Lemförder on November 3, 1951, but by January 1952, he had already withdrawn from the company.

[10] Quote from Werner Schwipps: *Annäherungen an Jürgen Ulderup. Der Lebensweg eines deutschen Unternehmers.* Bramsche, Germany, 1997. p. 56.

[11] Patent for a "Gelenk, insbesondere für den Kraftfahrzeugbau" ("joint, particularly for automobile manufacturing"), DPMA DE000001689587U, p. 2.

[12] Interview with Carlos Beja, May 6, 2014.

[13] Interview with Christian Peter Ulderup, January 27, 2015.

166 Shifting into high gear

[1] "Erwerb einer Beteiligung an der LEMFÖRDER METALLWAREN AG," Appendix to point 4.1 of the agenda of the supervisory board meeting on December 7, 1983, p. 1. Source: ZF Archive.

[2] cf. "Angaben zu dem Zusammenschlußvorhaben Zahnradfabrik Friedrichshafen/Lemförder Metallwaren" [draft from September 8, 1983, drawn up by MUELLER WEITZEL WEISNER Rechtsanwälte (Attorneys), Frankfurt am Main, Germany], p. 4. Source: ZF Archive.

[3] Interview with Max Mugler, June 25, 2013.

[4] cf. Purchase, assignment, and option contract [final draft, no date or signatures]. Source: ZF Archive.

[5] In 1982 (these figures were the basis for the merger negotiations), Lemförder generated 530 million deutschmarks in sales and employed 4,700 people. cf. "Erwerb einer Beteiligung an der LEMFÖRDER METALLWAREN AG," Appendix to point 4.1 of the agenda of the supervisory board meeting on December 7, 1983, p. 1. Source: ZF Archive.

[6] Interview with Horst Meyer, May 6, 2014.

[7] Interview with Ingrid Griepenstroh and Heidrun Schiller, May 6, 2014.

[8] 1989 annual report, Zahnradfabrik Friedrichshafen Aktiengesellschaft, p. 28.

[9] Rolf Dieterich: "Baurs Bilanz," in: *Schwäbische Zeitung,* July 6, 1989.

[10] The relative loss in purchasing power in West Germany between 1980 and 1989 was approximately 20.3 percent.

170 Footnotes, chapter: 1990–2005

172 A new economic horizon

[1] The term was coined by journalist Dirk Laabs (among others) and his book "Der deutsche Goldrausch – die wahre Geschichte der Treuhand," Munich, Germany, 2012.

[2] ZF-Ring 1/1990, p. 4.

[3] cf. The strategy paper "Auswahlkriterien für potentielle osteuropäische Märkte" dated February 27, 1990. Source: ZF Archive.

[4] A planned partnership with Russian truck producer Kamaz apparently failed in 1972 (the ZF Archive only contains a letter to the supervisory board chairman at the time, Max Grünbeck, dated July 13, 1972, which addresses project planning); a press release from ZF titled "ZF verstärkt die Zusammenarbeit mit der Sowjetunion" dated April 2, 1986 mentions a licensing agreement for hydrostatic forklift steering systems and a passenger car steering and synchronization unit signed in 1980 with a plant in Tolyatti (southern Russia) as the first successful partnership. Source: ZF-Archive.

[5] cf. "Übersicht über Lizenzgeschäfte der ZF" [drawn up by Martin Uellner, head of the central cooperation department], August 24, 1989, Appendix I, pp. 3–4. Source: ZF Archive.

[6] cf.: GDR contacts (note for ZF CEO Ernst Braun, drawn up by Martin Uellner), September 4, 1990. Source: ZF Archive.

[7] cf. Note from September 4, 1990 regarding Parchim (drawn up by: ZM br/st). Source: ZF Archive. According to this document, another factor complicating the situation was that American company Parker Hannifin Corporation was interested in purchasing the factory in Parchim; if the plant had produced ZF steering systems under license, ZF would have had to share expertise with its Cleveland-based competitor.

[8] cf.: GDR contacts (note for ZF CEO Ernst Braun, drawn up by Martin Uellner), September 4, 1990, p. 2. Source: ZF Archive.

[9] cf.: Von "Brennabor" bis ZF Brandenburg. Eine Industriegeschichte. Ed. Bertold Pavel. Berlin, Germany, 1996, pp. 186–187.

[10] Information zum Erwerb des Getriebewerks Brandenburg (GBW). Appendix to point 7.2 of the agenda of the supervisory board meeting on November 29, 1990, p. 3. Source: ZF Archive.

[11] cf. Von Brennabor bis ZF Brandenburg. Eine Industriegeschichte. Ed. Bertold Pavel. Berlin, Germany, 1996, p. 167; p. 234.

[12] Transcript of a supervisory board meeting at ZF Friedrichshafen Aktiengesellschaft on March 20, 1991, p. 12. Source: ZF Archive.

[13] Interview with Klaus Bleyer, June 27, 2013.

176 Pioneers on the assembly line

[1] This text is primarily based on the following complete overview of the history of the Brandenburg plant: *Von "Brennabor" bis ZF Brandenburg. Eine Industriegeschichte*, Ed. Bertold Pavel. Berlin, Germany, 1996.

180 Manufacturing goes cellular

[1] cf. 1991 annual report, ZF Friedrichshafen AG, p. 11.
[2] cf. e.g. ibid., p. 4.
[3] *ZF-Ring* 5/1991, pp. 10–11.
[4] Interview with Karlheinz Erbacher, June 28, 2013.
[5] *Automobil-Produktion* May 1992, pp. 19–22.
[6] *ZF-Ring* 1/1993, p. 21.
[7] "Der Krieger." [interview with José Ignacio López], in: *brand eins* 10/2006, p. 94.
[8] Interview with Giorgio Donà, September 25, 2014.
[9] "1993 wird das erwartete harte Jahr für unsere Branche," ZF CEO Klaus Bleyer in: *ZF-Ring* 1/1993, p. 2.
[10] cf. 1993 annual report, ZF Friedrichshafen AG, p. 6.
[11] Interview with Johann Kirchgässner, November 12, 2014.

190 Greater opportunities, greater responsibility

[1] Interview with Siegfried Goll, June 25, 2013.
[2] cf. *ZF-Ring* 1/1991, p. 17.
[3] cf. *ZF-Ring* 3/1993, p. 5.
[4] cf. ZF 1994 annual report, p. 35.
[5] Interview with Elizabeth Umberson, November 25, 2013.
[6] *ZF-Ring* 3/1995, p. 17.
[7] "Vom Zulieferer zum 'Systempartner:' das Beispiel ZF," in: *Frankfurter Allgemeine Zeitung*, November 4, 1997.
[8] cf. ZF-Ring 1/1994, p. 17.
[9] This term was used for the first time at the Frankfurt International Motor Show (IAA) in 1993 and in the 1993 annual report. cf. ZF-Ring 1/1994. p. 14. – 1993 annual report, ZF Friedrichshafen AG, p. 9.

196 Back to the future

[1] cf. Wolfgang von Zeppelin: "Das ZEPPELIN NT-Projekt" [internal dossier, ca. 1996]. Source: ZF Archive.
[2] cf. Transcript of a supervisory board meeting at ZF Friedrichshafen AG on December 8, 1993, p. 11.
[3] Interview with Max Mugler, June 25, 2013.

198 "Like a bolt and a nut"

[1] Interview with Siegfried Goll, June 25, 2013.
[2] *ZF-Ring interNational Compact. ZF Sachs-Special.* December 2001, p. 21.
[3] Interview with Hermann Sigle, September 21, 2011. Conducted by Andreas Dornheim, Walter Erke, and Daniel Schmitz in the process of assessing the history of Fichtel & Sachs. Transcript courtesy of Andreas Dornheim.
[4] 2001 annual report, ZF Friedrichshafen AG, p. 10.
[5] Interview with Hans-Georg Härter, June 24, 2013.

204 SACHS: Vom Fahrrad zum Fahrwerk

[1] On the history of the Sachs company and family, cf. inter alia: Ernst Bäumler: *Fortschritt und Sicherheit. Der Weg des Werkes Fichtel & Sachs*. Munich, Germany, 1961. – Wilfried Rott: *Sachs. Unternehmer, Playboys, Millionäre*. Munich, Germany, 2005. – We would also refer to the substantive new research being done on the history of Fichtel & Sachs by Andreas Dornheim. A comprehensive work is set to be published in 2015.
[2] This article appeared in the magazine Radchronik. cf. Bäumler, *Fortschritt und Sicherheit*, p. 34.

214 Footnotes, chapter: 2005–2015

216 Innovating in an age of economic uncertainty

[1] cf. 2005 annual report, ZF Friedrichshafen AG, p. 16.
[2] Comprehensive information on this subject can be found on the website of the German Federal Ministry for the Environment, Nature Conservation, Building and Nuclear Safety, for example. cf. e.g.: http://www.bmub.bund.de/fileadmin/bmu-import/files/pdfs/allgemein/application/pdf/eu_verordnung_co$_2$_emissionen_pkw.pdf
[3] ZF drive, Issue 3, 2009, p. 15.
[4] Ibid.

222 From newcomer to number 3

[1] Interview with Elizabeth Umberson, November 25, 2013.
[2] cf. Vestas. 2 MW Platform. [manufacturer's brochure, 2014].
[3] cf. ZF press releases on this subject dated July 25, 2011 and November 16, 2011.
[4] Interview with Elizabeth Umberson, November 25, 2013.

228 Global citizens and local heroes

[1] Interview with Klaus Bleyer, June 27, 2013.
[2] "Das Geld für Kunst und Kultur wird nicht mehr auf der Straße gefunden," in: Schwäbische Zeitung (daily newspaper), August 3, 1996.
[3] Interview with Peter Köpf, June 24, 2013.

236 TRW: From the streets to space and back again

[1] The following account of the history of TRW draws heavily from this study: Davis Dyer: *TRW: Pioneering Technology and Innovation since 1900*. Boston, MA, USA, 1998.
[2] This refers to patent US451345 A from April 28, 1891: "Method of Electric Welding."
[3] "Once it focused on making valves, and until its patents expired, the company all but printed money," cited in: Dyer, *TRW*, p. 12.
[4] "Addressing a mass meeting of employees, Lovell won a loud ovation by suggesting that TRW change its advertising slogan to, 'the last 300,000 miles are on us,'" cited in: Dyer, *TRW*, p. 301.
[5] This refers to regulation No. 208 of the Federal Motor Vehicle Safety Standards (FMVSS).

ACKNOWLEDGEMENTS

This book was made possible through the cooperation of many people at ZF. Countless current and former employees, managers, and associates of the company were generous enough to share their memories and historical accounts with us. Without their help, we would not have been able to tell the story of ZF's development – from its founding to the present day – from so many different perspectives or in such vivid detail. We would like to thank our interviewees:

Ernst Beck, Adam Beisert, Carlos Beja, Dr. Klaus Bleyer, Hansjörg Dach, Ottmar Dichtl, Giorgio Donà, Karlheinz Erbacher, Georg Federle, Franz Fuchs, Herta and Otto Gillhausen, Dr. Siegfried Goll, Ingrid Griepenstroh, Hans-Georg Härter, former government minister Martin Herzog, Maurice Kelijian, Heribert Kiebler, Hans Kirchgässner, Peter Köpf, Julius Maier, Horst Meyer, Max Mugler, Eberhard Sauter, Willi Schacher, Roland Schäffler, Heidrun Schiller, Ali Serdar, Walter Schmalzigaug, Alfred Schobinger, Klara Schultheiß, Josef Schwarz, Dr. Stefan Sommer, Rudolf Spannbauer, Hermann Stahl, Veronika Strobel, Christian Ulderup, and Elizabeth Umberson.

Properly capturing the major and minor moments of ZF's 100-year history in writing is such a complex, monumental task that a single author can hardly hope to do it justice. For this reason, we were fortunate that our team could count on the advice and wisdom of experts in a number of important areas. Thanks to their careful scrutiny of the manuscript and the many helpful contributions they made, we are confident that the contents of this work will stand the test of time – if this book should contain any errors, the author is the one to blame! We would like to thank the following people in particular for their guidance on specific topics:

- Jürgen Bleibler: the history leading up to ZF's founding
- Oswald Burger: Nazism in the Lake Constance region
- Prof. Andreas Dornheim: Fichtel & Sachs, Mannesmann Sachs, ZF Sachs
- Andrea Fischer: Zeppelin NT
- Regina Michel: ZF Art Foundation
- Manfred Sauter: ZF 1945–1965
- Dr. Christa Tholander: Nazism and forced labor in Friedrichshafen
- Janine Vogler: ZF in motor sports
- Barbara Waibel: Zeppelin Foundation, ZF until 1933
- Dr. Georg Wieland: ZF 1945–1965
- Johannes Winterhagen: the history of ZF technology

As is so often the case with works such as this one, many more people were involved in the production process than the title page and publishing information indicate. Among many others unfortunately not listed here, we would like to express our heartfelt thanks to:

- Rita Kessler, Ulrike Harder, and Krešimir Marenić for their extensive, professional organizational support in Friedrichshafen
- Rika Jackisch for coordinating and acquiring photo material at the Dielingen site
- Daniel Schmitz for coordinating and acquiring photo material at the Schweinfurt site
- Melanie Kollath and Simone Wagner for designing and implementing the layout on the publisher's end
- Jutta Groen and Anja Weddig for coordinating on the publisher's behalf
- Monika Briemle and Tim Müller for the portrait photos of our interviewees
- Joachim Burkhardt, Maximilian Kaltenhäuser, Sascha Schmidt, and Dr. Petra Spona for producing interview excerpts

Finally, we would like to thank the people who supported the entire writing process, which took approximately a year and a half: Tim Sander, a partner at timefab, was involved in the creation of the manuscript from the very beginning. Before the work was handed off to ZF, he provided constructive criticism on every chapter, convinced the author to change course wherever necessary, and cleared a number of roadblocks on the path to the successful completion of the project. Matthias Lenz, Head of Corporate Communications at ZF Friedrichshafen AG, had a decisive influence on the production of this work: he conducted the historical eyewitness interviews, worked on the design, and read and approved the individual chapters, always with an eye to the company's best interest, and always allowing the author an enormous degree of creative freedom. It is in large part thanks to Mr. Lenz that this book is more than a mere chronicle of ZF's rise – it is "history in motion."

Friedrichshafen and Leipzig, Germany, April 2015

Gisela Mattes
Stephan Paetrow

About the author

Stephan Paetrow was born in 1978. He studied modern
history, philosophy, and English in Jena and Nottingham
and wrote his master's thesis on Johann Gustav Droysen's
theory of history. He has authored a range of publications
on the history of various companies, including two volumes
on Carl Zeiss AG. In 2013, he co-founded the Leipzig-
and Berlin-based agency timefab, which specializes in
public history and heritage communication.

INDEX OF NAMES

PICTURE CREDITS

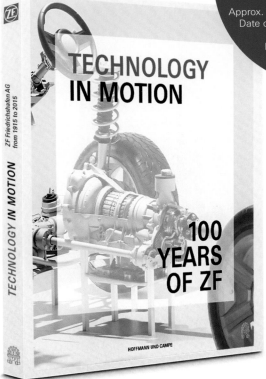

**TECHNOLOGY
IN MOTION**

ZF Friedrichshafen AG
from 1915 to 2015

Approx. 272 pages, including illustrations
Date of publication: September 2015

ISBN 978-3-455-50393-7

About the book

A transmission for Zeppelins, the first automatic transmission for passenger cars, and trucks that park by remote control – the 100-year history of ZF reflects the development of motorized transportation as a whole. ZF and its technologies are evidence of the fact that innovation does not occur by coincidence; it is the result of societal, economic, and technological growth. This book, which commemorates the anniversary of ZF Friedrichshafen AG in September 2015, clearly outlines the background and functions of the products that form the foundation for the company's success.

About the author

Johannes Winterhagen, owner and manager of the delta eta editorial agency, lives in Frankfurt am Main, Germany and works as a freelance journalist specializing in science and technology. He writes articles on the subject of energy and transportation and has been published in renowned German publications such as "Frankfurter Allgemeine Zeitung," "Automobilwoche," and "bild der wissenschaft."